A CUSTOM EDITION FOR THE UNIVERSITY OF OREGON

EVOLUTION OF HUMAN SEXUALITY

COMPILED BY FRANCES J. WHITE, Ph.D.

Taken from:

Human Sexuality: Meeting Your Basic Needs
by Tina S. Miracle, Andrew W. Miracle, and Roy F. Baumeister

Physical Anthropology and Archaeology
by Carol R. Ember, Melvin Ember, and Peter N. Peregrine

Biological Science
by Scott Freeman

PEARSON
Custom
Publishing

PEARSON
Prentice
Hall

Cover art: *Shindig*, by George Herman.

Excerpts taken from:

Human Sexuality: Meeting Your Basic Needs
by Tina S. Miracle, Andrew W. Miracle, and Roy F. Baumeister
Copyright © 2003 by Pearson Education, Inc.
Published by Prentice Hall
Upper Saddle River, New Jersey 07458

Physical Anthropology and Archaeology
by Carol R. Ember, Melvin Ember and Peter N. Peregrine
Copyright © 2002 by Pearson Education, Inc.
Published by Prentice Hall

Biological Science
by Scott Freeman
Copyright © 2002 by Prentice Hall

Printed in the United States of America

10 9 8 7 6 5 4 3 2 1

ISBN 0-536-86104-8

2004500114

AR/JM

Please visit our web site at *www.pearsoncustom.com*

PEARSON CUSTOM PUBLISHING
75 Arlington Street, Suite 300, Boston, MA 02116
A Pearson Education Company

Contents

Chapter 1   **Genetics and Evolution** 2
Taken from: *Physical Anthropology and Archaeology*
by Carol R. Ember, Melvin Ember, and Peter N. Peregrine

Chapter 2   **The Living Primates** 21
Taken from: *Physical Anthropology and Archaeology*,
by Carol R. Ember, Melvin Ember, and Peter N. Peregrine

Chapter 3   **Behavior** 40
Taken from: *Biological Science*,
by Scott Freeman

Chapter 4   **Human Sexual Anatomy and Physiology** 58
Taken from: *Human Sexuality*,
by Tina S. Miracle, Andrew W. Miracle, and Roy F. Baumeister

Chapter 5   **Sexual Arousal and Response** 106
Taken from: *Human Sexuality*,
by Tina S. Miracle, Andrew W. Miracle, and Roy F. Baumeister

Appendix A   **What's Love Got to Do With It? Sex Among
Our Closest Relatives is a Rather Open Affair** 133
Reprinted from *Discover*,
by Meredith F. Small

Appendix B   **Notes** 137
Taken from: *Physical Anthropology and Archaeology*,
by Carol R. Ember, Melvin Ember, and Peter N. Peregrine

Appendix C   **Bibliography** 141
Taken from: *Physical Anthropology and Archaeology*,
by Carol R. Ember, Melvin Ember, and Peter N. Peregrine

Lab Reports 163

Genetics and Evolution

CAROLI LINNÆI
EQUITIS DE STELLA POLARI,
ARCHIATRI REGII, MED. & BOTAN. PROFESS. UPSAL.;
ACAD. UPSAL. HOLMENS. PETROP. BEROL. IMPER.
LOND. MONSPEL. TOLOS. FLORENT. SOC.

SYSTEMA NATURÆ

PER
REGNA TRIA NATURÆ,

SECUNDUM

CLASSES, ORDINES,
GENERA, SPECIES,
CUM
CHARACTERIBUS, DIFFERENTIIS,
SYNONYMIS, LOCIS.

TOMUS I.

EDITIO DECIMA, REFORMATA.

Cum Privilegio Sæ Ræ Mtis Sveciæ.

HOLMIÆ,
IMPENSIS DIRECT. LAURENTII SALVII,
1758.

CHAPTER OUTLINE

The Evolution of Evolution

The Principles of Natural Selection

Heredity

Sources of Variability

The Origin of Species

Natural Selection of Behavioral Traits

Taken from: *Physical Anthropology and Archaeology* by Carol R. Ember, Melvin Ember, and Peter N. Peregrine

stronomers estimate that the universe has been in existence for some 15 billion years, plus or minus a few billion. To make this awesome history more understandable, Carl Sagan devised a calendar that condenses this span into a single year.[1] Using as a scale 24 days for every billion years and 1 second for every 475 years, Sagan moves from the "Big Bang," or beginning of the universe, on January 1 to the origin of the Milky Way on May 1. September 9 marks the beginning of our solar system, and September 25 the origin of life on earth. At 10:30 in the evening of December 31, the first humanlike primates appear. Sagan's compression of history provides us with a manageable way to compare the short span of human existence with the total time span of the universe. Humanlike beings have been around for only about 90 minutes out of a 12-month period! In this book we are concerned with what has happened in the last few hours of that year.

Some 55 million to 65 million years ago, the first primates appeared. They were ancestral to all living primates, including monkeys, apes, and humans. The early primates may or may not have lived in trees, but they had flexible digits and could grasp things. Later, about 35 million years ago, the first monkeys and apes appeared. About 15 million years ago, some 20 million years after the appearance of monkeys and apes, the immediate apelike ancestors of humans probably emerged. About 4 million years ago the first humanlike beings appeared. Modern-looking humans evolved only about 100,000 years ago.

How do we account for the biological and cultural evolution of humans? The details of the emergence of primates and the evolution of humans and their cultures are covered in subsequent chapters. In this chapter we focus on how the modern theory of evolution developed and how it accounts for change over time.

The Evolution of Evolution

Traditional Western ideas about nature's creatures were very different from Charles Darwin's theory of *evolution*, which suggested that different species developed, one from another, over long periods of time. In the fifth millennium B.C., the Greek philosophers Plato and Aristotle believed that animals and plants form a single, graded continuum going from more perfection to less perfection. Humans, of course, were at the top of this scale. Later Greek philosophers added the idea that the creator gave life or "radiance" first to humans, but at each subsequent creation some of that essence was lost.[2] Macrobius, summarizing the thinking of Plotinus, used an image that was to persist for centuries, the image of what came to be called the "chain of being": "The attentive observer will discover a connection of parts, from the Supreme God down to the last dregs of things, mutually linked together and without a break. And this is Homer's golden chain, which God, he says, bade hand down from heaven to earth."[3]

Belief in the chain of being was accompanied by the conviction that an animal or plant species could not become extinct. In fact, all things were linked to each other in a chain, and all links were necessary. Moreover, the notion of extinction threatened people's trust in God; it was unthinkable that a whole group of God's creations could simply disappear.

The idea of the chain of being persisted through the years, but it was not discussed extensively by philosophers, scientists, poets, and theologians until the eighteenth century.[4] Those discussions prepared the way for evolutionary theory. It is ironic that, although the chain of being did not allow for evolution, its idea that there was an order of things in nature encouraged studies of natural history and comparative anatomical studies, which stimulated the development of the idea of evolution. People were also now motivated to look for previously unknown creatures. Moreover, humans were not shocked when naturalists suggested that humans were close to apes. This notion was perfectly consistent with the idea of a chain of being; apes were simply thought to have been created with less perfection.

Early in the eighteenth century, an influential scientist, Carolus Linnaeus (1707–1778), classified plants and animals in a *systema naturae,* which placed humans in the same order (Primates) as apes and monkeys. Linnaeus did not suggest an evolutionary relationship between humans and apes; he mostly accepted the notion that all species were created by God and fixed in their form. Not surprisingly, then, Linnaeus is often viewed as an antievolutionist. But Linnaeus's hierarchical classification scheme, in descending order going from kingdom to class, order, genus, and species, provided a framework for the idea that humans, apes, and monkeys had a common ancestor.[5] See Figure 3–1.

Others did not believe that species were fixed in their form. According to Jean Baptiste Lamarck (1744–1829), acquired characteristics could be inherited and therefore species could evolve; individuals who in their lifetime developed characteristics helpful to survival would pass those characteristics on to future generations, thereby changing the physical makeup of the species. For example, Lamarck explained the long neck of the giraffe as the result of successive generations of giraffes stretching their necks to reach the high leaves of trees. The stretched muscles and bones of the necks were somehow transmitted to the offspring of the neck-stretching giraffes, and eventually all giraffes came to have long necks. But because Lamarck and later biologists failed to produce evidence to support the hypothesis that acquired characteristics can be inherited, this explanation of evolution is now generally dismissed.[6]

By the nineteenth century, some thinkers were beginning to accept evolution while others were trying to refute it.[7] For example, Georges Cuvier (1769–1832) was a leading opponent of evolution. Cuvier's theory of *catastrophism* proposed that a quick series of catastrophes accounted for changes in the earth and the fossil record.

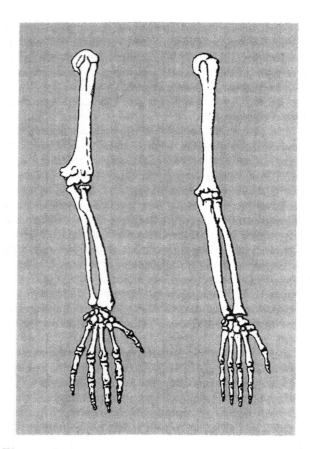

Figure 3–1

The idea that chimpanzees and humans descend from a common ancestor is suggested by anatomical similarities, such as in their forelimbs. Chimpanzee forelimb skeleton (left); human forelimb skeleton (right).

species through the mechanism of natural selection. While Darwin was completing his book on the subject, Lyell sent him a manuscript by Alfred Russel Wallace (1823–1913), a naturalist who had independently reached conclusions about the evolution of species that matched Darwin's own.[8] In 1858, the two men presented the astonishing theory of *natural selection* to their colleagues at a meeting of the Linnaean Society of London.[9]

In 1859, when Darwin published *The Origin of Species by Means of Natural Selection*,[10] he wrote, "I am fully convinced that species are not immutable; but that those belonging to what are called the same genera are lineal descendants of some other and generally extinct species, in the same manner as the acknowledged varieties of any one species."[11] His conclusions outraged those who believed in the biblical account of creation, and the result was bitter controversy that continues to this day.[12]

Until 1871, when his *The Descent of Man* was published, Darwin avoided stating categorically that humans were descended from nonhuman forms, but the implications of his theory were clear. People immediately began to take sides. In June 1860, at the annual meeting of the British Association for the Advancement of Science, Bishop Wilberforce saw an opportunity to attack the Darwinists. Concluding his speech, he faced Thomas Huxley, one of the Darwinists' chief advocates, and inquired, "Was

Charles Darwin. (*Source:* Gemalde von John Collier, 1883, "Charles Robert Darwin." Ol auf Leinwand. 125.7 x 96.5 cm. London, National Portrait Gallery/1024. Bildarchiv Preussischer Kulturbesitz. Photo: Jochen Remmer.)

Cataclysms and upheavals such as Noah's flood had killed off previous sets of living creatures, which each time were replaced by new creations.

Major changes in geological thinking occurred in the nineteenth century. Earlier, the geologist James Hutton (1726–1797) had questioned catastrophism, but his work was largely ignored. In contrast, Sir Charles Lyell's (1797–1875) volumes of the *Principles of Geology* (1830–1833), which built on Hutton's earlier work, received immediate acclaim. Their concept of *uniformitarianism* suggested that the earth is constantly being shaped and reshaped by natural forces that have operated over a vast stretch of time. Lyell also discussed the formation of geological strata and paleontology. He used fossilized fauna to define different geological epochs. Lyell's works were read avidly by Charles Darwin before and during Darwin's now-famous voyage on the *Beagle*. The two corresponded and subsequently became friends.

After studying changes in plants, fossil animals, and varieties of domestic and wild pigeons, Charles Darwin (1809–1882) rejected the notion that each species was created at one time in a fixed form. The results of his investigations pointed clearly, he thought, to the evolution of

it through his grandfather or his grandmother that he claimed descent from a monkey?" Huxley responded,

> If . . . the question is put to me would I rather have a miserable ape for a grandfather than a man highly endowed by nature and possessing great means and influence and yet who employs those faculties and that influence for the mere purpose of introducing ridicule into a grave scientific discussion—I unhesitatingly affirm my preference for the ape.[13]

The Principles of Natural Selection

Darwin was not the first person to view the creation of new species in evolutionary terms, but he was the first to provide a comprehensive, well-documented explanation —natural selection—for the way evolution had occurred. **Natural selection** is the main process that increases the frequency of adaptive traits through time. The operation of natural selection involves three conditions or principles.[14] The first is *variation:* Every species is composed of a great variety of individuals, some of which are better adapted to their environment than others. The existence of variety is important. Without it, natural selection has nothing on which to operate; without variation, one kind of characteristic could not be favored over another. The second principle of natural selection is *heritability:* Offspring inherit traits from their parents, at least to some degree and in some way. The third principle of natural selection is *differential reproductive success:* Since better adapted individuals generally produce more offspring over the generations than the poorer adapted, the frequency of adaptive traits gradually increases in subsequent generations. A new species emerges when changes in traits or geographic barriers result in the reproductive isolation of the population.

When we say that certain traits are adaptive or advantageous, we mean that they result in greater reproductive success in a particular environment. The phrase *particular environment* is very important. Even though a species may become more adapted to a particular environment over time, we cannot say that one species adapted to its environment is "better" than another species adapted to a different environment. For example, we may like to think of ourselves as "better" than other animals, but humans are clearly less adapted than fish for living under water, than bats for catching flying insects, than raccoons for living on suburban garbage.

Although the theory of natural selection suggests that disadvantageous or maladaptive traits will generally decline in frequency or even disappear eventually, it does not necessarily follow that all such traits will do so. After all, species derive from prior forms that have certain structures. This means that not all changes are possible; it also means that some traits are linked to others that might have advantages that outweigh the disadvantages. Choking may be very maladaptive for any animal, yet all vertebrates are capable of choking because their digestive and respiratory systems cross in the throat. This trait is a genetic legacy, probably from the time when the respiratory system developed from tissue in the digestive system of some ancestral organism. Apparently, the propensity to choke has not been correctable evolutionarily.[15]

Changes in a species can be expected to occur as the environment changes or as some members of the species move into a new environment. With environmental change, different traits become adaptive. The forms of the species that possess the more adaptive traits will become more frequent, whereas those forms whose characteristics make continued existence more difficult or impossible in the modified environment will eventually become extinct.

Consider how the theory of natural selection would explain why giraffes became long-necked. Originally, the necks of giraffes varied in length, as happens with virtually any physical characteristic in a population. During a period when food was scarce, those giraffes with longer necks, who could reach higher tree leaves, might be better able to survive and suckle their offspring, and thus they would leave more offspring than shorter-necked giraffes. Because of heredity, the offspring of long-necked giraffes are more likely to have long necks. Eventually, the shorter-necked giraffes would diminish in number and the longer-

The giraffe's long neck is adaptive for eating tree leaves high off the ground. When food is scarce, longer-necked giraffes would get more food and reproduce more successfully than shorter-necked giraffes; in this environment, natural selection would favor giraffes with longer necks.

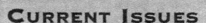

CURRENT ISSUES

Is Evolution Slow and Steady or Fast and Abrupt?

Darwin's evolutionary theory suggested that new species emerge gradually over time. Through the process of natural selection, frequencies of traits would slowly change, and eventually a new species would appear. But Darwin did not explain why so much speciation has occurred. If trait frequencies change only gradually over time, wouldn't descendant populations retain their ability to interbreed and wouldn't they, therefore, continue to belong to the same species?

In the 1930s and 1940s, Theodosius Dobzhansky, Julian Huxley, Ernst Mayr, George Simpson, and others advanced what came to be called the "modern synthesis" in evolutionary theory, adding what was known from genetics about heredity. Mutation and the recombination of genes now provided for genetic variety. The driving force of change was still adaptation to environments through natural selection; gene frequencies of a population presumably changed slowly as adaptive traits (because of existing genes or mutations) increased in prevalence and maladaptive traits decreased. As for speciation, the development and divergence of different species, the modern synthesis postulated that it would occur when subpopulations became isolated by geographic barriers or when different subpopulations encountered different climatic conditions or moved into new ecological niches; those environmental isolating processes would eventually result in the development of re-

productive isolation and therefore new species.

This gradualist view of evolution was challenged in 1972 by Niles Eldredge and Stephen Jay Gould. Their alternative model of evolution is referred to as "punctuated equilibrium." They still assume that natural selection is the primary mechanism of evolutionary change, but they see the pace of evolution quite differently. In their view, new species evolve quickly; but once a successful species emerges, its characteristics are likely to change very little over long periods of time. Thus, in contrast to the modern synthesis, Eldredge and Gould do not think it is common for the world's species to change gradually into descendant species. Rather, species are born more or less abruptly, they have lifetimes during which they do not change much, and they become extinct. As examples, Eldredge and Gould cite the history of North American trilobites and Bermudan land snails. In both groups of animals, it looks as if the different species did not change for a long period of time—millions of years for some species—but then certain species seem to have been quickly replaced by related species from nearby areas. In short, Eldredge and Gould believe that the succession of one species after another involves replacement from outside more often than gradual change over time.

Evolution may or may not occur as the model of punctuated equilibrium specifies, but most

evolutionists today agree that change could occur relatively quickly. Recent research suggests that some relatively quick climate changes in the earth's history helped bring about massive extinctions of species and families of species and exponential increases in the subsequent number of new families. For example, there is considerable evidence that a large meteorite collided with the earth at the end of the Cretaceous geological period, about 65 million years ago. Louis Alvarez and his colleagues proposed that so much dust was sent into the atmosphere by the collision that the earth was shrouded in darkness for months, if not longer. Some investigators now think that the meteorite impact may have also triggered a great deal of volcanic activity, even on the opposite side of the world, which would also have reduced solar radiation to the earth's surface. Not only the dinosaurs disappeared about 65 million years ago, so also did many sea animals and plants. Afterward, the earth saw the proliferation of many other kinds of animals, such as fish, lizards, birds, and mammals, as well as flowering trees. As we shall see in the chapter on primate evolution, our own biological order, the Primates, is believed to have emerged around that time.

Peter Grant recently studied the same finches on the Galápagos Islands that partially inspired Darwin's theory. But, unlike Darwin, Grant had the chance to see natural selection in action. And it was surprisingly quick. Central

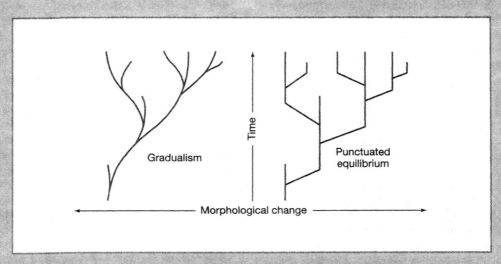

A Graphical Depiction of Gradual versus Punctuated Evolutionary Change

to the project was the attachment of colored bands to each individual bird, which allowed each bird to be identified at a distance. In the midst of the project, in 1977, when half the birds had been banded, there was a serious drought. Of the two main species of finch on one island, the cactus finch and the medium finch, only the cactus finches were able to breed, but they had no surviving offspring. During the next 18 months, 85 percent of the adult medium finches disappeared. Those finches that survived tended to be larger and to have larger beaks than the ones that died. Why larger beaks? Both species of finch eat seeds, but small seeds produced by grasses and herbs are scarce in a drought; bigger seeds are more available. So it seems that natural selection under conditions of drought favored finches with

bigger beaks, which are better at cracking the husks of large seeds.

If it were not for the fact that wet years, which favor smaller finches, occur between years of drought, we might see the quick evolution of new finch species. It is estimated that 20 drought episodes would be sufficient to produce a new species of finch. Darwin's (and Grant's) finches do not really provide an example of punctuated equilibrium (no replacement from outside occurred), but they do suggest that evolutionary change could be a lot quicker than Darwin imagined.

Controversy continues over whether evolution is slow and steady or fast and abrupt. But many scholars, including Gould, point out that there is no need to pit one model against the other. Both may be correct in different instances. In any case much more

investigation of evolutionary sequences is needed to help us evaluate the competing theoretical models.

Sources: Ian Tattersall, "Paleoanthropology and Evolutionary Theory," in Peter N. Peregrine, Carol R. Ember, and Melvin Ember, eds., *Physical Anthropology: Original Readings in Method and Practice* (Upper Saddle River, NJ: Prentice Hall, 2002); Charles Devillers and Jean Chaline, *Evolution: An Evolving Theory* (New York: Springer-Verlag, 1993); Peter R. Grant, "Natural Selection and Darwin's Finches," *Scientific American,* October 1991, 82–87; Jonathan Weiner, *Beak of the Finch* (New York: Vintage, 1994).

necked giraffes would increase. The resultant population of giraffes would still have variation in neck length but on the average would be longer-necked than earlier forms.

Natural selection does not account for all variation in the frequencies of traits. In particular, it does not account for variation in the frequencies of neutral traits—that is, those traits that do not seem to confer any advantages or disadvantages on their carriers. Changes in the frequencies of neutral traits may result rather from random processes that affect gene frequencies in isolated populations—*genetic drift*—or from matings between populations—*gene flow*. We discuss these other processes later in the chapter.

OBSERVED EXAMPLES OF EVOLUTION

Because the process of evolution may involve nearly imperceptible gradations over generations, it is usually difficult to observe directly. Nevertheless, because some life forms reproduce rapidly, some examples of natural selection have been observed over relatively short periods in changing environments.

For example, scientists think they have observed natural selection in action in British moths. In 1850, an almost black moth was spotted for the first time in Manchester. That was quite unusual, for most of the moths were speckled gray. A century later, 95 percent of the moths in industrial parts of Britain were black; only in the rural areas were the moths mostly gray. How is this to be explained? It seems that in the rural areas, the gray-speckled moth is hard to spot by bird predators against the lichen growing

The changes that occurred in the moth population in different areas of England show natural selection in action. Before industrialization, tree trunks were lighter and light-colored moths predominated. (Rural areas today, with little or no industrial air pollution, show that natural selection in unpolluted areas still favors light-colored moths.) But with industrial pollution and the darkening of tree trunks, light-colored moths became more visible to predators. Darker-colored moths quickly increased in number in the new industrial environment.

on the bark of trees. But in industrial areas, lichen is killed by pollution. The gray-speckled moths, formerly well adapted to blend into their environment, became clearly visible against the darker background of the lichen-free trees and were easier prey for birds. In contrast, the black moths, which previously would have had a disadvantage against the lighter bark, were now better adapted for survival. Their dark color was an advantage, and subsequently the darker moths became the predominant variety in industrial regions.

How can we be sure that natural selection was the mechanism accounting for the change? Consistent evidence comes from a series of experiments performed by H.B.D. Kettlewell. He deliberately released specially marked moths, black and gray, into two areas of England—one urban industrial and one rural—and then set light traps to recapture them subsequently. The proportions of the two kinds of moths recovered tell us about differential survival. Kettlewell found that proportionately more black moths compared with gray moths were recovered in the urban industrial area. Just the reverse happened in the rural area; proportionately more gray-speckled moths were recovered.[16] The same transformation—the switch to darker color—occurred in 70 other species of moth, as well as in a beetle and a millipede. It did not occur just in Britain; it also happened in other highly polluted areas, the Ruhr area of Germany and in the Pittsburgh area of the United States. Moreover, in the Pittsburgh area, antipollution measures in the last 40 years have apparently caused the black moth to dwindle in number once again.[17]

The type of natural selection in the moth example is called **directional selection** because a particular trait seems to be positively favored and the average value shifts over time toward the adaptive trait. But there can also be **normalizing selection.** In this type of selection the average value does not change, but natural selection removes the extremes.[18] An example is the birthweight of babies. Both very low birthweights and very high birthweights are disadvantageous and would be selected against. Directional and normalizing selection both assume that natural selection will either favor or disfavor genes, but there is a third possibility—balancing selection.[19] **Balancing selection** occurs when a *heterozygous* (varied) combination of *alleles* (genes) is positively favored even though a *homozygous* (genes in the pairs are the same) combination is disfavored. In the chapter on human variation, we discuss a trait that apparently involves balancing selection—sickle-cell anemia—which is found in persons of West African ancestry, among other populations.

Another well-known example of observed natural selection is the acquired resistance of houseflies to the insecticide DDT. When DDT was first used to kill insects, beginning in the 1940s, several new, DDT-resistant strains of housefly evolved. In the early DDT environment, many houseflies were killed, but the few that survived were the ones that reproduced, and their resistant characteristics became common to the housefly populations. To the cha-

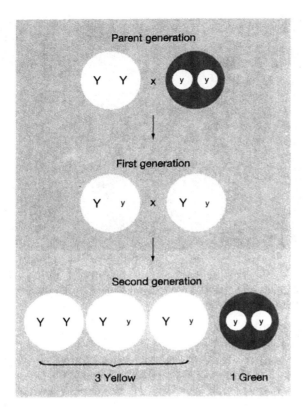

Figure 3–2

When Mendel crossed a plant having two genes for yellow peas (YY) with a plant having two genes for green peas (yy), each offspring pea was yellow but carried one gene for yellow and one gene for green (Yy). The peas were yellow because the gene for yellow is dominant over the recessive gene for green. Crossing the first generation yielded three yellow pea plants for each green pea plant.

grin of medical practitioners, similar resistances develop in bacteria. A particular antibiotic may lose its effectiveness after it comes into wide use because new, resistant bacterial strains emerge. These new strains will become more frequent than the original ones because of natural selection. In the United States now, a few strains are resistant to *all* antibiotics on the market, a fact that worries medical practitioners. One possible way to deal with the problem is to stop using antibiotics for a few years, so resistance to those antibiotics might not develop or develop only slowly.

The theory of natural selection answered many questions, but it also raised at least one whose answer eluded Darwin and others. The appearance of a beneficial trait may assist the survival of an organism, but what happens when the organism reproduces by mating with members that do not possess this new variation? Will not the new adaptive trait eventually disappear if subsequent generations mate with individuals that lack this trait? Darwin knew variations were transmitted through heredity, but he did not have a clear model of the mode of inheritance.

Gregor Mendel's pioneering studies in the science of genetics provided the foundation for such a model, but his discoveries did not become widely known until 1900.

Heredity

GREGOR MENDEL'S EXPERIMENTS

Mendel (1822–1884), a monk and amateur botanist who lived in what is now the Czech Republic, bred several varieties of pea plants and made detailed observations of their offspring. He chose as breeding partners plants that differed by only one observable trait. Tall plants were crossed with short ones, and yellow ones with green, for example.

When the pollen from a yellow pea plant was transferred to a green pea plant, Mendel observed a curious phenomenon: All of the first-generation offspring bore yellow peas. It seemed that the green trait had disappeared. But when seeds from this first generation were crossed, they produced both yellow and green pea plants in a ratio of three yellow to one green pea plant (see Figure 3–2). Apparently, Mendel reasoned, the green trait had not been lost or altered; the yellow trait was simply **dominant** and the green trait was **recessive**. Mendel observed similar results with other traits. Tallness dominated shortness, and the factor for smooth-skinned peas dominated the factor for wrinkled ones. In each cross, the 3-to-1

Gregor Mendel.

9

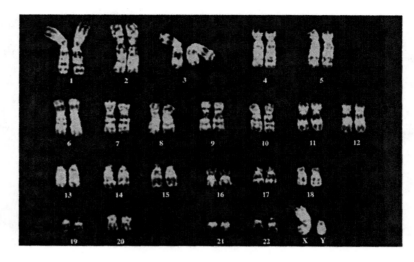

This karyotype shows the 23 paired chromosomes in a normal human male. Note the small Y chromosome at the bottom right that makes this individual male.

ratio appeared in the second generation. Self-fertilization, however, produced different results. Green pea plants always yielded green pea plants, and short plants always produced short plants.

From his numerical results, Mendel concluded that some yellow pea plants were pure (homozygous) for that trait, whereas others also possessed a green factor (the plants were heterozygous). That is, although two plants might both have yellow peas, one of them might produce offspring with green peas. In such cases, the genetic makeup, the **genotype,** differed from the observable appearance, or **phenotype.**

GENES: THE CONVEYORS OF INHERITED TRAITS

Mendel's units of heredity were what we now call **genes.** He concluded that these units occurred in pairs for each trait and that offspring inherited one unit of the pair from each parent. Each member of a gene pair or group is called an **allele.** If the two genes, or alleles, for a trait are the same, the organism is **homozygous** for that trait; if the two genes for a characteristic differ, the organism is **heterozygous** for that trait. A pea plant that contains a pair of genes for yellow is homozygous for the trait. A yellow pea plant with a dominant gene for yellow and a recessive gene for green, although phenotypically yellow, has a heterozygous genotype. As Mendel demonstrated, the recessive green gene can reappear in subsequent generations. But Mendel knew nothing of the composition of genes or the processes that transmit them from parent to offspring. Many years of scientific research have yielded much of the missing information.

The genes of higher organisms (not including bacteria and primitive plants such as green-blue algae) are located on ropelike bodies called **chromosomes** within the nucleus of every one of the organism's cells. Chromosomes, like genes, usually occur in pairs. Each allele for a given trait is carried in the identical position on corresponding chromosomes. The two genes that determined the color of

Mendel's peas, for example, were opposite each other on a pair of chromosomes.

MITOSIS AND MEIOSIS The body cells of every plant or animal carry chromosome pairs in a number appropriate for its species. Humans have 23 pairs, or a total of 46 chromosomes, each carrying many times that number of genes. Each new body cell receives this number of chromosomes during cellular reproduction, or **mitosis,** as each pair of chromosomes duplicates itself.

    CD-ROM Simulation II-2

But what happens when a sperm cell and an egg cell unite to form a new organism? What prevents the human baby from receiving twice the number of chromosomes characteristic of its species—23 pairs from the sperm and 23 pairs from the egg? The process by which the reproductive cells are formed, **meiosis,** ensures that this will not happen (see Figure 3–3). Each reproductive cell contains *half* the number of chromosomes appropriate for the species. Only one member of each chromosome pair is carried in every egg or sperm. At fertilization, the human embryo normally receives 23 *separate* chromosomes from its mother and the same number from its father, which add up to the 23 pairs.

DNA As we have said, genes are located on chromosomes. Each gene carries a set of instructions encoded in its chemical structure. It is from this coded information carried in genes that a cell makes all the rest of its structural parts and chemical machinery. It appears that in most living organisms, heredity is controlled by the same chemical substance, **DNA**—deoxyribonucleic acid. An enormous amount of research has been directed toward understanding DNA—what its structure is, how it duplicates itself in reproduction, and how it conveys or instructs the formation of a complete organism.

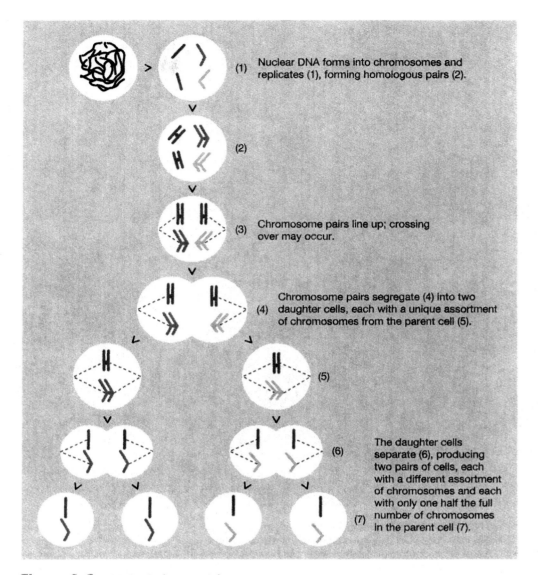

Figure 3–3 *Meiosis (sex cells)*

The figure labels read:

(1) Nuclear DNA forms into chromosomes and replicates (1), forming homologous pairs (2).

(2)

(3) Chromosome pairs line up; crossing over may occur.

(4) Chromosome pairs segregate (4) into two daughter cells, each with a unique assortment of chromosomes from the parent cell (5).

(5)

(6) The daughter cells separate (6), producing two pairs of cells, each with a different assortment of chromosomes and each with only one half the full number of chromosomes in the parent cell (7).

(7)

 CD-ROM Simulation II-3

One of the most important keys to understanding human development and genetics is the structure and function of DNA. In 1953, the American biologist James Watson, with the British molecular biologist Francis Crick, proposed that DNA is a long, two-stranded molecule shaped like a double helix[20] (see Figure 3–4). Genetic information is stored in the linear sequences of the bases; different species have different sequences, and every individual is slightly different from every other individual. Notice that in the DNA molecule each base always has the same opposite base; adenine and thymine are paired, as are cytosine and guanine. The importance of this pattern is that the two strands carry the same information, so that when the double helix unwinds each strand can form a template for a new strand of complementary bases.[21] Because DNA stores the information required to make up the cells of an organism, it has been called the language of life. As George and Muriel Beadle put it,

> the deciphering of the DNA code has revealed our possession of a language much older than hieroglyphics, a language as old as life itself, a language that is the most living language of all—even if its letters are invisible and its words are buried deep in the cells of our bodies.[22]

Once it was understood that genes are made of DNA, concerted efforts were begun to map DNA sequences and their locations on the chromosomes of different organisms. A project known as the human genome project set out to assemble a complete genetic map for humans. In July 2000, the initial mapping of the human genome was

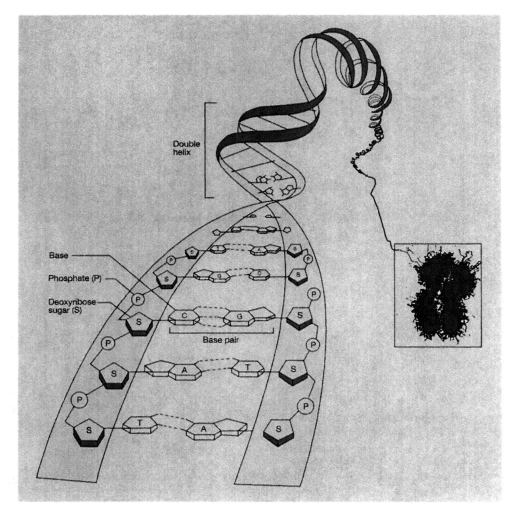

Figure 3–4 *The DNA molecule consists of two spiral sugar-phosphate strands. The strands are linked by the nitrogenous bases adenine (A), guanine (G), thymine (T), and cytosine (C). When the DNA molecule reproduces, the bases separate and the spiral strands unwind. Each original strand serves as a mold along which a new complementary chain is formed.* Source: From *The Language of Heredity* by Paul Berg and Maxine Singer. Reprinted by permission of University Science Books, 55D Gate Five Road, Sausalito, Ca 94965.

completed. While much work remains, this is a significant achievement and will certainly lead to breakthroughs in our understanding of how the genetic code functions.[23]

 CD-ROM Simulation II-4

MESSENGER RNA DNA stores the information to make cells, but it does not directly affect the formation of cells. One type of ribonucleic acid (RNA), **messenger RNA (mRNA),** is copied from a portion of DNA and moves outside the cell nucleus to direct the formation of proteins.[24] Proteins have so many functions that they are considered to be responsible for most of the characteristics of an organism. They act as catalysts for synthesizing DNA and RNA and for the activities of cells; they also contribute many structural elements that determine the shape and movement of cells.[25] Messenger RNA is like DNA in that it has a linear sequence of bases attached to a sugar-phosphate backbone, but it is slightly different chemically. One difference is that messenger RNA has the base uracil instead of the base thymine. Messenger RNA also has a different sugar-phosphate backbone and is single- rather than double-stranded. Messenger RNA is formed when a double-stranded DNA molecule unwinds and forms a template for the mRNA. After a section of DNA is copied, the mRNA releases from the DNA and leaves the nucleus, and the double helix of the DNA is re-formed.[26]

PROTEIN SYNTHESIS Once the mRNA is released from the DNA, it travels out of the cell nucleus and into the body of the cell. There it attaches to a structure in the cell called a **ribosome,** which uses the information on the mRNA to make proteins. The ribosome essentially "reads" the chemical bases on the mRNA in commands that tell the ribosome the specific amino acids to join together to form a protein (see Figure 3–5). For example, the mRNA sequence adenine, adenine, guanine (AAG) tells the ribosome to place the amino acid lysine in that location, whereas the sequence adenine, adenine, cytosine (AAC) calls for the amino acid histidine. There are also mRNA commands that tell the ribosome when to begin and when to stop constructing a protein. Thus, the DNA code copied onto mRNA provides all the information necessary for ribosomes to build the proteins that make up the structures of organisms and drive the processes of life.

 CD-ROM Simulation II-5

 Sources of Variability

Natural selection proceeds only when individuals within a population vary. There are two genetic sources of variation: genetic recombination and mutation.

GENETIC RECOMBINATION

The distribution of traits from parents to children varies from one offspring to another. Brothers and sisters, after all, do not look exactly alike, nor does each child resemble 50 percent of the mother and 50 percent of the father. This variation occurs because when a sperm cell or an egg is formed, the single member of each chromosome pair it receives is a matter of chance. Each reproductive cell, then, carries a random assortment of chromosomes and their respective genes. At fertilization, the egg and sperm that unite are different from every other egg carried by the mother and every other sperm carried by the father. A unique offspring is thus produced by a shuffling of the parents' genes. One cause of this shuffling is the random **segregation,** or sorting, of chromosomes in meiosis. Conceivably, an individual could get any of the possible assortments of the paternal and maternal chromosomes. Another cause of the shuffling of parental genes is **crossing-over,** the exchange of sections of chromosomes between one chromosome and another (Figure 3–6).[27] Thus, after meiosis, the egg and sperm do not receive just a random mixture of complete paternal and maternal chromosomes; because of crossing-over they also receive chromosomes in which some of the sections may have been replaced.

 CD-ROM Simulation II-6

The traits displayed by each organism are not simply the result of combinations of dominant and recessive genes, as Mendel had hypothesized. In humans, most traits are influenced by the activity of many genes. Skin color, for example, is the result of several inherited characteristics. A brownish shade results from the presence of a pigment known as *melanin;* the degree of darkness in the hue depends largely on the amount of melanin present and how it is distributed in the layers of the skin. Another factor contributing to the color of all human skin is the blood that flows in blood vessels located in the outer layers of the skin. Humans carry at least five different genes for the manufacture of melanin and many other genes for the other components of skin hue. In fact, almost all physical characteristics in humans are the result of the concerted action of many genes. Some traits are sex-linked. The X chromosome, which together with the presence or absence of a Y chromosome determines sex, may also carry the gene for hemophilia or the gene for color blindness. The expression of these two characteristics depends on the sex of the organism.

Genetic recombination produces variety, which is essential for the operation of natural selection. Ultimately, however, the major source of variability is mutation. This is because mutation replenishes the supply of variability, which is constantly being reduced by the selective elimination of less fit variants. Mutation also produces variety in organisms that reproduce asexually.

MUTATION

A **mutation** is a change in the DNA sequence. Such a change produces an altered gene. The majority of mutations are thought to occur because of occasional mismating of the chemical bases that make up DNA. Just as a typist will make errors in copying a manuscript, so will DNA, in duplicating itself, occasionally change its code.[28] A mutation will result from such an error. Some mutations have more drastic consequences than others. Suppose the error is in one base on a DNA strand. The effect depends on what that portion of the DNA controls. The effect may be minimal if the product hardly affects the organism. On the other hand, if the change occurs at a place where the DNA regulates the production of many proteins, the effect on the organism can be serious.[29]

Although it is very difficult to estimate the proportions of mutations that are harmful, neutral, or beneficial, there is no doubt that some mutations have lethal consequences. We can discuss the relative merits or disadvantages of a mutant gene only in terms of the physical, cultural, and genetic environment of that gene.[30] Galactosemia, for example, is caused by a recessive mutant gene and usually results in mental retardation and blindness. But it can be prevented by dietary restrictions begun at an early age. In this instance, the intervention of human culture counteracts the mutant gene and allows the afflicted individual to lead a normal life. Thus, some cultural factors can modify the effects of natural selection by helping

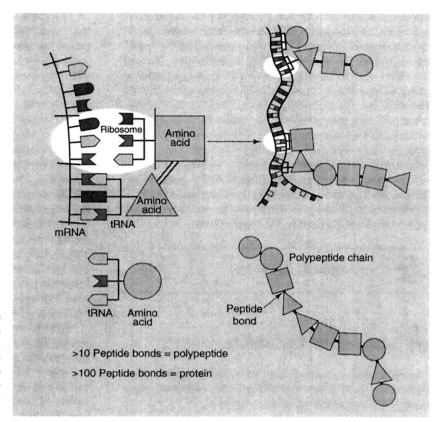

Figure 3–5 *Translation and Protein Synthesis*

The mRNA copy of the cellular DNA is "read" by a ribosome that attaches the amino acid with the corresponding transfer RNA (tRNA) to a growing chain of amino acids (called a polypeptide chain because the amino acids are linked together by peptide bonds). A chain more than 100 amino acids long is called a protein.

to perpetuate a harmful mutant gene. People with the galactosemia trait who are enabled to function normally can reproduce and pass on one of the recessive genes to their children. Without cultural interference, natural selection would prevent such reproduction. Usually, natural selection acts to retain only those mutations that aid survival.

Even though most mutations may not be adaptive, those that are will multiply in a population relatively quickly, by natural selection. As Theodosius Dobzhansky has suggested:

> Consistently useful mutants are like needles in a haystack of harmful ones. A needle in a haystack is hard to find, even though one may be sure it is there. But if the needle is valuable, the task of finding it is facilitated by setting the haystack on fire and looking for the needle among the ashes. The role of the fire in this parable is played in biological evolution by natural selection.[31]

The black moth that was spotted in Manchester in 1850 probably resulted from a mutation. If the tree trunks had been light colored, that moth or its offspring probably would have died out. But as industrialization increased and the tree trunks became darker, a trait that was once maladaptive became adaptive.

Genetic recombination and mutation are the sources of new variations, but evolutionary biologists have identified two other processes that are important in distributing those variations through populations: genetic drift and gene flow.

GENETIC DRIFT

The term **genetic drift** refers to various random processes that affect gene frequencies in small, relatively isolated populations. Genetic drift is also known as the *Wright effect*, after the geneticist Sewall Wright, who first directed attention to this process. Over time in a small population, genetic drift may result in a neutral or nearly neutral gene becoming more or less frequent just by chance.[32]

One variety of genetic drift, called the *founder principle*, occurs when a small group recently derived from a larger population migrates to a relatively isolated location.[33] If a particular gene is absent just by chance in the migrant group, the descendants are also likely to lack that gene, assuming that the group remains isolated. Similarly, if all members of the original migrant group just by chance carried a particular gene, their descendants would also be likely to share that gene. Isolation can occur for physical reasons, such as when a group moves to a previously uninhabited place and does not return. The populations that traveled over the Bering land bridge from Asia to North America could not readily return when the sea level rose. This may explain why Native Americans have a higher proportion of individuals with type O blood than other populations—the first migrants may have had, by

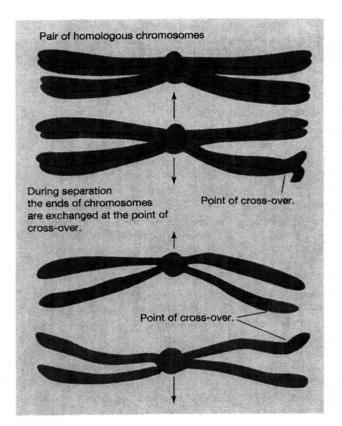

Pair of homologous chromosomes

During separation the ends of chromosomes are exchanged at the point of cross-over.

Point of cross-over.

Point of cross-over.

Figure 3–6   *Crossing Over*

Source: Noel T. Boaz and Alan J. Almquist, *Biological Anthropology.* Copyright © 1997. Reprinted by permission of Pearson Education, Inc., Upper Saddle River, NJ 07458.

chance, a predominance of individuals with type O blood.

Or the isolation can occur for social reasons. A religious sect of Dunkers emigrated from Germany to the United States in the early 1700s. The fact that the 50 original families kept to themselves probably explains why some of their gene frequencies differ from what is found in both the German and general U.S. populations.[34]

GENE FLOW

Gene flow is the process whereby genes pass from one population to another through mating and reproduction. Unlike the other processes of natural selection and genetic drift, which generally increase the differences between populations in different environments, gene flow tends to work in the opposite direction—it *decreases* differences between populations. Two populations at opposite ends of a region may have different frequencies of a particular gene, but the populations located between them have an intermediate gene frequency because of gene flow between them. The variation in gene frequency from one end of the region to the other is called a **cline.** In Europe, for example, there is a cline in the distribution of blood type B, which gradually diminishes in frequency from east to west.[35]

Most genetically determined characteristics in humans have gradually or clinally varying frequencies as one moves from one area to another. Neighboring regions have more similar gene frequencies than regions widely separated. But these clines do not always coincide, which makes the concept of "race" as applied to humans not very useful for understanding human biological variation.[36] We discuss this in more detail in the chapter on human variation.

Gene flow may occur between distant as well as close populations. Long-range movements of people, to trade or raid or settle, may result in gene flow. But they do not always do so.

The Origin of Species

One of the most controversial aspects of Darwin's theory was the suggestion that one species could, over time, evolve into another. A **species** is a population that consists of organisms able to interbreed and produce fertile and viable offspring. In general, individuals from one species cannot successfully mate with members of a different species because of genetic and behavioral differences. If members of different species did mate, it is unlikely that the egg would be fertilized, or, if it were, that the embryo would survive. If the offspring were born, it would soon die or be infertile. But how could one species evolve into another? What is the explanation for this differentiation? How does one group of organisms become so unlike another group with the same ancestry that it forms a totally new species?

Speciation, or the development of a new species, may occur if one subgroup of a species finds itself in a radically different environment. In adapting to their separate environments, the two populations may undergo enough genetic changes to prevent them from interbreeding, should they renew contact. Numerous factors can prevent the exchange of genes. Two species living in the same area may breed at different times of the year, or their behavior during breeding—their courtship rituals—may be distinct. The difference in body structure of closely related forms may in itself bar interbreeding. Geographic barriers may be the most common barriers to interbreeding.

Once species differentiation does occur, the evolutionary process cannot be reversed; the new species can no longer mate with other species related to its parent population. Humans and gorillas, for example, have the same distant ancestors, but their evolutionary paths have diverged irreversibly.

Natural Selection of Behavioral Traits

Until now we have discussed how natural selection might operate to change a population's physical traits, such as the

CURRENT ISSUES
Do We Need to Fear Genetic Engineering?

So much is known about molecular genetics that it is now possible to alter individual genes and even whole organisms in very precise ways. The revolution occurred very quickly after the structure of DNA was first identified in 1953 by James Watson and Francis Crick. Particular genetic traits could then be linked to particular sequences of DNA messages. In the 1970s, the development of recombinant DNA techniques allowed researchers to splice pieces of DNA from one organism into the DNA of another, in precise locations. Researchers learned how to make copies by putting these "recombined" strands into host organisms such as bacteria, which reproduce by cloning. The applications of these techniques are potentially enormous. Biotechnology companies are already doing genetic engineering to manufacture medicines (such as insulin and a vaccine against hepatitis B) and to produce more desirable plant and animal products (for example, a strain of

tomato that can be shipped when it's ripe without spoiling). They are also working on how to reintroduce altered cells into organisms to fix genetic defects. As of now, about 4,000 human disorders are known to be caused by defects in a few genes; theoretically, they should be fixable some day by genetic engineering. As more becomes known about the precise location of genes and the DNA sequences that convey particular information, much more engineering will be possible. Already some imagine that genetic therapy will eventually cure various cancers and heart disease.

Might there be risks associated with such interventions? Some fear that recombinant DNA engineering may have disastrous consequences. Could a dangerous runaway strain of bacteria or virus be produced in the lab? Might a kind of Frankenstein be produced? Could unscrupulous governments mandate certain kinds of alterations? Do we have reason to entertain such fears?

It is important to remind ourselves that although DNA alteration by recombinant techniques is new, genetic engineering is not new. Humans have genetically altered plants and animals for thousands of years. We usually do not call it genetic engineering—we call it domestication or breeding. To be sure, the mechanism of traditional genetic engineering, selective breeding, is different from DNA splicing, but the effect is genetic alteration nonetheless. By breeding for preferred traits, humans are able to produce breeds of horses, dogs, cattle, varieties of corn and beans, and all of the other animals and plants we depend on for food, fiber, and other materials and chemicals. All of them are different, often very different, from their wild progenitors. Humans have also domesticated micro-organisms. An example that goes back thousands of years is the yeast used for brewing beer and baking bread; a more recent example is a particular mold used to produce penicillin. And

color of moths or the neck length of giraffes. But natural selection can also operate on the behavioral characteristics of populations. Although this idea is not new, it is now receiving more attention. The approaches called **sociobiology**[37] and **behavioral ecology**[38] involve the application of evolutionary principles to the behavior of animals. Behavioral ecology is interested in how all kinds of behavior are related to the environment; sociobiology is particularly interested in social organization and social behavior. The typical behaviors of a species are assumed to be adaptive and to have evolved by natural selection. For example, why do related species exhibit different social behaviors even though they derive from a common ancestral species?

Consider the lion, as compared with other cats. Although members of the cat family are normally solitary

creatures, lions live in social groups called *prides*. Why? George Schaller has suggested that lion social groups may have evolved primarily because group hunting is a more successful way to catch large mammals in open terrain. He has observed that not only are several lions more successful in catching prey than are solitary lions, but several lions are more likely to catch and kill large and dangerous prey such as giraffes. Then, too, cubs are generally safer from predators when in a social group than when alone with their mothers. Thus, the social behavior of lions may have evolved primarily because it provided selective advantages in the lions' open-country environment.[39]

It is important to remember that natural selection operates on expressed characteristics, or the *phenotype*, of an individual. In the moth example, the color of the moth is

live vaccines that are deliberately weakened viruses, as, for example, in the vaccine against polio, have already been widely used to prevent illness.

So what does our past engineering tell us about the risks of future engineering? In general, the past suggests that no serious harm is attributable to domestication. In fact, domesticated animals and plants are less likely to do well if reintroduced into the wild than their wild cousins. They usually need human help to eat, to get shelter from the elements, and to care for their offspring. So why should genetic engineering be any different? It has basically the same purpose as selective breeding—humans want organisms, large or small or microscopic, to be useful to humans. So far, the available evidence indicates that organisms altered genetically to satisfy human needs are no threat to humans because they are unlikely to survive without human assistance. Needless to say, that does not obviate the need to test for risks. It is reassuring that even though DNA in nature can cross over from one organism to another, such natural genetic alter-ation is not generally harmful to us.

People may mostly be afraid that a dangerous microbe could be accidentally released from a laboratory and multiply uncontrollably. But, as already noted, any microbe or new genetic form is unlikely to be as hardy as its wild cousins. If a bacterium is mistakenly released, it is not going into an artificially empty environment like a sterile petri dish. The natural environment is already filled with bacteria (most of them beneficial to humans), as well as organisms that attack bacteria. In short, it is not so easy to produce a harmful microbe.

The improbability of making destructive organisms does not mean that humans should not guard against the possibility. That is why we have government agencies to certify new products, along with guidelines for testing procedures and oversight panels. A new product of recombinant DNA research has to be approved before it can be widely used.

Can humans use such technology for eugenic purposes, such as creating superhumans or for biological warfare? Possibly. But recombinant DNA tech-niques are not the problem. After all, the lack of such technology has not prevented genocide, ethnic cleansing, sterilization, and rape. The absence of recombinant technology did not prevent the use of natural biological weapons (such as smallpox-infected blankets given to Native Americans in the nineteenth century) or the manufacture and use of poison gas in World War I and since. It is not technology or the absence of it that explains evil; it is other things. If we want to reduce the risk of human violence, we have to understand why it occurs. More research might help make us safer.

Sources: Allan M. Campbell, "Microbes: The Laboratory and the Field," Bernard D. Davis, "The Issues: Prospects versus Perceptions" and "Summary and Comments: The Scientific Chapters," and Henry I. Miller, "Regulation," all in Bernard D. Davis, ed., *The Genetic Revolution: Scientific Prospects and Public Perceptions* (Baltimore: Johns Hopkins University Press, 1991), pp. 28–44, 1–8, 239–65, 196–211; Paul Berg and Maxine Singer, *Dealing with Genes: The Language of Heredity* (Mill Valley, CA: University Science Books, 1992), pp. 221–44.

part of its phenotype, subject to natural selection. Behavior is also an expressed characteristic. If hunting in groups, a behavioral trait, gets you more food, then individuals who hunt in groups will do better. But we must also remember that natural selection requires traits to be heritable. Can the concept of heritability be applied to learned behavior, not just genetically transmitted behavior? And, even more controversially, if the concept of heritability can include learning, can it also include cultural learning?

Early theorizing in sociobiology and behavioral ecology appeared to emphasize the genetic component of behavior. For example, Edward O. Wilson, in his book *Sociobiology,* defined sociobiology as "the systematic study of the biological causes of behavior."[40] But Bobbi Low points out that, although the term *biology* may have been interpreted to mean "genetic," most biologists understand that expressed or observable characteristics are the results of genes and environment, and life history, all interacting. Behavior is a product of all three. If we say that some behavior is heritable, we mean that the child's behavior is more likely to resemble the parents' behavior than the behavior of others.[41] Learning from a parent could be an important part of why the offspring is like the parent. If the child is more like the parent than like others, then the likeness is heritable, even if it is entirely learned from the parent.

The sociobiological approach has aroused considerable controversy in anthropology, probably because of its apparent emphasis on genes, rather than experience and

Prides of lions that live in open country are more successful in catching large animals than are solitary lions. This social behavior may have evolved because it provided selective advantages in the lion's open-country environment.

learning, as determinants of human behavior. Anthropologists have argued that the customs of a society may be more or less adaptive because cultural behaviors also have reproductive consequences. It is not just an individual's behavior that may have reproductive consequences. So does natural selection also operate in the evolution of culture? Most biologists think not. They say there are substantial differences between biological and cultural evolution. How do cultural evolution and biological evolution compare? To answer this question, we must remember that the operation of natural selection requires three conditions, as we aleady noted: variation, heritability or mechanisms that duplicate traits in offspring, and differential reproduction because of heritable differences. Do these three requirements apply to cultural behavior?

In biological evolution, variability comes from genetic recombination and mutation. In cultural evolution, it comes from recombination of learned behaviors and from invention.[42] Cultures are not closed or reproductively isolated, as species are. A species cannot borrow genetic traits from another species, but a culture can borrow new things and behaviors from other cultures. The custom of growing corn, which has spread from the New World to many other areas, is an example of this phenomenon. As for the requirement of heritability, although learned traits obviously are not passed to offspring through purely genetic inheritance, parents who exhibit adaptive behavioral traits are more likely to "reproduce" those traits in their children, who may learn them by imitation or by parental instruction. Children and adults may also copy adaptive traits they see in people outside the family. Finally, as for the requirement of differential reproduction, it does not matter whether the trait in question is genetic or learned or both. As Henry Nissen emphasized, "behavioral incompetence leads to extinction as surely as does morphological disproportion or deficiency in any vital organ. Behavior is subject to selection as much as bodily size or resistance to disease."[43]

Many theorists are comfortable with the idea of applying the theory of natural selection to cultural evolution, but others prefer to use different terminology when dealing with traits that do not depend on purely genetic transmission from one generation to the next. For example, Robert Boyd and Peter Richerson discuss human behavior as involving "dual inheritance." They distinguish cultural transmission, by learning and imitation, from genetic transmission, but they emphasize the importance of understanding both and the interaction between them.[44] William Durham also deals separately with cultural transmission, using the term *meme* (analogous to the term

Mountain lions live in wooded environments and hunt individually. Here we see one that has killed a mule deer in western Montana.

gene) for the unit of cultural transmission. He directs our attention to the interaction between genes and culture, calling that interaction "coevolution," and provides examples of how genetic evolution and cultural evolution may lead to changes in each other, how they may enhance each other, and how they may even oppose each other.[45]

So biological and cultural evolution in humans may not be completely separate processes. As we will discuss, some of the most important biological features of humans—such as our relatively large brains—may have been favored by natural selection because our ancestors made tools, a cultural trait. Conversely, the cultural trait of informal and formal education may have been favored by natural selection because humans have a long period of immaturity, a biological trait.

As long as the human species continues to exist and the social and physical environment continues to change, there is reason to think that natural selection of biological and cultural traits will also continue. However, as humans learn more and more about genetic structure they will become more and more capable of curing genetically caused disorders and even altering the way evolution proceeds. Today, genetic researchers are capable of diagnosing genetic defects in developing fetuses, and parents can and do decide often whether to terminate a pregnancy. Soon genetic engineering will probably allow humans to fix defects and even try to "improve" the genetic code of a growing fetus. Whether and to what extent humans should alter genes will undoubtedly be the subject of continuing debate. Whatever the decisions we eventually make about genetic engineering, they will affect the course of human biological and cultural evolution.

🦕 Summary

1. If we think of the history of the universe in terms of 12 months, the history of human-like primates would take up only about one and a half hours. The universe is some 15 billion years old; modern-looking humans have existed for about 100,000 years.

2. Ideas about evolution took a long time to take hold because they contradicted the biblical view of events; species were viewed as fixed in their form by the creator. But in the eighteenth and early nineteenth centuries increasing evidence suggested that evolution was a viable theory. In geology, the concept of uniformitarianism suggested that the earth is constantly subject to shaping and reshaping by natural forces working over vast stretches of time. A number of thinkers during this period began to discuss evolution and how it might occur.

3. Charles Darwin and Alfred Wallace proposed the mechanism of natural selection to account for the evolution of species. Basic principles of the theory of natural selection are that (1) every species is composed of a great variety of individuals, some of which are better adapted to their environment than others; (2) offspring inherit traits from their parents at least to some degree and in some

way; and (3) since better adapted individuals generally produce more offspring over the generations than the poorer adapted, the frequency of adaptive traits increases in subsequent generations. In this way, natural selection results in increasing proportions of individuals with advantageous traits.

4. Mendel's and subsequent research in genetics and our understanding of the structure and function of DNA and mRNA help us to understand the biological mechanisms by which traits may be passed from one generation to the next.

5. Natural selection depends on variation within a population. The four sources of biological variation are genetic recombination, mutation, genetic drift, and gene flow.

6. Speciation, the development of a new species, may occur if one subgroup becomes separated from other subgroups. In adapting to different environments, these subpopulations may undergo enough genetic changes to prevent interbreeding, even if they reestablish contact. Once species differentiation occurs, it is believed that the evolutionary process cannot be reversed.

7. Natural selection can also operate on the behavioral characteristics of populations. The approaches called sociobiology and behavioral ecology involve the application of evolutionary principles to the behavior of animals. Much controversy surrounds the degree to which the theory of natural selection can be applied to human behavior, particularly cultural behavior. There is more agreement that biological and cultural evolution in humans may influence each other.

🦕 Glossary Terms

allele	homozygous
balancing selection	meiosis
behavioral ecology	messenger RNA (mRNA)
chromosome	mitosis
cline	mutation
crossing-over	natural selection
directional selection	normalizing selection
DNA	phenotype
dominant	recessive
gene	ribosome
gene flow	segregation
genetic drift	sociobiology
genotype	speciation
heterozygous	species

🦕 Critical Questions

1. Do you think the theory of natural selection is compatible with religious beliefs? Explain your reasoning.

2. How might the discovery of genetic cures and the use of genetic engineering affect the future of evolution?

3. Why do you think humans have remained one species?

Internet Exercises

1. Explore the Evolution and the Nature of Science Institutes (ENSI) Web site at **http://www.indiana.edu/~ ensiweb/**, and go through several of the evolution lessons.

2. Visit the home page of *Evolution* (*International Journal of Organic Evolution*) at **http://lsvl.la.asu.edu/ evolution/**. By looking at the table of contents, provide a bibliography of at least 15 articles related to human evolution.

3. Visit the Museum of Paleontology's evolution exhibit halls at **http://www.ucmp.berkeley.edu/history/ evolution.html**, and write a review of the exhibits presented there.

Suggested Reading

BOYD, R., AND RICHERSON, P. J. *Culture and the Evolutionary Process*. Chicago: University of Chicago Press, 1985. The authors develop mathematical models to analyze how biology and culture interact under the influence of evolutionary processes.

BRANDON, R. N. *Adaptation and Environment*. Princeton, NJ: Princeton University Press, 1990. After defining basic concepts regarding adaptation and the theory of natural selection, the author emphasizes that the process of adaptation and its outcomes cannot be understood without analysis of the environment.

CHIRAS, D. D. *Human Biology: Health, Homeostasis, and the Environment*, 2nd ed. St. Paul, MN: West, 1995. An introductory textbook in human biology. See chapters 3–5 for a detailed discussion of chromosomes, DNA, RNA, principles of heredity, and genetic engineering.

DEVILLERS, C., AND CHALINE, J. *Evolution: An Evolving Theory*. New York: Springer-Verlag, 1993. Aimed at the general audience, this book addresses the questions: What is the place of humans in the living world? What is evolution? How can the observed data be explained? Appendixes give more detailed information.

DOBZHANSKY, T. *Mankind Evolving: The Evolution of the Human Species*. New Haven, CT: Yale University Press, 1962. A classic demonstration that the mechanisms of evolution, primarily natural selection, are still active.

DURHAM, W. H. *Coevolution: Genes, Culture, and Human Diversity*. Stanford, CA: Stanford University Press, 1991. A discussion of the evolution of culture that considers how theory and research point to the interaction of genes and culture in human populations.

EISELEY, L. *Darwin's Century: Evolution and the Men Who Discovered It*. New York: Anchor Books, 1958. A classic history of evolutionary thought and the growth of modern evolutionary theory.

MAYR, E. *The Growth of Biological Thought: Diversity, Evolution, and Inheritance*. Cambridge, MA: Belknap Press of Harvard University Press, 1982. A history of ideas that discusses the successful and unsuccessful attempts to understand problems in the study of evolution.

MAYR, E. *One Long Argument: Charles Darwin and the Genesis of Modern Evolutionary Thought*. Cambridge, MA: Harvard University Press, 1993. A concise look at evolutionary theory.

2

The Living Primates

CHAPTER OUTLINE

Common Primate Traits

Classification of Primates

The Various Primates

Explanations of Variable Primate Adaptations

Distinctive Human Traits

Taken from: *Physical Anthropology and Archaeology* by Carol R. Ember, Melvin Ember, and Peter N. Peregrine

he goal of *primatology,* the study of primates, is to understand how different primates have adapted anatomically and behaviorally to their environments. The results of such studies may help us to understand the behavior and evolution of the human primate.

But how can living primates such as chimpanzees tell us anything about humans or the primates that were our ancestors? After all, each living primate species has its own history of evolutionary divergence from the earliest primate forms. All living primates, including humans, evolved from earlier primates that are now extinct. Nonetheless, by observing how humans and other primates differ from and resemble each other, we may be able to infer how and why humans diverged from the other primates.

In conjunction with fossil evidence, anatomical and behavioral comparisons of living primates may help us reconstruct what early primates were like. For example, if we know that modern primates that swing through the trees have a particular kind of shoulder bone structure, we can infer that similar fossil bones probably belonged to an animal that also swung through the trees. Differing adaptations of living primates may also suggest why certain divergences occurred in primate evolution. If we know what traits belong to humans, and to humans alone, this knowledge may suggest why the line of primates that led to humans branched away from the line leading to chimpanzees and gorillas.

In this chapter we first examine the common features of the living primates. Next we introduce the different animals that belong to the order Primates, focusing on the distinctive characteristics of each major type. Then we discuss possible explanations of some of the varying adaptations exhibited by the different primate species. We close with a look at the traits that make humans different from all other primates. The purpose of this chapter is to help us understand more about humans. Therefore, we emphasize the features of primate anatomy and behavior that perhaps have the greatest bearing on human evolution.

Common Primate Traits

All primates belong to the class Mammalia, and they share all the common features of mammals. Except for humans, the bodies of primates are covered with dense hair or fur, which provides insulation. Even humans have hair in various places, though perhaps not always for insulation. Mammals are *warm-blooded;* that is, their body temperature is more or less constantly warm and usually higher than that of the air around them. Almost all mammals give birth to live young that develop to a considerable size within the mother and are nourished by suckling from the mother's mammary glands. The young have a relatively long period of dependence on adults after birth. This period is also a time of learning, for a great deal of adult mammal behavior is learned rather than instinctive. Play is a learning technique common to mammal young and is especially important to primates, as we shall see later in this chapter.

The primates have a number of physical and social traits that set them apart from other mammals.

PHYSICAL FEATURES

No one of the primates' physical features is unique to primates; animals from other orders share one or more of the characteristics described below. But the complex of all these physical traits *is* unique to primates.[1]

Many skeletal features of the primates reflect an **arboreal** (tree-living) existence. All primate hind limbs are structured principally to provide support, but the "feet" in most primates can also grasp things (see Figure 4–1). Some primates—orangutans, for instance—can suspend themselves from their hind limbs. The forelimbs are especially flexible, built to withstand both pushing and pulling forces. Each of the hind limbs and forelimbs has one bone in the upper portion and two bones in the lower portion (with the exception of the tarsier). This feature has little changed since the time of the earliest primate ancestors. It has remained in modern primates (although many other mammals have lost it) because the double bones give great mobility for rotating arms and legs.

Another characteristic structure of primates is the clavicle, or collarbone. The clavicle also gives primates great freedom of movement, allowing them to move the shoulders both up and down and back and forth. Although humans obviously do not use this flexibility for arboreal activity, they do use it for other activities. Without a clavicle we could not throw a spear or a ball; no fine tools could be made and no doorknobs turned if we did not have rotatable forearms.

Primates generally are **omnivorous;** that is, they eat all kinds of food, including insects and small animals, as well as fruits, seeds, leaves, and roots. The teeth of primates reflect this omnivorous diet. The chewing teeth—the **molars** and **premolars**—are unspecialized, particularly in comparison with those of other groups of animals, such as the grazers. The front teeth—the **incisors** and **canines**—are often very specialized, principally in the lower primates. For example, in many prosimians the slender, tightly packed lower incisors and canines form a "dental comb" the animals use in grooming or for scraping hardened tree gum (which is a food for them) from tree trunks.[2]

Primate hands are extremely flexible. All primates have **prehensile**—grasping—hands, which can be wrapped around an object. Primates have five digits on both hands and feet (in some cases, one digit may be reduced to a stub), and their nails, with few exceptions, are broad and flat, not clawlike. This structure allows them to grip objects; the hairless, sensitive pads on their fingers, toes, heels, and palms also help them to grip. Most primates have **opposable thumbs,** a feature that allows an even more precise and powerful grip.

Vision is extremely important to primate life. Com-

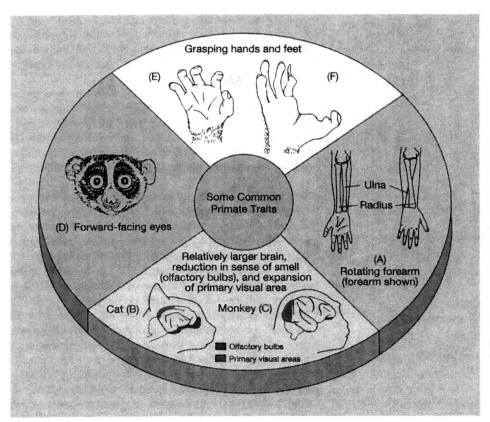

Figure 4–1 *Some Common Primate Traits*

Source: (A) From Ronald G. Wolff, *Functional Chordate Anatomy* (Lexington, MA: D. C. Heath and Company, 1991), p. 255. Reprinted with permission of D. C. Heath. (B, C) From Terrence Deacon, "Primate Brains and Senses," in Stephen Jones, Robert Martin, and David Pilbeam, eds., *The Cambridge Encyclopedia of Human Evolution* (New York: Cambridge University Press, 1992, p. 110. (D) From Matt Cartmill, "Non-Human Primates," in ibid., p. 25. (E, F) From ibid., p. 24. Copyright © by Cambridge University Press. Reprinted by permission of Cambridge University Press.

pared with other mammals, primates have a relatively larger portion of the brain devoted to vision rather than smell. Primates are characterized by *stereoscopic*, or depth, *vision*. Their eyes are directed forward rather than sideways, as in other animals—a trait that allows them to focus on an object (insects or other food or a distant branch) with both eyes at once. Most primates also have color vision, perhaps to recognize when plant foods are ready to eat.

Another important primate feature is a large brain relative to body size. That is, primates generally have larger brains than animals of similar size, perhaps because their survival depends on an enormous amount of learning, as we discuss later. In general, animals with large brains seem to mature more slowly and to live longer than animals with small brains.[3] The more slowly an animal matures and the longer it lives, the more it can learn.

Finally, the primate reproductive system sets this order of animals apart from other mammals. Males of most primate species have a pendulous penis that is not attached to the abdomen by skin, a trait shared by a few other animals, including bats and bears. Females of most primate species have two nipples on the chest (a few prosimians have more than two nipples). The uterus is usually constructed to hold a single fetus (only the marmosets and tamarins typically give birth to twins), not a litter, as with most other animals. This reproductive system can be seen as emphasizing quality over quantity—an adaptation possibly re-lated to the dangers of life in the trees, particularly the risk of falls.[4] Primate infants tend to be relatively well developed at birth, although humans, apes, and some monkeys have helpless infants. Most infant primates, except humans, can cling to their mothers from birth. Primates typically take a long time to mature. For example, the rhesus monkey is not sexually mature until about 3 years of age, the chimpanzee not until about age 9.

SOCIAL FEATURES

For the most part, primates are social animals. And just as physical traits such as grasping hands and stereoscopic vision may have developed as adaptations to the environment, so may have many patterns of social behavior. For most primates, particularly those that are **diurnal**—that is, active during the day—group life may be crucial to survival, as we will see later in this chapter.

DEPENDENCY AND DEVELOPMENT IN A SOCIAL CONTEXT Social relationships begin with the mother and other adults during the fairly long dependency period of primates. (For the dependency period of primates, the infancy and juvenile phases, see Figure 4–2.) The prolonged dependency of infant monkeys and apes probably offers an evolutionary advantage in that it allows infants more time to observe and learn the complex behaviors essential to survival while enjoying the care and protection of mature adults.

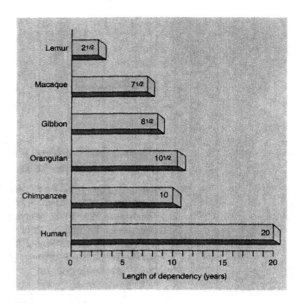

Figure 4–2 *A Comparison of the Dependency Periods of Primate Offspring*

Source: Data from Alison Jolly, *The Evolution of Primate Behavior,* 2nd ed. (New York: Macmillan, 1985), p. 292.

Primates without a warm, social relationship with a mother or another individual do not appear to develop appropriate patterns of social interaction. In a series of classic experiments with rhesus monkeys, Harry Harlow investigated the effects of maternal neglect and isolation on offspring.[5] He found that as a result of either inadequate mothering or isolation from other infants, some monkeys are unable to lead normal social lives. They develop aberrant sexual activities and may even become juvenile delinquents. Harlow mated socially deprived female monkeys with well-adjusted males. When these females gave birth, their behavior was not at all motherly, and they

often rejected their babies entirely. Their abnormal behavior was offered as evidence that mothering is more than instinctive. Harlow's experiments underline the importance of maternal care and attention for monkeys and, as a corollary, for humans.

In many primate groups the mother is not the only individual providing care to the dependent young. Among gray langur monkeys, the birth and subsequent rearing of a baby absorb the attention of most female members of the troop.[6] And in some primate species, the father may spend as much time caring for infants as the mother.[7]

PRIMATES AT PLAY Harlow's investigations have provided other information about social learning in young primates. The experiments that showed the importance of maternal care to baby rhesus monkeys also revealed that play is another crucial ingredient of normal development during the dependency period. Just as monkeys raised without mothers showed abnormal behavior as adults, so did monkeys raised with mothers but with no peers to play with. In fact, when some of the monkeys raised without mothers were allowed a regular playtime with peers, many of them behaved more normally. Subsequent work has supported Harlow's findings.[8]

Play is important for learning.[9] It provides practice for the physical skills necessary or useful in adulthood. For example, young monkeys racing through the trees at top speed are gaining coordination that may save their lives if they are chased by predators later on. Play is also a way of learning social skills, particularly in interacting and communicating with other members of the group. Some dom-

Primates can learn from direct teaching, but they learn mostly by imitation and trial-and-error.

Endangered Primates

In contrast to many human populations that are too numerous for their resources, many populations of nonhuman primates face extinction because they are not numerous enough. The two trends—human overpopulation and nonhuman primate extinctions—are related. Were it not for human expansion in many parts of the world, the nonhuman primates living in those habitats would not be endangered. Various lemur and other prosimian species of Madagascar, the mountain gorilla and red colobus monkeys of Africa, and the lion tamarin monkeys of Brazil are among the species most at risk.

Many factors are responsible for the difficulties faced by nonhuman primates, but most of them are directly or indirectly the result of human activity. Perhaps the biggest problem is the destruction of tropical rain forest, the habitat of most nonhuman primates, because of encroaching agriculture and cattle ranching and the felling of trees for wood products. The people who live in these areas are partly responsible for the threats to nonhuman primates—population pressure in the human populations increases the likelihood that more forest will be cleared and burned for agriculture, and

A golden lion tamarin.

in some areas nonhuman primates are an important source of hunted food. But world market forces are probably more important. The increasing need for "American" hamburger in fast food restaurants has accelerated the search for places to raise beef inexpensively. There is also enormous demand for wood products from tropical forests; Japan imports half of all the timber from rain forests to use for plywood, cardboard, paper, and furniture.

Some would argue that it is important to preserve all species. Primatologists remind us that it is especially important to preserve primate diversity. One reason is the scientific one of need-

ing those populations to study and understand how humans are similar and different and how they came to be that way. Another reason is the usefulness of nonhuman primates in biomedical research on human diseases; we share many of our diseases, and many of our genes, with our primate relatives. (As we noted in the first chapter, chimpanzees share 99 percent of their genes with humans.) The film *The Planet of the Apes*, in which the humans are subordinate to the apes, tells us that the primates in zoos could have been us.

So how can nonhuman primates be protected from us? There really are only two major ways: Either human population growth in many places has to be curtailed, or we have to preserve substantial populations of nonhuman primates in protected parks and zoos. Both are difficult but humanly possible.

Sources: Russell A. Mittermeier and Eleanor J. Sterling, "Conservation of Primates," in Steve Jones, Robert Martin, and David Pilbeam, eds., *The Cambridge Encyclopedia of Human Evolution* (Cambridge: Cambridge University Press, 1992), pp. 33–36; Toshisada Nishida, "Introduction to the Conservation Symposium," in Naosuke Itoigawa, Yukimaru Sugiyama, Gene P. Sackett, and Roger K. R. Thompson, *Topics in Primatology*, vol. 2 (Tokyo: University of Tokyo Press, 1992), pp. 303–304.

inance relationships seem to be established partly through the rough-and-tumble games that older juveniles play, where winning depends on such factors as size, strength, and agility. These qualities, or the lack of them, may influence the individual's status throughout adult life. (Other factors also help determine an individual's status. For instance, the mother's status has been shown to be very important in some primates.[10])

LEARNING FROM OTHERS   We know that primates, nonhuman and human alike, learn many things in social groups. Among humans, children often imitate others, and adults often deliberately teach the young. In English we say, "Isn't it cute how Tommy 'apes' his father." But do apes (and monkeys) imitate others, or do they just learn to do similar things whether or not a model is observed? There is controversy among researchers as to how much imitation versus independent learning occurs in nonhuman primates. Even more arguable is whether deliberate teaching occurs among nonhuman primates.[11]

Some fieldworkers have suggested that chimpanzees may learn by imitation to use tools. For example, Jane Goodall cited an occasion when a female with diarrhea picked up a handful of leaves to wipe her bottom. Her 2-year-old infant watched closely, and then twice picked up leaves to wipe its own, clean behind.[12] Termite "fishing," using a grass stalk to withdraw termites from a termite mound, is probably the best known example of chimpanzee tool use. Immature chimpanzees in the wild have been observed to watch attentively and pick up stalks while others are "fishing." And mothers let their infants hold on to the stalks while the mothers "fish." But some observers do not think these reports provide clear evidence of imitation or teaching. Even though the mother lets the infant hold on to the "fishing" stalk, the infant is doing the activity with her, not watching it and then independently repeating it soon after.[13]

Classification of Primates

Classification provides a useful way to refer to groups of species that are similar in biologically important ways.

Sometimes classification schemes vary because the classifiers emphasize somewhat different aspects of similarity and difference. For instance, one type of classification stresses the evolutionary branching that led to the primates of today; another the quantity of shared features. A third approach considers the evolutionary lines as well as similarity and difference of features, but not all features are equally weighted. More "advanced" and specialized features that develop in an evolutionary line are emphasized.[14] Figure 4–3 gives a classification scheme that follows this last approach.[15]

Despite the different ways to classify, there is generally little disagreement about how the various primates should be classified. Most of the disagreement, as we shall see when we discuss the various primates, revolves around the classification of tarsiers and humans.

The order Primates is often divided into two suborders: the **prosimians**—literally, premonkeys—and the **anthropoids.** The prosimians include lemurs, lorises, and tarsiers. The anthropoid suborder includes New World monkeys, Old World monkeys, the lesser apes (gibbons, siamangs), the great apes (orangutans, gorillas, chimpanzees), and humans.

The Various Primates

Now that we have discussed their common features, let us focus on some of the ways in which the primates living in the world today vary.

Figure 4–3   *A Simplified Classification of the Living Primates*

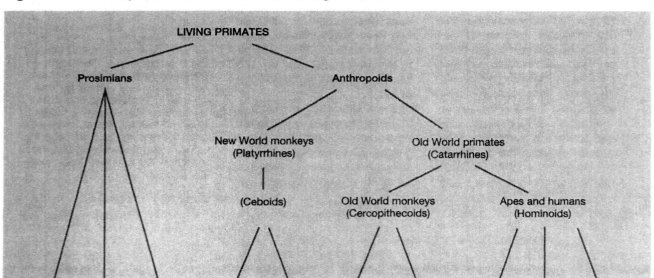

Prosimians such as these ring-tailed lemurs depend much more on smell than do anthropoids. Prosimians also have more mobile ears, whiskers, longer snouts, and relatively fixed facial expressions.

The bushbaby is a small arboreal prosimian that eats both fruit and insects. It is an energetic nocturnal animal that moves by vertical clinging and leaping.

PROSIMIANS

The prosimians resemble other mammals more than the anthropoid primates do. For example, the prosimians depend much more on smell for information than do anthropoids. Also in contrast with the anthropoids, they typically have more mobile ears, whiskers, longer snouts, and relatively fixed facial expressions. The prosimians also exhibit many traits shared by all primates, including grasping hands, stereoscopic vision, and enlarged visual centers in the brain.

LEMURLIKE FORMS Lemurs and their relatives, the indris and the aye-ayes, are found only on two island areas off the southeastern coast of Africa, Madagascar and the Comoro Islands. These primates range in size from the mouse lemur to the 4-foot-long indri. Members of the lemur group usually produce single offspring, although twins and even triplets are common in some species. Many of the species in this group are **quadrupeds**—animals that move on all fours; they walk on all fours in the trees as well as on the ground. Some species, such as the indris, use their hind limbs alone to push off from one vertical position to another in a mode of locomotion called **vertical clinging and leaping.**

Lemurs are mostly vegetarians, eating fruit, leaves, bark, and flowers. Lemur species vary greatly in their group size. Many lemur species, particularly those that are **nocturnal** (active during the night), are solitary during their active hours. Others are much more social, living in groups ranging in size from a small family to as many as 60 members.[16] An unusual feature of the lemurlike primates is that females often dominate males, particularly over access to food. In most primates, and in most other mammals, female dominance is rarely observed.[17]

LORISLIKE FORMS Members of the loris group, found in both Southeast Asia and sub-Saharan Africa, are all nocturnal and arboreal. They eat fruit, tree gum, and insects, and usually give birth to single infants.[18] There are two major subfamilies, the lorises and the bushbabies (galagos), and they show wide behavioral differences. Bushbabies are quick, active animals that hop between branches and tree trunks in the vertical-clinging-and-leaping pattern. On the ground they often resort to a kangaroolike hop. Lorises are much slower, walking sedately along branches hand over hand in the quadrupedal fashion.

With the use of searchlights and technical aids such as radio tracking, field researchers have learned a good deal about these nocturnal primates. For example, we know that among bushbabies, females, particularly mothers and young adult daughters, stay together in small groups,

Nocturnal tree-living tarsiers, like this one in the Philippines, are the only primates that depend completely on animal foods. Their enormous eyes equip them to find insects and other prey in the night. Their elongated ankle bones (tarsals) make them very good at vertical clinging and leaping.

whereas the males disperse. Newborns are born in nests or hollows of trees (which related females may share), and mothers return to nurse them regularly. A few days after birth, a mother may carry her infant in her mouth to nearby trees, "parking" it while she eats.[19]

TARSIERS The nocturnal, tree-living tarsiers, found now only on the islands of the Philippines and Indonesia, are the only primates that depend completely on animal foods. They are usually insect-eaters, but they sometimes capture and eat other small animals. They are well equipped for night vision, possessing enormous eyes, extraordinary eyesight, and enlarged visual centers in the brain. The tarsiers get their name from their elongated tarsal bones (the bones of the ankle), which give them tremendous leverage for their long jumps. Tarsiers are very skilled at vertical clinging and leaping. They live in family groups composed of a mated pair and their offspring. Like some higher primates, male and female tarsiers sing together each evening to advertise their territories.[20]

The classification of tarsiers is somewhat controversial. Instead of placing them with the suborder prosimians, as we have done here, some classifiers group tarsiers with anthropoids. In this other classification scheme the suborders of primates are labeled *strepsirhines* (which includes lemurs and lorises) and *haplorhines* (which includes tarsiers and anthropoids). Tarsiers have chromosomes similar to those of other prosimians; they also have claws for grooming on some of their toes, more than two nipples, and a uterus shaped like that of other prosimians (two-horned). Like bushbabies, tarsiers move about through

Figure 4–4 *Features of Platyrrhines and Catarrhines*

Source: Based on Noel T. Boaz and Alan J. Almquist, *Biological Anthropology.* Copyright © 1997. Reprinted by permission of Pearson Education, Inc., Upper Saddle River, NJ 07458.

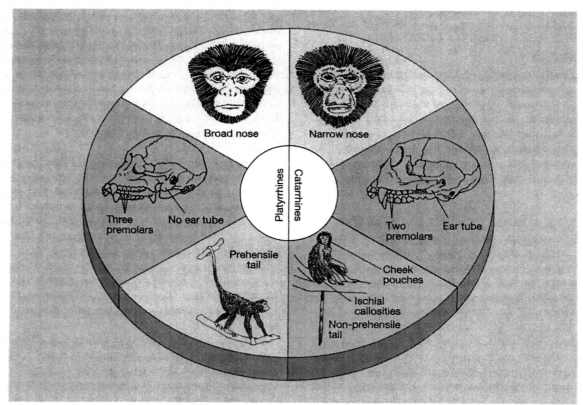

vertical clinging and leaping. In other respects tarsiers are more like the anthropoids. They have a reduced dependence on smell; not only are their noses smaller, but they lack the wet, doglike snout of lemurs. In common with the anthropoids, their eyes are closer together and are protected by bony orbits. Reproductively, the tarsier, like anthropoids, has a placenta that allows contact between the mother's blood and that of the fetus.[21]

ANTHROPOIDS

The anthropoid suborder includes humans, apes, and monkeys. Most anthropoids share several traits in varying degree. They have rounded braincases; reduced, nonmobile outer ears; and relatively small, flat faces instead of muzzles. They have highly efficient reproductive systems. They also have highly dextrous hands.[22] The anthropoid order is divided into two main groups: **platyrrhines** and **catarrhines** (see Figure 4–4). These groups take their names from the nose shape of the different anthropoids, but as we shall see they differ in other features as well. Platyrrhines have broad, flat-bridged noses, with nostrils facing outward; these monkeys are found only in the New World, in Central and South America. Catarrhines have narrow noses with nostrils facing downward. Catarrhines include monkeys of the Old World (Africa, Asia, and Europe), as well as apes and humans.

The squirrel monkey, like all platyrrhines, almost never leaves the trees. It is well suited to an arboreal lifestyle; note how it uses both hands and feet to grasp branches.

NEW WORLD MONKEYS Besides the shape of the nose and the position of the nostrils, other anatomical features distinguish the New World monkeys (platyrrhines) from the catarrhine anthropoids. The New World species have three premolars, whereas the Old World species have two. Some New World monkeys have a prehensile (grasping) tail; no Old World monkeys do. All the New World monkeys are completely arboreal; they vary a lot in the size of their groups; and their food ranges from insects to nectar and sap to fruits and leaves.[23]

Two main families of New World monkeys have traditionally been defined. One family, the *callitrichids*, contains marmosets and tamarins; the other family, the *cebids*, contains all the other New World monkeys. Although scholars recognize some problems with this division, it is a useful one for gaining a basic understanding of the New World monkeys. The callitrichids are very small, have claws instead of fingernails, and give birth to twins who mature in about two years. Perhaps because twinning is so common and the infants have to be carried, callitrichid mothers cannot take care of them alone. Fathers and older siblings have often been observed carrying infants. Indeed, males may do more carrying than females. Callitrichid groups may contain a mated pair (monogamy) or a female mated to more than one male (polyandry). The callitrichids eat a lot of fruit and tree sap, but like other very small primates, they obtain a large portion of their protein requirements from insects.[24]

Cebids are generally larger than callitrichids, take about twice as long to mature, and tend to bear only one offspring at a time.[25] The cebids vary widely in size, group composition, and diet. For example, squirrel monkeys weigh about 2 pounds, whereas woolly spider monkeys weigh more than 16 pounds. Some cebids have small groups with one male-female pair, others have groups of up to 50 individuals. Some of the smallest cebids have a diet of leaves, insects, flowers, and fruits, whereas others are mostly fruit-eaters with lesser dependence on seeds, leaves, or insects.[26]

OLD WORLD MONKEYS The Old World monkeys, or **cercopithecoids,** are related more closely to humans than to New World monkeys. They have the same number of teeth as apes and humans. The Old World monkey species are not as diverse as their New World cousins, but they live in a greater variety of habitats. Some live both in trees and on the ground; others, such as the gelada baboon, are completely **terrestrial,** or ground-living. Macaques are found both in tropical jungles and on snow-covered mountains, and they range from the Rock of Gibraltar to Africa to northern India, Pakistan, and Japan. There are two major subfamilies of Old World monkeys.

Colobine Monkeys The colobine group includes Asian langurs, the African colobus monkeys, and several other species. These monkeys live mostly in trees, and their diet consists principally of leaves and seeds. Their digestive tracts are equipped to obtain maximum nutrition from a

Grooming is an important part of social behavior for Old World monkeys. Here two Japanese macaques groom one another.

high-cellulose diet; they have pouched stomachs, which provide a large surface area for breaking down plant food, and very large intestinal tracts.

One of the most noticeable features of colobines is the flamboyant color typical of newborns. For example, in one species dusky gray mothers give birth to brilliant orange babies.[27] Observational studies suggest that the colobines

This langur, like all catarrhines, has a relatively narrow nose with nostrils that point downward. Langurs are Asian members of the colobine family and are primarily leaf-eaters.

are also unusual among the primates (except for humans) in that mothers let other group members take care of their infants shortly after birth. But males who are not members of the group are dangerous for infants; males trying to enter and take over a group have been observed to kill infants. Although this description may suggest that a one-male group is the typical group structure, there does not appear to be a typical pattern for a given species. When more than one site of a species has been studied, both one-male and multiple-male groups have been found.[28]

Cercopithecine Monkeys The cercopithecine subfamily of monkeys includes more terrestrial species than any other subfamily of Old World monkeys. Many of these species are characterized by a great deal of **sexual dimorphism** (the sexes look very different); the males are larger, have longer canines, and are more aggressive than the females. Cercopithecines depend more on fruit than do colobines. They are also more capable of surviving in arid and seasonal environments.[29] Pouches inside the cheeks allow cercopithecines to store food for later eating and digestion. An unusual physical feature of these monkeys is the *ischial callosities*, or callouses, on their bottoms—an adaptation that enables them to sit comfortably in trees or on the ground for long periods of time.[30]

Studies of baboons and macaques suggest that closely related females form the core of a local group, or *troop*. In large groups, which are common among rhesus monkeys,

A troop of baboons in Kenya spends most of its time on the ground.

many social behaviors seem to be determined by degree of biological relatedness. For example, an individual is most likely to sit next to, groom, or help an individual who is closely related maternally.[31] Moreover, a closely related subgroup is likely to stay together when a large troop divides.[32]

THE HOMINOIDS: APES AND HUMANS The **hominoid** group includes three separate families: the lesser apes, or **hylobates** (gibbons and siamangs); the great apes, or **pongids** (orangutans, gorillas, and chimpanzees); and humans, or **hominids.** Several characteristics distinguish the hominoids from the other primates. Their brains are relatively large, especially the areas of the cerebral cortex associated with the ability to integrate data. All hominoids have fairly long arms, short, broad trunks, and no tails. The wrist, elbow, and shoulder joints of hominoids allow a greater range of movement than in other primates. Hominoid hands are longer and stronger than those of other primates. These skeletal features probably evolved along with the hominoids' unique abilities in suspensory locomotion. Unlike other anthropoids, who move quadrupedally along the ground or along tops of tree branches, hominoids often suspend themselves from below the branches and swing or climb hand over hand from branch to branch.[33] This suspensory posture also translates to locomotion on the ground; all hominids, at least occasionally, move bipedally, as we discuss in more detail in the chapter on the first hominids.

The dentition of hominoids demonstrates some unique features as well (see Figure 4–5). Hominoid molars are flat and rounded compared to those of other anthropoids, and have what is called a **"Y-5" pattern** on the lower molars—that is, the lower molars have five cusps with a Y-shaped groove opening toward the cheek running between them. Other anthropoids have what is called a **bilophodont** pattern—their molars have two long ridges or "loafs" running parallel to the cheeks. All hominoids except for humans also have long canine teeth that project beyond the tops of the other teeth, and a corresponding space on the opposite jaw, called a **diastema,** where the canine sits when the jaws are closed. The contact of the upper canine and the lower third premolar creates a sharp cutting edge, in part due to the premolar being elongated to accommodate the canine.[34] These dental features are related to the hominoids' diets, which often include both fibrous plant materials, which can be efficiently cut with sharp canines against elongated premolars, and soft fruits, which can be efficiently chewed with wide, flat molars.

The skeletal and dental features shared by the hominoids point toward their common ancestry. Their blood proteins show many similarities, too. This blood likeness is particularly strong among chimpanzees, gorillas, and humans. For this reason, primatologists think chimpanzees and gorillas are evolutionarily closer to humans than are the lesser apes and orangutans, which probably branched off at some earlier point. We discuss the fossil evidence that supports an early split for the orangutans in the next chapter.

Gibbons and Siamangs The agile gibbons and their close relatives the siamangs are found in the jungles of Southeast Asia. The gibbons are small, weighing only about 11 to 15 pounds. The siamangs are somewhat larger, but no more than 25 pounds. Both are mostly fruit-eaters, although they also eat leaves and insects. They are spectacular **brachiators;** their long arms and fingers let them swing hand over hand through the trees.[35] A gibbon can move more than 30 feet in a single forward swing.

Figure 4–5

Difference in dentition between an Old World monkey (left) and an ape (right). In Old World monkeys the cusps of the lower molars form two parallel ridges; in apes, the five cusps form a Y-shaped pattern. Source: Adapted from Noel T. Boaz and Alan J. Almquist, Essentials of Biological Anthropology (Upper Saddle River, NJ: Prentice Hall, 1999), p. 164.

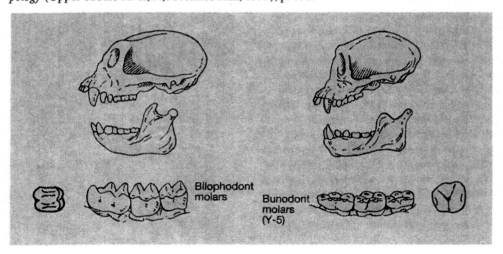

A white-handed gibbon demonstrates its ability as a brachiator.

Gibbons and siamangs live in small family groups consisting of an adult pair, who appear to mate for life, and one or two immature offspring. When the young reach adulthood, they are driven from home by the adults. There is little sexual dimorphism—males and females do not differ in size or appearance—nor is there any clear pattern of dominance by either sex. These lesser apes are also highly territorial; an adult pair advertises their territory by singing and defends it by chasing others away.[36]

Orangutans Orangutans survive only on the islands of Borneo and Sumatra. Unlike gibbons and siamangs, they are clearly recognizable as males or females. Males not only weigh almost twice as much as females (up to 200 pounds), but they also have large cheek pads, throat pouches, beards, and long hair.[37] Like gibbons and siamangs, orangutans are primarily fruit-eaters and arboreal. They are the heaviest of the arboreal primates, and perhaps for this reason they move slowly and laboriously through the trees. Orangutans are unusual among the higher primates in living basically solitary lives, except for mothers and their young; however, a recent field study of orangutans on Sumatra found that groups of as many as 10 adults fed together in the same tree.[38]

Different ideas have been proposed about the solitary habit of the orangutans that live in the mountainous areas of Borneo. One is that there may be insufficient food in any one tree or home range to support more than a single adult orangutan, a pretty large animal, as animals go. To obtain sufficient food each day without having to travel over a huge area, orangutans thus may live alone rather than in groups.[39] Another idea is that animals live in groups when they are subject to heavy predation; the large size of orangutans may make them immune to attacks from most animals, so living alone may be a viable option.[40] A third idea, which on the face of it seems opposite to the second, is that living alone may be an adaptation to heavy predation by humans. The orangutan's best defense against humans with guns may be to hide alone in the trees.[41]

Gorillas Gorillas are found in the lowland areas of western equatorial Africa and in the mountain areas of Congo, Uganda, and Rwanda.[42] Unlike the other apes, who are mostly fruit-eaters, gorillas mostly eat other parts of plants—stems, shoots (for example, bamboo), pith, leaves, roots, and flowers. The amount of fruit eaten varies greatly. In many populations fruit-eating is rare; in some, however, fruit is a common part of the diet.[43]

Gorillas are by far the largest of the surviving apes. In their natural habitats, adult males weigh up to 450 pounds and females up to 250 pounds. To support the weight of massive chests, gorillas travel mostly on the ground on all fours in a form of locomotion known as **knuckle walking:** They walk on the thickly padded middle joints of their fingers. Gorillas' arms and legs, especially those of the young, are well suited for climbing. As adults, their heavier bodies make climbing more precarious.[44] They sleep on the ground or in tub-shaped nests they make from non-food plants each time they bed down.[45]

Gorillas tend to live in groups consisting of a dominant male, called a *silverback*, other adult males, adult females, and immature offspring. Both males and females, when mature, seem to leave the groups into which they were

A young gorilla shows how it knuckle-walks. The back feet are flat on the ground, and only the knuckles of the "hands" touch the ground.

born to join other groups. The dominant male is very much the center of attention; he acts as the main protector of the group and the leader in deciding where the group will go next.[46]

Chimpanzees Perhaps because they are more sociable and easier to find, chimpanzees have been studied far more than gorillas. Chimpanzees live in the forested areas of Africa, from Sierra Leone in the west to Tanzania in the east.

There are two distinct species of chimpanzee—the common chimpanzee (*Pan troglodytes*) and the *bonobo*, or pygmy, chimpanzee (*Pan paniscus*). While they share many features in common (indeed, they were not recognized as distinct species until 1929), bonobos tend to be more slender than common chimpanzees, with longer limbs and digits, smaller heads, darker faces, and a distinct part in their hair. Unlike common chimpanzees, bonobos show almost no sexual dimorphism in dentition or skeletal structure. More significant seem to be differences in social behavior. Bonobos are more gregarious than common chimpanzees, and groups tend to be more stable. Groups also tend to be centered around females rather than males.[47] Some of these behavioral differences have led some scholars to suggest that bonobos are likely to be more closely related to humans than common chimpanzees,[48] although this view remains controversial.[49]

Although they are primarily fruit-eaters, chimpanzees

A bonobo mother with infant. Her slender limbs, dark face, and the part in her hair are some of the traits that distinguish bonobos from common chimpanzees.

Chimpanzees, though they spend much time in the trees, can also move very quickly on the ground.

show many similarities to their close relatives, the gorillas. Both are arboreal and terrestrial. Like gorillas, chimpanzees are good climbers, especially when young, and they spend many hours in the trees. But they move best on the ground, and when they want to cover long distances they come down from the trees and move by knuckle walking. Occasionally, they stand and walk upright, usually when they are traveling through tall grass or are trying to see long distances. Chimpanzees sleep in tree nests that they carefully prepare anew, complete with a bunch of leaves as a pillow, each time they bed down.[50]

Chimpanzees (including bonobos) are less sexually dimorphic than the other great apes. Males weigh a little more than 100 pounds on the average, females somewhat less. But males have longer canines.

For some time it was thought that chimpanzees ate only plant food. Although most of their diet is vegetarian, among common chimpanzees a significant amount comes from meat. After three decades of studies at Gombe Park in Tanzania and elsewhere, researchers have found that common chimpanzees not only eat insects, small lizards, and birds, but they also actively hunt and kill larger animals.[51] They have been observed hunting and eating monkeys, young baboons, and bushbucks in addition to smaller prey. At Gombe, the red colobus monkey is by far the most often hunted animal. So it is not only humans who endanger other primates (recall the box "Endangered Primates"); the red colobus monkey population is very small in areas of intense chimpanzee hunting. Hunting appears to be undertaken more often during the dry season when food is scarce.[52] Prey is caught mostly by the males, which hunt either alone or in small groups. It is then shared with—or, perhaps more accurately, begged by—as many as 15 other chimpanzees in friendly social gatherings that may last up to nine hours.[53]

Despite considerable observation, the organization of chimpanzee social groups is still not clear. Groups of common chimpanzees usually are multimale and multifemale, but the size may range considerably from a few to 100 or so members. In Gombe, males typically remain in their natal group throughout life, and females often move to a neighboring group; but males in Guinea do not tend to stay in their natal groups.[54] It appears that chimpanzees come together and drift apart depending upon circumstances such as the availability of food and the risk of predation.[55]

Hominids According to the classification we use here, the hominoids we call hominids include only one living species—modern humans. Humans have many distinctive characteristics that set them apart from other anthropoids and other hominoids, which lead many to place humans in a category separate from the pongids. (These traits are discussed later in this chapter and also throughout much of the rest of the book.) However, others believe that the differences are not so great as to justify a separate hominid category for humans. For example, humans, chimpanzees, and gorillas are very similar in their proteins and DNA. And it is widely agreed that the lines leading to humans, chimpanzees, and gorillas diverged from a common ancestor perhaps 5 million to 6 million years ago.[56] Whether we stress the similarities or differences between humans and apes does not matter that much; what does matter is that we try to understand the reasons for those similarities and differences.

Explanations of Variable Primate Adaptations

Thus far we have discussed the common features of primates and introduced the different primates that survive in the world today. Now let us examine possible explanations, suggested by research, of some of the ways in which the surviving primates vary.

BODY SIZE

Surviving primates vary enormously in body size, ranging from the 2 or so ounces of the average gray mouse lemur to the 350 pounds of the average male gorilla. What accounts for this sizable variation? Three factors seem to predict body size—the time of day the species is active, where it is active (in the trees or on the ground), and the kinds of food eaten.[57] All the nocturnal primates are small; and among the primates active during the day, the arboreal ones tend to be smaller than the terrestrial ones. Finally, species that eat mostly leaves tend to be larger than species that eat mostly fruits and seeds.

Why do these factors predict size? One important consideration is the general relationship in mammals between body weight and energy needs. Generally, larger animals require more absolute energy, but smaller animals require much more energy for their body weight. That being so, smaller animals (and small primates) need more energy-rich food. Insects, fruits, tree gum, and sap are full of calories and tend to be more important in the diet of small primates. Leaves are relatively low in energy, so leaf-eaters have to consume a lot of food to get enough energy. They

Figure 4–6

As this graph shows, larger animals generally have larger brains. Primates generally have even larger brains than we would expect from their body weight. Note that most of the primates (as indicated by the colored circles) fall above the line showing the relationship between brain weight and body weight. The brains in primates are about twice as heavy as the brains of non-primate mammals of the same body weight. Source: *From Terrence W. Deacon, "Primate Brains and Senses," in Stephen Jones, Robert Martin, and David Pilbeam, eds.,* The Cambridge Encyclopedia of Human Evolution *(New York: Cambridge University Press, 1992), p. 111. Copyright © by Cambridge University Press. Reprinted by permission of Cambridge University Press.*

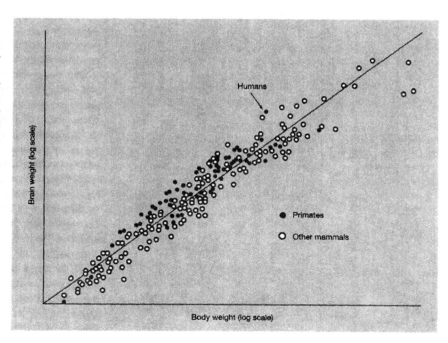

also need large stomachs and intestines to extract the nutrients they need, and a bigger gut in turn requires a bigger skeleton and body.[58] Small primates, which eat insects and other rich foods, probably would compete with birds for food. However, most very small primates are nocturnal, whereas most forest-living birds are diurnal.

Energy requirements may also explain why arboreal primates are usually smaller. Moving about in trees usually requires both vertical and horizontal motion. The energy required to climb vertically is proportional to weight, so larger animals require more energy to climb. But the energy for traveling horizontally, as on the ground, is not proportionate to weight, so larger animals use energy more efficiently on the ground than in the trees.[59] An additional consideration is the amount of weight that can be supported by small tree branches, where foods such as fruits are mostly located. Small animals can go out to small branches more safely than large animals. Also, ground dwellers might be bigger because large size is a protection against predation.[60]

RELATIVE BRAIN SIZE

Larger primates usually have larger brains, but larger animals of all types generally have larger brains (see Figure 4–6). Thus primatologists are interested in *relative brain size,* that is, the ratio of brain size to body size.

Perhaps because human primates have the largest brain relatively of any primate, we tend to think a larger brain is "better." However, a large brain does have "costs." From an energy perspective, the development of a large brain requires a great deal of metabolic energy; therefore it should not be favored by natural selection unless the benefits outweigh the costs.[61]

Fruit-eating primates tend to have relatively larger brains than leaf-eating primates do. This difference may be due to natural selection in favor of more capacity for memory, and therefore relatively larger brains, in fruit-eaters. Leaf-eaters may not need as much memory, because they depend on food that is more readily available in time and space, and therefore they may not have to remember where food might be found. In contrast, fruit-eaters may need greater memory and brain capacity because their foods ripen at different times and in separate places that have to be remembered to be found.[62] The brain requires large supplies of oxygen and glucose. Because leaf-eating primates do not have as much glucose in their diets as fruit-eating primates, they may also not have the energy reserves to support relatively large brains.[63]

GROUP SIZE

Primate groups vary in size from solitary males and females with young (orangutans) to a few individuals and young (for example, gibbons) to 100 or more individuals in some Old World monkey troops.[64] What factors might account for such variation?

Nocturnal activity is an important predictor not only of small body size but also of small group size. Nocturnal primates feed either alone or in pairs.[65] John Terborgh has noted that most nocturnal predators hunt by sound, so a nocturnal animal might best avoid attack by being silent.[66] Groups are noisy, and therefore nocturnal animals might be more likely to survive by living alone or in pairs.

On the other hand, a large group might provide advantages in the daytime. The more eyes, ears, and noses a group has, the more quickly a would-be predator might be detected—and perhaps avoided. Also, a larger group would have more teeth and strength to frighten or mob a predator that actually attacked.[67] But this line of reasoning would lead us to expect that all diurnal terrestrial species would have large groups. Yet not all do. Other factors must be operating. One seems to be the amount and density of food. If food resources occur in small amounts and in separate places, only small groups can get enough to eat; if food occurs in large patches, there will be enough to support large groups.[68] An additional factor may be competition over resources. One suggestion is that substantial but separated patches of resources are likely to be fought over, and therefore individuals living in larger groups might be more likely to obtain access to them.[69]

Distinctive Human Traits

We turn now to some of the features that distinguish us—humans—from the other primates. Although we like to think of ourselves as unique, many of the traits we discuss here are at the extreme of a continuum that can be traced from the prosimians through the apes.

PHYSICAL TRAITS

Of all the primates, only humans consistently walk erect on two feet. Gibbons, chimpanzees (particularly bonobos), and gorillas (and some monkeys too) may stand or walk on two feet some of the time, but only for very short periods. All other primates require thick, heavy musculature to hold their heads erect; this structure is missing in humans, for our heads are more or less balanced on top of our spinal columns. A dish-shaped pelvis (peculiar to humans), a lumbar curve in the spine, straight lower limbs, and arched, nonprehensile feet are all related to human **bipedalism.** Because we are fully bipedal, we can carry objects without impairing our locomotor efficiency. (In the chapter on the first hominids we consider the effects that bipedalism may have had on such diverse traits as toolmaking, prolonged infant dependency, and the division of labor by gender.)

Although many primates have an opposable thumb, which enables them to grasp and examine objects, the greater length and flexibility of the human thumb allow us to handle objects with greater dexterity. We are capable of both a power grip, to hold large or heavy objects firmly, and a precision grip, to hold small or delicate objects without dropping or breaking them. We also have remarkable hand-eye coordination, as well as a remarkably sophisticated brain.

The human brain is large and complex, particularly the **cerebral cortex,** the center of speech and other higher mental activities. The brain of the average adult human measures more than 1,300 cubic centimeters, compared with 525 cubic centimeters for the gorilla, the primate with the next largest brain. The frontal areas of the human brain are also larger than those of other primates, so that humans have more prominent foreheads than monkeys or gorillas. Humans have special areas of the brain that are dedicated to speech and language. The large human brain requires an enormous amount of blood, and the way blood is carried to and from the brain is also unique.[70] We'll talk more about the human brain and its evolution in the chapter on the emergence of the genus *Homo.*

Human teeth reflect our completely omnivorous diet, and they are not very specialized, which may reflect the fact that we use tools and cooking to prepare our food. As discussed earlier, other hominoids have long canines and a diastema, whereas human canines do not usually project beyond the tops of the other teeth. This allows humans to move their jaws both vertically and horizontally when chewing; horizontal movement would be prevented by the long upper canines of the other hominoids. Human molars have thicker enamel than the molars of other hominoids, and both horizontal movement and thickened molars may be related to a dietary emphasis on coarse grains and seeds, something we'll discuss further in the chapter on the first hominids. The human jaw is shaped like a parabolic arch, rather than a U-shape, as in the apes, and is composed of relatively thin bones and light muscles. Humans have chins; other primates do not.

One other distinctive human trait is the sexuality of human females, who may engage in intercourse at any time throughout the year; most other primate females engage in sex only periodically, just around the time they can conceive.[71] Humans are also unusual among the primates in having female-male bonding.[72] Later, in the discussion of the origins of culture, we examine some theories suggesting why male-female bonding, which in humans we call "marriage," may have developed. It used to be thought that more or less continuous female sexuality may be related to female-male bonding, but comparative research on mammals and birds contradicts this idea. Those mammals and birds that have more frequent sex are not more likely to have male-female bonding.[73]

Why, then, does human female sexuality differ from that of most other primates? One suggestion is that more or less continuous female sexuality became selectively advantageous in humans after female-male bonding developed in conjunction with local groups consisting of at least several adult males and adult females.[74] More specifically, the combination of group living *and* male-female bonding—a combination unique to humans among the primates—may have favored a switch from the common higher-primate pattern of periodic female sexuality to the pattern of more or less continuous female sexuality. Such a switch may have been favored in humans because periodic rather than continuous female sexuality would undermine female-male bonding in multimale-multifemale groups.

Field research on nonhuman primates strongly suggests that males usually attempt to mate with any females ready to mate. If the female (or females) a male was bonded to was not interested in sex at certain times, but other females in the group were, it seems likely that the male would try to mate with those other females. Frequent "extramarital affairs" might jeopardize the male-female bond and thereby presumably reduce the reproductive success of both males and females. Hence natural selection may have favored more or less continuous sexuality in human females if humans already had the combination of group living (and the possibility of "extramarital affairs") and marriage. If bonded adults lived alone, as do gibbons, noncontinuous female sexuality would not threaten bonding, because "extramarital" sex would not be likely to occur. Similarly, seasonal breeding would also pose little threat to male-female bonds, because all females would be sexually active at more or less the same time.[75] So the fact that the combination of group living and male-female bonding occurs only in humans may explain why continuous female sexuality developed in humans. The bonobo, or pygmy chimpanzee, female does engage in intercourse throughout the year, but bonobos do not have male-female bonding and the females are not interested in sex quite as often as human females.[76]

BEHAVIORAL ABILITIES

In comparison with other primates, a much greater proportion of human behavior is learned and culturally patterned. As with many physical traits, we can trace a continuum in the learning abilities of all primates. The great apes, including orangutans, gorillas, and chimpanzees, are probably about equal in learning ability.[77] Old and New World monkeys do much less well in learning tests, and, surprisingly, gibbons perform more poorly than most monkeys.

TOOLMAKING The same kind of continuum is evident in inventiveness and toolmaking. There is no evidence that any nonhuman primates except great apes use tools, although several species of monkeys use "weapons"—branches, stones, or fruit dropped onto predators below them on the ground. Chimpanzees both fashion and use tools in the wild. As we have noted, they strip leaves from sticks and then use the sticks to "fish" termites from their mound-shaped nests. They use leaves to mop up termites, to sponge up water, or to wipe themselves clean.

One example of chimpanzee tool use suggests planning. In Guinea, West Africa, observers watched a number of chimpanzees crack oil palm nuts with two stones. The "platform" stone had a hollow depression; the other stone was used for pounding. The observers assumed that the stones had been brought by the chimpanzees to the palm trees, because no stones like them were nearby and the chimps were observed to leave the pounding stone on top of or near the platform stone when they were finished.[78] Observers in other areas of West Africa have also reported that chimpanzees use stones to crack nuts. In one location in Liberia, an innovative female appeared to have started the practice; it seems to have been imitated within a few months by 13 others who previously showed no interest in the practice.[79]

In captivity, chimpanzees have also been observed to be inventive toolmakers. One mother chimpanzee was seen examining and cleaning her son's teeth, using tools she had fashioned from twigs. She even extracted a baby tooth he was about to lose.[80]

Humans have usually been considered the only toolmaking animal, but observations such as these call for modification of the definition of toolmaking. If we define toolmaking as adapting a natural object for a specific purpose, then at least some of the great apes are toolmakers too. Perhaps it would be more accurate to say humans are the only habitual toolmaking animal, just as we say

Chimps in the wild use tools—in this case, a stick to pry insects out of a fallen tree trunk. As far as we know, though, they don't use tools to make other tools, as humans do.

humans are the only habitual bipedal hominoid, even though the other hominoids all can and do walk bipedally sometimes. As far as we know, though, humans are unique in their ability to use one tool to make another.

LANGUAGE   Only humans have spoken, symbolic language. But, as with toolmaking abilities, the line between human language and the communications of other primates is not as sharp as we once thought. In the wild, vervet monkeys make different alarm calls to warn of different predators. Observers playing tape recordings of these calls found that monkeys responded to them differently, depending on the call. If the monkeys heard an "eagle" call, they looked up; if they heard a "leopard" call, they ran high into the trees.[81]

Common chimpanzees are also communicative, using gestures and many vocalizations in the wild. Researchers have used this "natural talent" to teach chimpanzees symbolic language in experimental settings. In their pioneering work, Beatrice T. Gardner and R. Allen Gardner raised a female chimpanzee named Washoe and trained her to communicate with startling effectiveness by means of American Sign Language hand gestures.[82] After a year of training, she was able to associate gestures with specific activities. For example, if thirsty, Washoe would make the signal for "give me" followed by the one for "drink." As she learned, the instructions grew more detailed. If all she wanted was water, she would merely signal for "drink." But if she craved soda pop, as she did more and more, she prefaced the drink signal with the sweet signal—a quick touching of the tongue with her fingers. Later, the Gardners had even more success in training four other chimpanzees, who were taught by fluent deaf users of American Sign Language.[83]

Bonobos have provided strong evidence that they understand simple grammatical "rules," very much like 2-year-old humans. Pointing to graphic symbols for different particular meanings, a bonobo named Kanzi regularly communicated sequences of types of symbols; for example, he would point to a symbol for a verb ("bite") and then point to a symbol for an object ("ball," "cherry," "food").[84]

OTHER HUMAN TRAITS   Although many primates are omnivores, eating insects and small reptiles in addition to plants—some even hunt small mammals—only humans hunt very large animals. Also, humans are one of the few primates that are completely terrestrial. We do not even sleep in trees, as many other ground-living primates do. Perhaps our ancestors lost their perches when the forests receded, or cultural advances such as weapons or fire may have eliminated the need to seek nightly shelter in the trees. In addition, as we have noted, we have the longest dependency period of any of the primates, requiring extensive parental care and support for up to 20 years or so.

Finally, humans are unlike almost all other primates in having a division of labor by gender in food-getting and food sharing in adulthood. Among nonhuman primates, both females and males forage for themselves after infancy. Humans have more gender-role specialization, perhaps because men, unencumbered by infants and small children, were freer to hunt and chase large animals.

Having examined our distinctive traits and the traits we share with other primates, we need to ask what selective forces may have favored the emergence of primates, what forces may have favored the line of divergence leading to the first hominids, and what forces led to the emergence of the genus *Homo*. These questions are the subjects of the next three chapters.

Summary

1. Although no living primate can be a direct ancestor of humans, we do share a common evolutionary history with the other surviving primates. Studying the behavioral and anatomical features of our closest living relatives may help us make inferences about primate evolution. Studying distinctive human traits may help us understand why the line of primates that led to humans branched away from the line leading to chimpanzees and gorillas.

2. No one trait is unique to primates. However, primates do share the following features: two bones in the lower part of the leg and in the forearm, a collarbone, flexible prehensile (grasping) hands, stereoscopic vision, a relatively large brain, only one (or sometimes two) offspring at a time, long maturation of the young, and a high degree of dependence on social life and learning.

3. The order Primates is divided into two suborders: the prosimians and the anthropoids. Compared with the anthropoids, prosimians depend more on smell for information. They have mobile ears, whiskers, longer snouts typically, and relatively fixed facial expressions. Anthropoids have rounded braincases; reduced, nonmobile outer ears; and relatively small, flat faces instead of muzzles. They have highly dextrous hands.

4. The anthropoid order is divided into two main groups: platyrrhines (monkeys of the New World) and catarrhines. The catarrhines are subdivided into cercopithecoids (Old World monkeys) and hominoids (apes and humans). The anthropoid apes consist of the hylobates, or lesser apes (gibbons and siamangs), and the pongids, or great apes (orangutans, gorillas, and chimpanzees).

5. Along with the gorilla, the chimpanzee has proteins and DNA remarkably similar to those of humans, as well as anatomical and behavioral similarities to humans. Wild chimpanzees have been seen to create and use tools, modifying a natural object to fulfill a specific purpose. High conceptual ability is also demonstrated by both the chimpanzee's and the gorilla's facility in learning sign language.

6. Variable aspects of the environment, differences in activity patterns, and variation in diet may explain many of the traits that vary in the primates. Nocturnal primates tend to be small and to live alone or in very small groups. Among diurnal species, the arboreal primates tend to be

smaller and to live in smaller social groups than terrestrial primates. Fruit-eaters have relatively larger brains than leaf-eaters.

7. The differences between humans and the other anthropoids show us what makes humans distinctive as a species. Humans are totally bipedal; they walk on two legs and do not need the arms for locomotion. The human brain, particularly the cerebral cortex, is the largest and most complex. In contrast to females of almost all other primates, human females may engage in sexual intercourse at any time throughout the year. Human offspring have a proportionately longer dependency stage. And in comparison with other primates, more human behavior is learned and culturally patterned. Spoken, symbolic language and the use of tools to make other tools are uniquely human behavioral traits. Humans also generally have a division of labor in food-getting and food sharing in adulthood.

Glossary Terms

anthropoids
arboreal
bilophodont
bipedalism
brachiators
canines
catarrhines
cercopithecoids
cerebral cortex
diastema
diurnal
hominids
hominoid
hylobates
incisors
knuckle walking

molars
nocturnal
omnivorous
opposable thumbs
platyrrhines
pongids
prehensile
premolars
prosimians
quadrupeds
sexual dimorphism
terrestrial
vertical clinging
 and leaping
"Y-5" pattern

Critical Questions

1. How could you infer that a fossil primate lived in the trees?
2. Why are primates so smart?
3. Under what conditions would the ability to communicate be adaptive?
4. Why are humans immature for so long?

Internet Exercises

1. The Duke University Primate Center (**http://www. duke.edu/web/primate/index.html**) is devoted to research on and conservation of prosimians. Click on the Animals button and read about how prosimians differ from anthropoidal primates and the differences among lemurs, lorises, galagos, pottos, and tarsiers. Also, use this site to find out which prosimians are most endangered.

2. Visit the Primate Gallery site at **http://www. selu. com/~bio/PrimateGallery/main.html** and read about the primate of the week. Look at the new images at **http:// www.selu.com/~bio/PrimateGallery/new/images. html**.

3. Visit the Great Ape Project at **http://www. greatapeproject.org/** and click on the latest news reports. Read one of the reports of interest to you and summarize the article.

4. Want to hear some primate vocalizations? Go to the Web site at **http://www.indiana.edu/~primate/primates. html** and listen to vocalizations from a number of different primates.

Suggested Reading

CHENEY, D., AND SEYFARTH, R. *How Monkeys See the World.* Chicago: University of Chicago Press, 1990. A thoughtful, balanced attempt to find out how monkeys think and the extent to which their view of the world is similar to ours.

FLEAGLE, J. G., JANSON, C. H., AND REED, K. E., EDS. *Primate Communities.* Cambridge: Cambridge University Press, 1999. An interesting collection of essays examining variation in primate communities.

GRAY, J. P. *Primate Sociobiology.* New Haven, CT: HRAF Press, 1985. A survey and discussion of empirical studies that tested 396 possible explanations, mostly derived from sociobiological theory, of many aspects of variation in primate behavior.

JONES, S., MARTIN, R., AND PILBEAM, D., EDS. *The Cambridge Encyclopedia of Human Evolution.* Cambridge: Cambridge University Press, 1992. About a third of this comprehensive book reviews information about primate classification, conservation, aspects of and variation in physique, physiology, behavior, and cognitive abilities of the living primates.

MCGREW, W. *Chimpanzee Material Culture: Implications for Human Evolution.* Cambridge: Cambridge University Press, 1992. A careful description and analysis of tool use among chimpanzees.

PARKER, S. T., AND GIBSON, K. R., EDS. *"Language" and Intelligence in Monkeys and Apes: Comparative Developmental Perspectives.* New York: Cambridge University Press, 1990. A volume of 20 papers that apply frameworks from human developmental psychology and evolutionary biology to comparative studies of primate abilities.

ROWE, N. *The Pictorial Guide to the Living Primates.* East Hampton, NY: Pogonias Press, 1996. A beautiful successor to J. R. Napier and P. H. Napier's *Handbook of Living Primates* (New York: Academic Press, 1967), with a photograph or illustration of each of the living primates. This is the most complete collection of images yet published in a single source.

SMUTS, B. B., CHENEY, D. L., SEYFARTH, R. M., WRANGHAM, R. W., AND STRUHSAKER, T. T., EDS. *Primate Societies.* Chicago: University of Chicago Press, 1987. An extensive review, by some 50 primatologists, of primate species that have been studied in the wild.

Behavior

At its most fundamental level, an organism's behavior is based on receiving information about conditions in the environment and acting in response to that information. Viewed in this context, most organisms behave. Plants sense light and gravity and move or grow in response; many can also sense predators and release defense compounds in response. Numerous species of bacteria perceive changes in light, magnetic fields, or chemical concentrations and react by swimming to or from the stimulus. There are even predatory fungi that sense the presence of roundworms and then capture and eat them. In this chapter, however, we limit ourselves to examining the behavior from a single part of the tree of life: the animals.

Biologists analyze how animals behave at two levels. At the proximate, or mechanistic level, researchers ask how actions occur in terms of the neurological, hormonal, and skeletal-muscular mechanisms that cause the behavior. At the ultimate, or evolutionary level, investigators ask why actions occur in terms of their effect on reproductive success. Is a particular behavior adaptive—meaning that it increases an individual's ability to survive and reproduce in a particular environment? Analyses at the ultimate level also seek to explain the evolutionary origins of particular behavior patterns and analyze how they have changed through time.

As an example of proximate and ultimate causation, let's consider singing by male birds. As section 47.2 shows, researchers study birdsong at the proximate level by asking how hormones, neurons, and muscles interact to produce a vocalization. An experiment at the proximate level might involve manipulating the concentration of the sex hormones testosterone and estrogen and then analyzing whether the areas of the brain responsible for

This mated pair of red-crowned cranes is performing a courtship display named the unison call. In addition to exploring the genetic and cellular-level underpinnings of behavior, this chapter investigates how the unison call and other types of behavior evolve.

47.1   The Role of Genes

47.2   How Animals Act: Neural and Hormonal Control

47.3   The Adaptive Consequences of Behavior

47.4   The Evolution of Behavior

Taken from: *Biological Science,* by Scott Freeman

song change in response. At this level, an explanation for bird-song runs as follows. Sex hormones are released in response to environmental cues that indicate the onset of the breeding season. These hormones cause certain areas of the brain to grow; when neurons in these song control regions fire, they stimulate muscles around an organ called the syrinx. When these muscles respond, the syrinx vibrates. Song results.

At the ultimate level, research takes a different tack. As section 47.4 details, the function of a bird's song is to defend a territory for breeding and to attract a mate. A breeding territory contains food that birds need to raise offspring. Research at the ultimate level might look for correlations between the size of a male's song repertoire and his success in attracting mates, or involve adding food to a territory and documenting whether the resident male's singing rate increases in response. At this level, an explanation for birdsong runs as follows. Defending a reliable food supply and attracting a mate, through the use of the signal called song, is critical for successful reproduction. Birds that cannot or do not sing produce few offspring.

The important point to grasp about proximate and ultimate levels of analysis is that they are complementary. Studies at the proximate level explain how the behavior occurs; research at the ultimate level explains why. The goal of this chapter is to introduce how biologists study behavior at both levels.

To begin, let's explore some research on how genes affect behavior. Genes provide the link between proximate mechanisms and ultimate function. They code for the molecules involved in proximate mechanisms, and the frequency of certain alleles changes over time in response to mutation, natural selection, and other evolutionary processes.

47.1 The Role of Genes

Until the 1970s and 1980s, the genes that influence animal behavior represented a "black box." Biologists assumed that at least some behavioral traits were influenced by particular genes and alleles in addition to being affected by environmental conditions, but they knew almost nothing about the extent of this influence. Experimental and analytical tools for testing the assumption were simply lacking.

The situation is changing dramatically, however. Powerful techniques are now available to investigate behavioral genetics. This section begins by introducing two approaches for analyzing the genetic basis of behavior, and closes by investigating how genotypes and environmental conditions interact to produce behavior.

Are Behavioral Traits Influenced by Genes?

Does some of the variation in behavior observed among individuals result from variation in their genotypes? To introduce how biologists answer this question, let's consider alcohol

abuse in humans. Alcoholism is a behavioral disorder that tends to run in families. As a result, physicians have long suspected that it has a significant genetic component. But a plausible alternative hypothesis exists. Alcoholism could run in families not because family members share a genetic predisposition to the behavior, but simply because they share an environment that promotes alcohol abuse. How can researchers distinguish the two?

In an attempt to tease apart the effects of heredity and environment, Robert Cloninger and colleagues studied the children of alcoholics and of nonalcoholics. The researchers focused on a large group of Swedish men who had been adopted by nonrelatives at a very early age. The genetic parents of these men included both alcoholics and nonalcoholics. The boys had been assigned to their foster homes randomly, meaning without respect to either their biological or foster parents' behavior. Also, the vast majority of the boys had been placed as newborns or infants. Presumably, this was before their parental environment could exert a strong influence on their behavior.

In effect, these adoptive placements created a natural experiment. An experiment like this—where young are raised by non-relatives in randomly assigned environments—is called a cross-fostering experiment. Cross-fostering experiments are routinely performed on nonhuman animals. The logic is simple. If the cross-fostered offspring show the same type of behavior as their genetic parents, then the trait has a strong genetic basis; if offspring behave more like their foster parents, then the trait has a strong environmental basis. Here is the question that Cloninger and co-workers asked: Were the biological children of alcoholic parents more likely to become alcohol abusers than the biological children of nonalcoholic parents?

The data that answer this question are summarized in **Figure 47.1a** (page 916). Boys who had alcoholic biological fathers were almost nine times as likely to abuse alcohol as were boys whose biological fathers were nonalcoholics. This is strong evidence that certain alleles create a predisposition to alcoholism. Cloninger and co-workers realized, however, that this effect occurred in one type of alcoholism only. They termed this behavior teen-onset alcohol abuse.

A strikingly different pattern occurred in boys who did not develop alcoholism until they became adults. As the data in **Figure 47.1b** show, boys experienced an increased frequency of this syndrome only when alcohol abuse was also favored by their foster environment; that is, if their adoptive parents abused alcohol, too.

In short, the study revealed that there are two distinct types of alcoholism, and that the interaction between genetic background and environment is different in these two types. In teen-onset alcoholism, the expression of the trait is largely independent of whether alcohol abuse occurs in the home environment. In contrast, development of adult-onset alcoholism is heavily influenced by alcohol abuse at home.

Can We Find Specific Genes or Alleles Responsible for Certain Behavior Patterns?

Cross-fostering experiments can establish that a particular behavior has a genetic basis. Once this has been confirmed, researchers turn their attention to the next level of analysis, which is to locate and analyze the specific genes and alleles involved. When these have been identified and their mode of action has been explained, the genetic basis of behavior is largely understood. The black box is open.

In classical genetics, researchers begin a study by identifying a trait of interest. Then they search for the genes responsible for the trait by finding a mutant that does not show the trait. By carrying out the types of breeding experiments analyzed in Chapter 17, researchers can map the physical location of the mutant locus. Once the locus is pinpointed, investigators attempt to sequence the gene, produce the protein, and perform experiments focused on explaining how the gene product influences the phenotype. This approach is called **forward genetics** (Figure 47.2). The researcher starts with a normal phenotype and a mutant phenotype and attempts to determine the underlying genotype. (Box 47.1, page 918, explains how a newer approach, called **reverse genetics**, is used in behavior genetics. In reverse genetics, investigators start with a mutant gene and attempt to determine how it affects the phenotype.)

Normally, it is extremely difficult to do forward genetics with behavioral traits. This is because in most cases, dozens of different genes influence the expression of a behavior. For example, there is no single gene for behavioral disorders such as alcoholism. Instead, many genes are involved in the illness.

The products of these genes might affect the development of the brain, the behavior of individual neurons, the output of sensory organs, and so on. When many genes are involved, and when each has a small effect on the trait, it is difficult to map the loci involved.

Marla Sokolowski, however, was fortunate enough to discover an important behavioral trait controlled by a single gene. Consequently, she was able to use a forward genetics approach to uncover what may be the best example to date of a gene that influences behavior.

As an undergraduate research assistant, Sokolowski noticed that some of the fruit-fly larvae she was studying tended to move several centimeters after feeding in a particular location, while others tended to remain in place. She reared the two types of larvae separately and confirmed that as adults, the two forms also acted as either "rovers" or "sitters." Further, the same behavior was found in the wild. Sokolowski studied a population of fruit flies living in an apple orchard and found that rovers made up 70 percent of the population while sitters comprised 30 percent.

By breeding rovers and sitters that possessed other distinct genetic markers, Sokolowski and colleagues were able to map the gene responsible for the behavior. (Genetic mapping was explained in detail in Chapter 17.) The researchers named the locus *foraging* (*for*). Rovers have the *for^R* allele, while sitters have the *for^S* allele; heterozygotes act like rovers.

Exactly which gene is at this locus? Fortunately, the *Drosophila* genome has been sequenced. The locus called *for* happened to map at or near a previously identified gene called *dg2*. The protein product of *dg2* is a protein kinase that is acti-

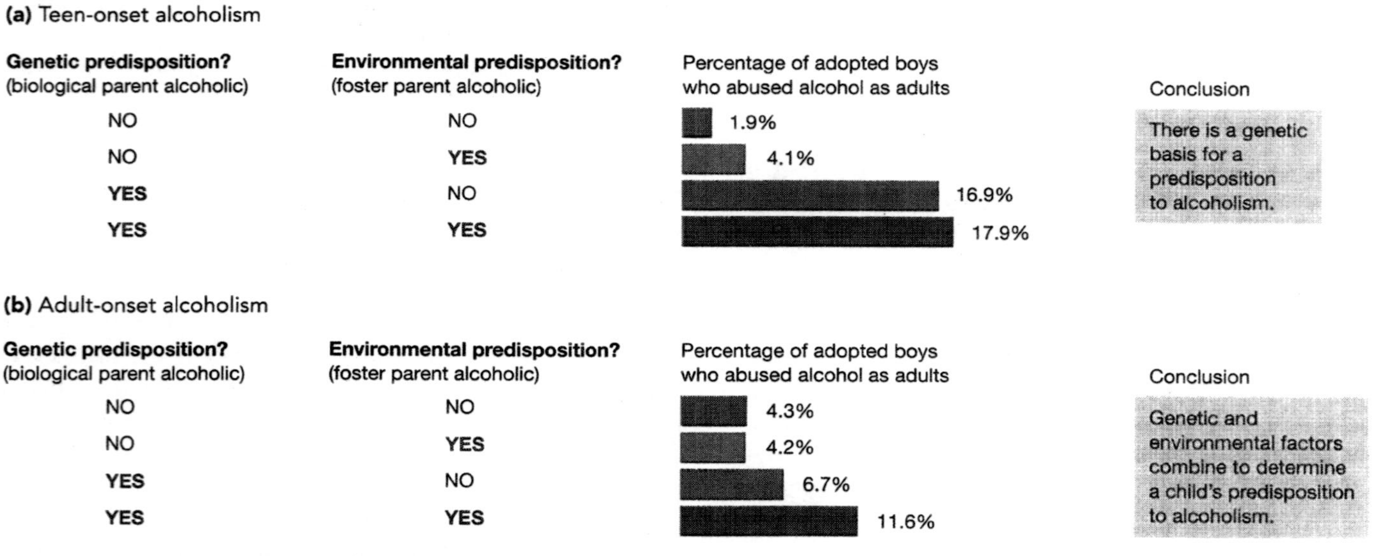

(a) Teen-onset alcoholism

Genetic predisposition? (biological parent alcoholic)	Environmental predisposition? (foster parent alcoholic)	Percentage of adopted boys who abused alcohol as adults	Conclusion
NO	NO	1.9%	There is a genetic basis for a predisposition to alcoholism.
NO	YES	4.1%	
YES	NO	16.9%	
YES	YES	17.9%	

(b) Adult-onset alcoholism

Genetic predisposition? (biological parent alcoholic)	Environmental predisposition? (foster parent alcoholic)	Percentage of adopted boys who abused alcohol as adults	Conclusion
NO	NO	4.3%	Genetic and environmental factors combine to determine a child's predisposition to alcoholism.
NO	YES	4.2%	
YES	NO	6.7%	
YES	YES	11.6%	

FIGURE 47.1 Analyzing Genetic Predispositions to Alcoholism
These data are for adopted boys who were placed in foster homes shortly after birth. **(a)** Teen-onset alcoholism was most likely to develop in boys whose biological parents were alcoholics, regardless of whether their foster parents abused alcohol. **(b)** Adult-onset alcoholism was more likely to develop only if boys had biological parents who abused alcohol and if their foster parents also abused alcohol. (A statistical test indicated that the observed differences between the first three categories probably arose by chance.)

FORWARD GENETICS

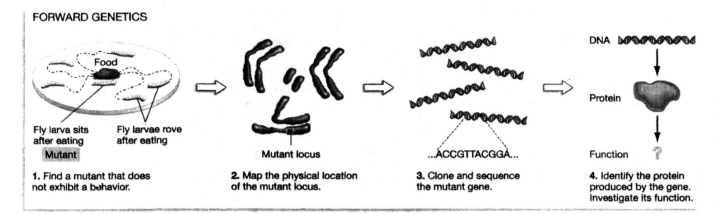

1. Find a mutant that does not exhibit a behavior.

2. Map the physical location of the mutant locus.

Mutant locus

3. Clone and sequence the mutant gene.

...ACCGTTACGGA...

DNA

Protein

Function ?

4. Identify the protein produced by the gene. Investigate its function.

Fly larva sits after eating
Mutant

Fly larvae rove after eating

Food

FIGURE 47.2 Forward Genetics
Forward genetics is based on identifying, analyzing, and mapping mutants. In effect, a researcher works from phenotype to genotype.

vated by cyclic guanosine monophosphate (cGMP). As several earlier chapters pointed out, protein kinases activate or deactivate certain proteins by phosphorylating them. The change in the protein often leads to the transcription or repression of certain genes and a dramatic change in the cell's activity.

Are *for* and *dg2* actually identical? To answer this question, Sokolowski and co-workers inserted extra copies of the *dg2* gene into eggs that were homozygous for the *for*^{S} allele (**Figure 47.3**). The control group in the experiment, which had the same sitter genotype, did not receive the extra copies of *dg2*. These eggs developed into sitters. But the transformed eggs hatched into larvae and then metamorphosed into adults that acted like rovers. This is convincing evidence that *for* and *dg2* are in fact the same gene. Follow-up experiments confirmed that the *for*^{R} allele produces more of the protein kinase than the *for*^{S} allele.

In section 47.3 we'll consider how roving and sitting affect the ability of flies to survive and reproduce in different habitats. In the meantime, let's take a closer look at how the genes involved in behavioral traits interact with various aspects of the environment.

Interactions Between Genes and the Environment

A common misconception about the genetic basis of behavior is to assume that traits can be "genetically determined." This is almost never the case. In the rover/sitter example just examined, the associations between certain alleles and certain types of behavior are statistical in nature—not deterministic. Fruit flies with the *for*^{R} allele tend to move more after feeding, on average, than fruit flies with the *for*^{S} allele. In this and most other cases, behavioral responses are not an either-or proposition.

The message here is that certain alleles create a disposition for a certain behavior, but they do not dictate or determine it. There are several reasons for this. To begin with, genes and alleles must be expressed. Their expression depends on regulatory molecules—often hormones or other developmental signals. The

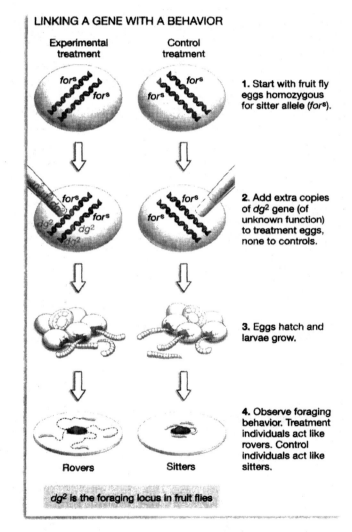

LINKING A GENE WITH A BEHAVIOR

Experimental treatment | Control treatment

1. Start with fruit fly eggs homozygous for sitter allele (*for*^{s}).

2. Add extra copies of *dg2* gene (of unknown function) to treatment eggs, none to controls.

3. Eggs hatch and larvae grow.

4. Observe foraging behavior. Treatment individuals act like rovers. Control individuals act like sitters.

Rovers | Sitters

dg2 is the foraging locus in fruit flies

FIGURE 47.3 What Convinced Researchers That *dg2* Was the *Foraging* Locus in Fruit Flies?
Researchers were able to produce the rover phenotype by injecting fly eggs with extra copies of the *dg2* gene. **QUESTION** In the second step, why did the researchers inject the eggs in the control treatment?

amount, timing, or duration of the signal has a huge effect on the amount of protein produced. Further, the proteins produced by genes interact with other proteins. In the rover/sitter example, the protein kinase has to receive a signal from a hormone or other molecule, and then respond by phosphorylating other proteins. Variation in these interactions will cause variation in the behavior.

In short, every allele interacts with other alleles within the individual. But the external environment also influences genes. To illustrate this point, let's examine a particularly startling phenomenon: female fish that change their sex and become male.

Many species of coral-reef fish have a distinctive mating system. Males defend territories that contain nesting sites and feeding areas. A group of females lives inside the boundaries of this territory. When these females spawn (lay eggs), the male

fertilizes the eggs. Thus, a single male monopolizes all of the matings in that territory. Invariably, this male is the largest individual in the group. This is logical because the male guards the territory, and because fights between fish are usually won by the biggest contestant.

When this male dies, however, something unusual happens. The largest female in the group changes sex. She becomes the dominant male, and begins fertilizing all of the eggs laid in the territory.

Why does she do this? What does the sex-changing female gain by making this switch? These questions are at the ultimate level, and they have been answered by Michael Ghiselin's "size-advantage hypothesis" (see **Box 47.2**). But how does the sex-switching female switch from an egg producer to a sperm pro-

BOX 47.1 Using Reverse Genetics to Study Behavior

The growth of molecular genetics during the 1970s and 1980s inspired an increasingly popular research strategy for understanding the genetic basis of traits. This strategy is called reverse genetics. The tactic hinges on knowing the identity of a particular protein and then designing experiments to understand its function (**Figure 1**). Reverse genetics is sometimes called the candidate gene approach because the first step is to find the gene that is hypothesized to be responsible for a certain phenotype.

In behavioral studies, reverse genetics has been especially useful for understanding how variation in certain neuro-

transmitters and receptors affects behavior. For example, consider the neurotransmitter called serotonin that was introduced in Chapter 42. In humans, variation in serotonin function has been implicated in alcohol abuse and in the emotional states called depression and anxiety. (Many common antidepressant medications act on serotonin or its receptors.) At least 14 different receptor proteins bind serotonin and mediate its effects, however. How do variations in these proteins affect behavior?

Lora Heisler and co-workers answered this question for a serotonin receptor in mice called 5-HT$_{1A}$. The researchers dis-

rupted the DNA sequences for this receptor. Mice that were homozygous for this mutation had no functioning copies of the 5-HT$_{1A}$ protein. When these individuals were tested in mazes, open-field environments, or cages with novel objects, they were much more likely to cower, hide, or show other anxiety-like behavior than normal mice. The result supports the hypothesis that this receptor is involved in modulating specific types of behavior. The experiment also illustrates the value of reverse genetics as a research strategy in behavioral genetics.

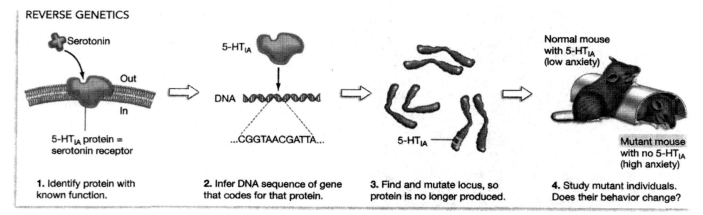

REVERSE GENETICS

Serotonin — Out — In — 5-HT$_{1A}$ protein = serotonin receptor

5-HT$_{1A}$ — DNA — ...CGGTAACGATTA...

5-HT$_{1A}$

Normal mouse with 5-HT$_{1A}$ (low anxiety)

Mutant mouse with no 5-HT$_{1A}$ (high anxiety)

1. Identify protein with known function.

2. Infer DNA sequence of gene that codes for that protein.

3. Find and mutate locus, so protein is no longer produced.

4. Study mutant individuals. Does their behavior change?

FIGURE 1
Reverse genetics is also called the candidate gene approach. In effect, a researcher works from genotype to phenotype.

ducer? How does her behavior change from submissive to aggressive? These questions are at the proximate level, and they are still unanswered.

Sex change in fish illustrates an important point. Organisms frequently have the genetic "tools" to act in several different ways, but their physical or social environment dictates which behavior they exhibit. Sex-switching fish do not change their genotype, just their physiology and behavior. This is a classic case of condition-dependent behavior. Now let's consider how the genes that influence behavior act, via nerve cells and hormonal signals.

47.2 How Animals Act: Neural and Hormonal Control

If genes create the potential for a certain behavior, how is this potential realized? Answering this question is the essence of the proximate approach to behavior. Because the nervous and endocrine systems initiate and modify behavior, answering proximate-level questions involves analyzing neuronal connections and hormone signaling pathways. Here we examine interactions among neurons, hormones, and behavior.

Birdsong

In 1981 Francisco Nottebohm shocked the scientific world by suggesting that each spring, adult male canaries grow new neurons in the brain centers responsible for producing song. Canaries sing in the spring during the breeding season, but they do not sing in the fall or winter. Nottebohm wanted to know whether these changes in song behavior might be correlated with changes in the size or shape of the brain's song centers. By examining and comparing the song centers in the brains of male canaries in spring and fall, Nottebohm demonstrated that dramatic changes occur. The song centers are much larger in spring than in fall. He proposed that neurons in these areas die each fall, and are replaced by new neurons generated each spring.

Nottebohm's hypothesis caused a sensation, for two reasons. First, if his hypothesis proved to be correct, similar neuron-generating areas might be found in humans and offer an avenue for treating patients with stroke damage or spinal cord injuries. Second, the idea contradicted accepted dogma, which was that the brains of adult vertebrates make few, if any, neurons.

Within three years, however, the hypothesis was confirmed in spectacular fashion. To establish that new neurons do indeed form, Steven Goldman and Nottebohm exploited a finding made by Mark Gurney and Masakazu Konishi. Gurney and Konishi had shown that when female birds are given injections of testosterone, the song centers in their brains enlarge and they begin to sing. Goldman and Nottebohm also injected females with testosterone, but they added radioactively labeled molecules of the deoxyribonucleic acid, thymidine. Because thymidine is incorporated into DNA when it is synthesized, these radioactive bases would specifically label the DNA in new nerve

BOX 47.2 Conditional Strategies and the Nature/Nurture Debate

The size-advantage hypothesis, developed by Michael Ghiselin, states that fish living in a harem breeding system, dominated by a single male, should switch from female to male when they become very large. (Note that fish have indeterminate growth, which means that they continue growing throughout their lives.) To understand why this switch should occur, suppose that a small female can lay 10 eggs a year, while a large female can lay 20 eggs a year. If six small females and two large females live in a harem, the male that owns the territory thus fertilizes 100 eggs each year. If the male dies, the largest female can increase the number of offspring she produces each year from 20 to 80 by changing sex and taking over the role of dominant male. Alleles that allow females to do this will increase rapidly in the population. It does not pay for smaller females to switch sex, though, because

they would be defeated in fights and have 0 offspring per year instead of 10.

Biologists refer to this type of behavior as a conditional strategy. The term is apt because the individuals involved are capable of behaving in several different ways. The behavior that they adopt depends on conditions—in this case, on the size and sex of other individuals in their social group. The critical point here is that individuals usually adopt the behavior that allows them to produce the most surviving offspring. This is an issue we return to in section 47.3.

Conditional strategies are also noteworthy because they shed light on an old controversy called the nature-nurture debate. This conflict, which raged for decades, was based on a stark dichotomy. Some researchers claimed that differences in the behavior of individuals were due primarily to differences in their genetic

makeup (or "nature"). Other investigators argued that behavioral differences among individuals were due to differences in the environments they experienced (or "nurture").

As the data analyzed in this chapter show, both points of view are incorrect. Do genes or the environment determine behavior? The short answer is both. The longer, more accurate answer is that in most cases genetic backgrounds create the potential for various types of behavior; the behavior exhibited depends on environmental conditions.

Instead of arguing about the primacy of nature or nurture, then, biologists have become more interested in collecting data that show how genetic predispositions and environmental conditions interact, and how the behaviors adopted by individuals allow them to survive and reproduce.

cells. As predicted, Goldman and Nottebohm found many radioactively labeled neurons in and around the growing song centers. This observation supported the hypothesis that new neurons are being formed, that the song center enlarges due to the synthesis of new cells, and that the expansion of song centers is contingent upon stimulation by testosterone.

To verify that these new neurons were actually involved in generating song, John Paton and Nottebohm did the experiment diagrammed in **Figure 47.4**. They began by injecting radioactively labeled thymidine into adult canaries to mark new neurons. Thirty days later, they recorded electrical impulses generated by individual neurons in the song centers. After making a recording and confirming that a particular cell functioned as a normal neuron, Paton and Nottebohm injected the cell with an enzyme called horseradish peroxidase. The chemical reaction catalyzed by this enzyme results in a product that acts as a dark stain. In this way, working neurons in the song center became permanently marked. When Paton and Nottebohm analyzed the resulting cells under the microscope, they found that some cells contained both radioactive thymidine and black stain (see Figure 47.4, right). This result corroborated that new neurons, which form in the song centers in response to stimulation by testosterone, actually function.

Figure 47.5 summarizes these experiments on the proximate control of birdsong. The figure contains a crucial step that we've yet to explore, however. What aspect of the social or physical environment signals the arrival of spring and triggers the release of testosterone? David Crews performed a series of ingenious experiments to investigate how different types of environmental cues affect sexual behavior in the green anole lizard.

Courtship, Copulation, and Egg-Laying in *Anolis* Lizards

Anolis carolinensis (**Figure 47.6a**) live in the woodlands of the southeastern United States. After spending the winter under a log or rock, males emerge in January and establish breeding territories. Females become active a month later; by May, they are laying an egg every 10–14 days. By the time the breeding season is complete three months later, females will have produced an amount of eggs equaling twice their body mass. **Figure 47.6b** maps this series of events, along with the changes occurring in the male and female reproductive systems.

What causes these dramatic, seasonal changes in behavior? The proximate answer is sex hormones—testosterone in males and estradiol in females. Testosterone is produced in the testes and estradiol in the ovaries. The evidence for these statements is direct. Testosterone injections induce sexual behavior in castrated males, while estradiol injections induce sexual activity in females whose ovaries have been removed.

Now the question becomes, what environmental cues trigger the production of sex hormones? To answer this question for females, Crews brought a large group of inactive adult lizards into the laboratory and divided them into five treatment groups. The environment was exactly the same in all treatments. Each individ-

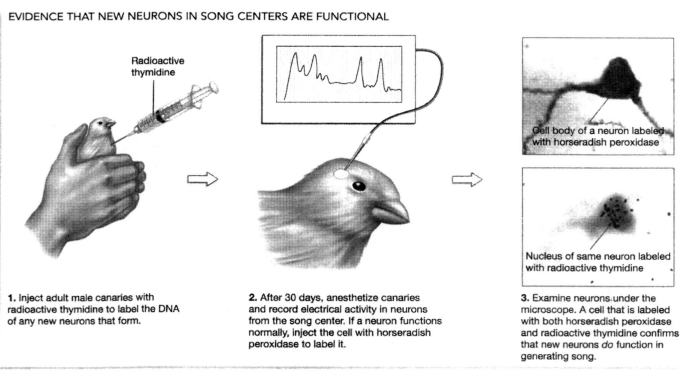

EVIDENCE THAT NEW NEURONS IN SONG CENTERS ARE FUNCTIONAL

Radioactive thymidine

Cell body of a neuron labeled with horseradish peroxidase

Nucleus of same neuron labeled with radioactive thymidine

1. Inject adult male canaries with radioactive thymidine to label the DNA of any new neurons that form.

2. After 30 days, anesthetize canaries and record electrical activity in neurons from the song center. If a neuron functions normally, inject the cell with horseradish peroxidase to label it.

3. Examine neurons under the microscope. A cell that is labeled with both horseradish peroxidase and radioactive thymidine confirms that new neurons *do* function in generating song.

FIGURE 47.4 Evidence That New Neurons in Song Centers Are Functional

ual received identical food, and in all treatments artificial lighting simulated the long days and short nights of spring. Further, high "daytime" temperatures were followed by slightly lower "nighttime" settings. Only the social setting varied among treatment groups: (1) single isolated females, (2) groups of females only, (3) single females each with a single male, (4) single females each with a group of castrated (non-breeding) males, or (5) single females each with a group of uncastrated (breeding) males.

Each week, Crews examined the ovaries of females in each group. He also monitored the ovaries of females in nearby natural habitats, since those females were not exposed to spring-like conditions. As **Figure 47.7** (page 922) shows, the differences in their reproductive systems were dramatic. Females

exposed to breeding males began producing eggs much earlier than the females placed in the other treatment groups. The experiment showed that two types of stimulation are necessary to produce the hormonal changes that lead to sexual behavior. Females need to experience spring-like light and temperatures *and* exposure to breeding males.

What aspect of male behavior causes the difference in female egg production? Crews suspected that visual stimulation from the male's courtship display was important. Specifically, he hypothesized that a flap of skin, called the dewlap, played a role in stimulating females to produce eggs. To court females, male anoles bob up and down and extend their dewlaps (see Figure 47.6a). To test this idea, Crews repeated the previous experiment, but

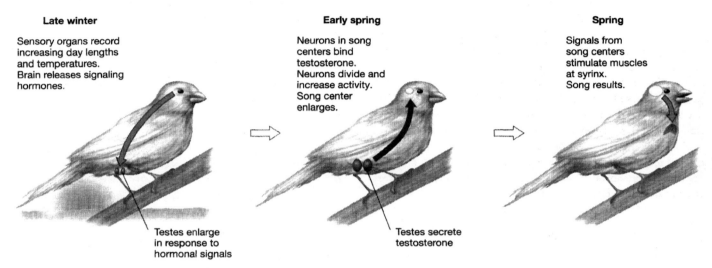

Late winter

Sensory organs record increasing day lengths and temperatures. Brain releases signaling hormones.

Testes enlarge in response to hormonal signals

Early spring

Neurons in song centers bind testosterone. Neurons divide and increase activity. Song center enlarges.

Testes secrete testosterone

Spring

Signals from song centers stimulate muscles at syrinx. Song results.

FIGURE 47.5 The Proximate Causes of Birdsong—A Summary Diagram
In male canaries, the capacity to sing results from interactions between environmental cues, hormonal signals, and the nervous system.

(a) Courting of *Anolis* lizards

(b) Changes in sexual organs through the year

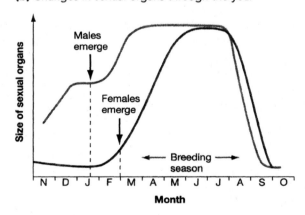

FIGURE 47.6 Sexual Behavior in *Anolis* Lizards
(a) A male *Anolis* lizard courting a nearby female. While bobbing up and down, the male is extending a flap of skin called a dewlap. (b) These graphs show changes in the sexual organs of *Anolis* lizards through the year. The red line indicates the relative size of the follicles inside a female's ovary. The blue line indicates the relative size of a male's testicles.

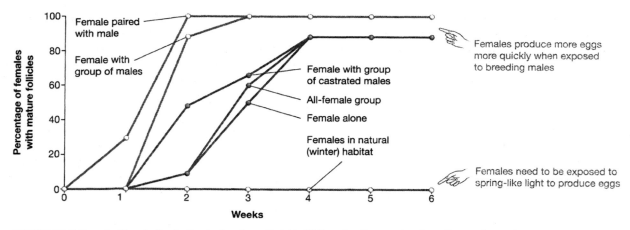

FIGURE 47.7 Female Lizards Begin Producing Eggs Quickly if They Are Exposed to Breeding Males and Spring-like Light
The percentage of female lizards with mature follicles is given on the y-axis, with data plotted for each of five treatment groups exposed to spring-like light and temperature and females left in natural (winter) habitat. Each data point represents the average value for a group of 6–10 females.

added a twist. He placed females with males that had intact dewlaps or with males whose dewlaps had been surgically removed. The result? Females grouped with dewlap-less males were slow to produce eggs—just as slow, in fact, as the females in the first experiment that had been grouped with castrated males. These females had not been courted at all. The result suggests that the dewlap is a key visual signal. The experiments succeeded in identifying the environmental cues that trigger hormone production and the onset of sexual behavior.

47.3 The Adaptive Consequences of Behavior

In addition to understanding how the nervous and endocrine systems control behavior at the proximate level, biologists would like to know why behavior exists at all. What is its function? How did different types of behavior come to be? At this level of analysis—the ultimate level—the questions are no longer about *how* animals do what they do, but why they do what they do.

To begin exploring the evolutionary significance of behavior, let's return to the research on fruit fly foraging that was introduced in section 47.1. Recall that flies with the *for^R* allele tend to rove, or move about, after feeding; while individuals with the *for^S* allele tend to remain stationary. Also recall that natural selection occurs if individuals with certain alleles survive better or reproduce more in certain environments than individuals with other alleles. Does natural selection favor *for^R* in some environments and *for^S* in others?

Natural Selection and Behavior

Marla Sokolowski and co-workers hypothesized that roving and sitting are feeding strategies that work best at different population densities, meaning in crowded or uncrowded condi-

tions. The logic here was that sitting should be favored when population density is low because sitters conserve energy and grow faster than rovers. Thus, in low-density situations where competition for food is virtually nonexistent, sitters should survive better and reproduce more than rovers do. Because sitters have more offspring than rovers, the *for^S* allele should increase in frequency under these conditions. But in high-density populations, the opposite is true. Food is extremely scarce. Rovers should be favored because they are more likely to find uneaten food as they move. In high-density situations, the *for^R* allele should increase in frequency.

To test these predictions, Sokolowski and colleagues did the experiment diagrammed in **Figure 47.8**. They began by placing mixtures of 50 rovers and sitters in jars with a prescribed amount of food and mixtures of about 1000 rovers and sitters in jars with the same amount of food. They let the flies in each treatment group breed. Then they randomly selected offspring—50 from the jar with 50 adults and 1000 from the jar with 1000 adults—to start the next generation. They repeated this sequence for a total of 74 generations.

What happened? Over time, a strong pattern emerged. The average distance traveled by larvae after feeding decreased in the low-density treatment groups but increased in the high-density groups. These results suggest that as predicted, sitting is favored when population density is low, while roving is advantageous when population density is high.

In general, if some variations in behavior allow individuals to survive better or to reproduce more than other individuals, then alleles associated with the advantageous behavior will increase in frequency in the population. As a result, the behavior of natural populations will change through time, or evolve, just as it did in the laboratory experiment by Sokolowski and colleagues.

If natural selection favors a certain behavioral trait in a certain environment, it is called an **adaptation**. An adaptation is a characteristic that increases the ability of individuals to survive and reproduce compared to individuals without the trait. In fruit flies, roving and sitting are adaptive in certain environments.

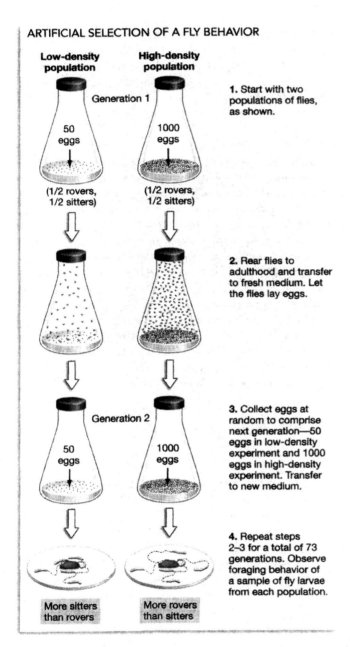

ARTIFICIAL SELECTION OF A FLY BEHAVIOR

Low-density population

High-density population

Generation 1

50 eggs

1000 eggs

(1/2 rovers, 1/2 sitters)

(1/2 rovers, 1/2 sitters)

1. Start with two populations of flies, as shown.

2. Rear flies to adulthood and transfer to fresh medium. Let the flies lay eggs.

Generation 2

50 eggs

1000 eggs

3. Collect eggs at random to comprise next generation—50 eggs in low-density experiment and 1000 eggs in high-density experiment. Transfer to new medium.

4. Repeat steps 2–3 for a total of 73 generations. Observe foraging behavior of a sample of fly larvae from each population.

More sitters than rovers

More rovers than sitters

FIGURE 47.8 Do Fruit Fly Rovers or Sitters Have an Advantage at Different Population Densities?
This type of protocol is called an artificial selection experiment. In this case, researchers selected flies that were able to thrive in low- or high-density populations. QUESTION In addition to changes in foraging behavior, what other traits might change in response to selection for the ability to survive and reproduce in low- and high-density populations? How would you test your hypotheses?

In many species, however, behavior is much more flexible than it is in fruit flies. Instead of tending to either rove or sit, an individual might be able to rove and sit. If individuals are capable of acting in several different ways, how do they choose what to do? To answer this question, let's consider territorial defense behavior in hummingbirds.

Flexible Behavior: Territorial Defense in Hummingbirds

Many types of animal behavior involve "decision-making." The phrase is in quotes because the decisions that animals make are probably not conscious in the human sense. Yet they are decisions nonetheless. In coral-reef fish that have the capacity to be either male or female, individuals "decide" which sex to become based on their social situation.

The question is, are these decisions adaptive? Let's explore this question by considering territorial behavior in hummingbirds. These tiny birds defend territories that contain the nectar and insects they eat. They use several different types of behavior in territory defense, including displaying the iridescent feathers found on their head or neck (**Figure 47.9**), calling, chasing, and fighting. Chasing away a competitor is considered an expensive behavior because it requires a great deal of energy, entails a risk of injury, and leaves the territory undefended. Calling or displaying, in contrast, is relatively inexpensive.

Which type of territory defense behavior should a hummingbird use when an intruder approaches? Paul Ewald and Gordon Orians proposed that hummingbirds should make choices based on the value of their territory at the time. This prediction was based on the observation that hummingbirds empty the nectar stores when they feed on flowers. Just after feeding, then, flowers offer few benefits to hummingbirds. If the choice of territorial defense behavior is adaptive, then hummingbirds should call or display at intruders soon after feeding, but chase

Hummingbirds have feeding territories.

FIGURE 47.9 Hummingbird Territorial Behavior Depends on the Value of the Territory
Hummingbirds defend feeding territories by chasing intruders or by calling at them.

them if enough time had passed for flowers to refill with nectar and for the territory owner to be hungry again.

To test these ideas, the biologists put feeders filled with a sugary solution on hummingbird territories. The feeders were designed so that only a small amount of food would be delivered at a time, however. Once the feeders were in place, the investigators recorded what happened on a minute-by-minute basis. (Box 47.3 highlights the importance of observation in behavioral studies.) When they compared how individuals behaved during different time intervals after feeding, they found interesting patterns. In the interval just after feeding, territory owners used displays more frequently when intruders approached, chased a lower percentage of intruders, and reduced the duration of chases. These results support the prediction that hummingbirds choose among behavioral options according to current conditions, and make choices in an adaptive manner.

Why Is Behavior Selfish?

When biologists analyze why an animal behaves in a certain way in a certain situation, they focus on the benefit to the individual. But when nonbiologists consider why animals behave in certain ways, they frequently suggest that individuals will do things "for the good of the species." Territorial behavior in birds, for example, was once thought to exist for the good of the species. The idea was that by spacing themselves out in a habitat, members of a species avoided depleting their food supplies and causing a population crash. Individuals that did not own a territory were thought to honor the existing territorial boundaries for the good of the species.

According to this view, individuals sacrifice themselves to benefit others. Over 35 years ago, however, George Williams pointed out that this type of behavior does not exist for a simple reason. Natural selection eliminates alleles that allow organisms to behave this way.

To understand Williams's logic, let's work through the following thought experiment. Suppose that the for^R allele in fruit flies acted for the good of the species. For example, individuals with the for^R allele might reduce their food intake when conditions became crowded, and thus leave more food for others. If individuals with the for^S allele ate normal amounts, though, they would eat the food that the for^R flies left alone. Thus, for^S flies would grow faster, survive better, and leave more offspring than for^R flies. As a result, the for^S allele would increase in frequency while for^R declined until it was eliminated. Williams pointed out that "selfish" alleles are guaranteed to win a competition with self-sacrificing alleles every time.

To drive this point home, consider the phenomenon of infanticide (infant-killing) in the langur monkeys of south Asia (**Figure 47.10a**). Langurs live in troops that frequently consist of one adult male, eight or more adult females, and their offspring. The troop defends a territory, often against bands of unmated males that roam about. In some cases the dominant member of an all-male band is able to evict the dominant territorial male, usually after weeks of intense fighting. After the new male takes over, infants in the troop are extremely likely to disappear.

What is the cause of death? Most biologists suspect infanticide by the new males. Sarah Hrdy has documented several instances when the new male in the troop attacked and mortally wounded langur infants (**Figure 47.10b**).

BOX 47.3 The Importance of Observation in Behavioral Studies

Virtually every study reviewed in this chapter is based on observation. Biologists watch what animals do and then ask how or why the behavior occurs. In many cases, finding an answer involves performing relatively simple experiments and carefully observing the outcome. For example, to test the hypothesis that hummingbirds use different types of territorial displays under different conditions, a biologist and an undergraduate assistant set feeders out on territories, recorded when territory owners fed, and observed how the owner responded to intruders.

Although the ability to make insightful observations is basic to all of the biological sciences, behavior may be the most observation-intensive field of study. Jane

Goodall's pioneering work on chimpanzee behavior is a classic example. Goodall had little formal training in biology and was able to make fundamental contributions solely through observation. Her discoveries included tool use, nest-making, the existence of coalitions among females and among males, and hunting. Her observations were so astute and accurate that she is now considered one of the world's leading primatologists.

One of the attractive aspects of observational studies of behavior is that they are relatively inexpensive and accessible. At least some behavioral biology can even be done at home or on a college campus. Ants, wasps, spiders, beetles, birds, and bees can be found and observed almost

anywhere. Suppose you ran across a line of ants retrieving pieces from a scrap of bread on a lawn. What would happen if you interrupted the line by placing a rock in the way? What happens when you remove any scents that might exist by wiping the line with rubbing alcohol? If the line is marked by a scent, are predators or competing species of ants able to sense it and use the signal to prey on ants or steal food?

Simple studies like these provide valuable practice in making observations, forming hypotheses, making predictions, and carrying out experimental tests. More than a few professional biologists got their start as undergraduate assistants on behavioral studies that emphasized observation.

Why does infanticide occur when new males take over? A group-selection argument would contend that the death of the infants benefits the species, by reducing population size and conserving resources. Hrdy's hypothesis, in contrast, is that the behavior benefits the individual perpetrators. She suggests that incoming males receive a reproductive benefit because the mothers of the dead infants respond by coming into estrus. (Nursing mothers do not ovulate. If their babies die and they stop nursing, they respond by ovulating.) This means that they are again ready to be fertilized and bear young. Instead of spending months or years helping to rear unrelated young, the new, dominant male kills them and quickly fathers his own offspring.

Data from lions collected by Craig Packer and Anne Pusey strongly support Hrdy's hypothesis. Lions live in social groups called prides. Prides are sometimes taken over by groups of incoming males. Packer and Pusey have shown that mothers whose offspring are victims of infanticide come into estrus eight months earlier, on average, than mothers with offspring who are not killed by males. The upshot is that males that commit infanticide do better, in terms of producing offspring, than males that do not commit infanticide.

Behavior like infanticide does not exist for the good of the species. It exists because alleles that encourage selfish behavior tend to increase in frequency.

Kin Selection and the Evolution of Cooperation: Alarm Calling in Prairie Dogs

The preceding discussion emphasizes that much of animal behavior is selfish—at least regarding its effects on the animal exhibiting the behavior and the recipient of this behavior. But this is by no means the entire story of behavior. Hundreds of examples of altruistic behavior exist in nature. In biology, **altruism** is defined as an act that has a cost to the actor, in terms of his or her ability to survive and reproduce, and a benefit to the recipient. It is the formal term for self-sacrificing behavior.

How can altruism exist, if theory proposes that selfish alleles are always favored? William Hamilton created a mathematical model that provided the answer. Hamilton asked: How could an allele that contributes to altruistic behavior increase in frequency in a population? To model the fate of these alleles, he represented the cost of the altruistic act to the actor as C and the benefit to the recipient as B. Both C and B are measured in units of offspring produced. His mathematical proof showed that the allele could spread if

$$Br - C > 0$$

where r is the **coefficient of relatedness**. The coefficient of relatedness is a measure of how closely the actor and beneficiary are related. Specifically, r measures the fraction of alleles in the actor and beneficiary that are identical by descent—that is, inherited from the same ancestor (see **Box 47.4**, page 926).

This result is called Hamilton's rule. It is important because it confirms that individuals can pass their genes on to the next generation not only by having their own offspring but also by helping close relatives produce more offspring. According to Hamilton's rule, if the benefits of altruistic behavior are high, if the benefits are dispersed to close relatives, and if the costs are low, then alleles associated with altruistic behavior will be favored by natural selection and will spread throughout the population. Biologists use the term **kin selection** to refer to natural selection that acts through benefits to relatives.

Does Hamilton's rule work? Do animals really favor relatives when they act altruistically? John Hoogland tested the

(a)

(b)

FIGURE 47.10 Infanticide Occurs in Nature When It Benefits the Perpetrators
(a) Two female langur monkeys intervene as a male, who has recently taken over the troop, attacks an infant (the infant's tail is visible above the male's head). (b) The infant is protected by its mother on the following morning. Note the wound in the infant's abdomen. QUESTION One of the females intervening on the infant's behalf is presumably its mother. Why would the other female help her in such a dangerous situation? What data would you gather to test your hypothesis?

theory by studying a behavior called alarm calling in Gunnison's prairie dogs. These burrowing mammals live in large communities, called towns, in the Four Corners region of the American Southwest (**Figure 47.11a**). When a badger, coyote, hawk, or other predator approaches a town, some prairie dogs give alarm calls that alert others to run to mounds and scan for the threat. Giving these calls is risky. In several species of ground squirrels and prairie dogs, researchers have shown that alarm-callers draw attention to themselves by calling and are in greater danger of being attacked.

To assess whether this selfless act is consistent with Hamilton's rule, Hoogland recorded the identity of the callers and listeners during 125 experiments. In these studies, a student assistant dragged a stuffed badger through the colony on a sled. Did alarm-callers preferentially help relatives, did non-

relatives usually receive the benefit, or was everyone alerted equally with no difference in benefits? The data in **Figure 47.11b** illustrate that Gunnison's prairie dogs are much more likely to call if relatives are nearby. This same pattern—of preferentially dispensing help to close relatives—has been observed in many other species of social mammals and birds. Most cases of altruism that have been analyzed to date are consistent with Hamilton's rule.

47.4 The Evolution of Behavior

As noted in the introduction to this chapter, biologists have two goals when they analyze behavior at the ultimate level. They want to understand why the behavior helps an individual produce more offspring, and they want to know the evolutionary

---

BOX 47.4 Calculating the Coefficient of Relatedness

The coefficient of relatedness, r, varies between 0.0 and 1.0. If individuals have no alleles that are identical because they were inherited from the same ancestor, then their r is 0.0. Because every gene in pairs of identical twins is identical by descent, their coefficient of relatedness is 1.0.

What about other relationships? **Figure 1a** shows the general scheme for calculating coefficients of relatedness between individuals whose place in a genealogy is known, using first cousins as an example. The thick arrows in **Figure 1b** mark the path of common descent, from one cousin (marked A) to its parent (marked B), to the parent's sibling (marked C), to the other cousin (marked D). In each case, the individuals on either side of an arrow share half of their alleles by descent. To understand why, recall how the process of meiosis distributes alleles to gametes. Meiosis distributes alleles from the diploid genome to the haploid gamete randomly. As a result, if you pick any two gametes at random, the probability of them having the same allele is 50 percent.

FIGURE 1
(a) This figure is the standard way of depicting human pedigrees, or family trees. **(b)** The thick arrows represent the genetic connections, or paths of common descent, between first cousins.

To find r, then, we have to calculate the probability that the same allele is shared by A and B, *and* B and C, *and* C and D. The calculation is $1/2 \times 1/2 \times 1/2$, or $1/8$. Using the same logic and

rules for combining probabilities, you can calculate r's for any two individuals. (Biologists who study altruism in nature have to do this routinely.)

(a) Structure of a pedigree

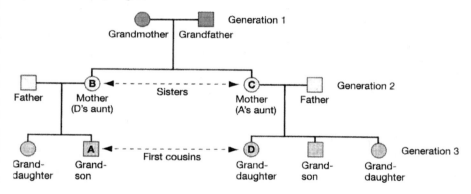

(b) Calculating coefficient of relatedness

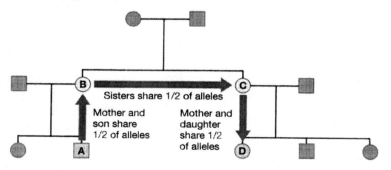

A and B (first cousins) share: $1/2 \times 1/2 \times 1/2 = 1/8$ alleles
Coefficient of relatedness (r) = 0.125

(a) Prairie dogs give alarm calls.

(b) When do prairie dogs give an alarm call?

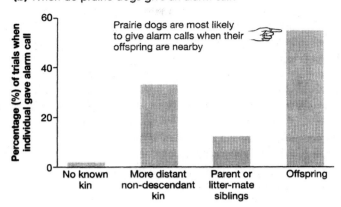

Prairie dogs are most likely to give alarm calls when their offspring are nearby

FIGURE 47.11 Prairie Dogs Give Alarm Calls if Relatives Are Nearby
(a) Prairie dogs are social animals that live in the grasslands of western North America. **(b)** This graph shows how likely prairie dogs are to give alarm calls, after detecting a predator, in four different situations: when no relatives are nearby, when cousins or more distant kin are around, when parents or siblings are within earshot, and when offspring are close.   **QUESTION** The researcher who gathered these data is not sure why prairie dogs are so unlikely to give alarm calls when parents or siblings are close by. Generate a hypothesis to explain the observation. How would you test your hypothesis?

origins of the behavior. Stated another way, how did the behavior originate, and how has it changed through time?

To appreciate why biologists want to study the evolutionary origins of behavior, consider facial expressions in humans. Distinct muscle movements produce changes in the position of our lips, eyebrows, and other features. We use these poses to communicate our emotional state. Across all human cultures, people use the same facial expressions to indicate greeting, happiness, surprise, anger, and fear. (In contrast, hand gestures and other aspects of body language are learned. They vary from culture to culture.) A few of these expressions are strikingly similar to behavior used by our close relatives, the chimpanzees, in the same contexts (**Figure 47.12**). Is this similarity coincidental, or did humans and chimps inherit some of their behavior from a common ancestor, who used the same types of facial expressions to communicate?

As a case study of how biologists answer questions like this, let's consider the evolution of a spectacular territorial bird display carried out by cranes.

Cranes are large, marsh-dwelling birds found everywhere but Antarctica and South America. Individuals can live over 80 years in captivity, and they mate for life. Mated pairs sing a set of alternating songs, called the unison call, as a duet (**Figure 47.13a**, page 928). The display is used in the context of courtship and defending a breeding territory.

All 15 crane species perform a unison call, and in all cranes the display is an **innate behavior**. It is not modified by learning. If a crane chick is reared by humans with no contact from other cranes, or if a chick is reared by a different crane species that acts as a foster parent, the individual will still perform a fully functional unison call—of its own species—as

an adult. Among the 15 species, however, the display varies widely in complexity.

How did the behavior evolve, and change through time? George Archibald answered this question by breaking the unison calls of the 15 species into a series of components. These components consist of motions and vocal inflections, some of which are unique to certain species and some of which are shared. Then Archibald proposed a hypothesis for how the display evolved. He assumed that complex displays are derived from simpler displays. For example, he proposed that the unison originated from a display called the alarm call. The alarm call is a short, loud blast given by a male or female crane when a predator approaches. It is closely related to the guard call, which is given by

FIGURE 47.12 Chimpanzee Facial Expressions
Some of the facial expressions used by chimpanzees are strikingly similar to those of humans.

either males or females when another crane enters their territory. The alarm calls and guard calls of all crane species are similar. Further, Archibald proposed that they are ancestral—meaning that these displays predated the advent of the unison call.

In two species of cranes that are native to Africa, the unison call is actually very similar to the guard-call and alarm-call. In these species the unison call consists of guard calls given alternately by a male and female that are paired. The vocalizations are accompanied by a simple visual display, consisting of head movements. In other species, however, the display is much more complex. Depending on the species, pairs may stand side by side or walk together as they call. In many species females begin the display, and male and female calls and postures are different.

Archibald grouped species whose motions and vocal inflections were similar and then ordered the display components from simple to complex. As a result of this analysis, he proposed that the unison call evolved in the order proposed in Figure 47.13b. The relationships establish a hypothesis for how

complex behavior might evolve, in a step-by-step fashion, from simpler behavior.

Carey Krajewski and colleagues tested this hypothesis by reconstructing the evolutionary history of the 15 crane species. These researchers compared the composition of DNA sequences in both nuclear and mitochondrial genomes, and used these data to group species whose genes are similar. This analysis resulted in the relationships shown in Figure 47.13c. Compare parts (b) and (c), and note that the evolutionary relationships estimated from the genetic data are remarkably similar to the relationships of the unison-call display. Stated another way, the assumption that complex unison calls are derived from simpler behavior leads to a match between the history of the species and the history of the display. This result supports the validity of the assumption about how the behavior actually evolved. By reconstructing history in this way, researchers can understand how particular behavior patterns originated and changed through time.

(a) Crane courtship display

(b) Tree based on complexity of courtship displays

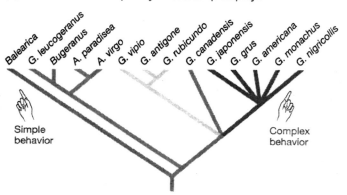

(c) Tree based on DNA sequences

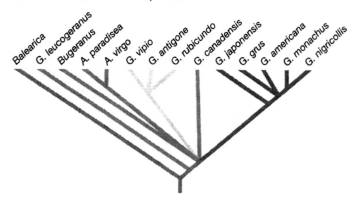

FIGURE 47.13 The Evolution of Crane Courtship Displays
(a) Cranes are long-legged, long-necked birds that live in marshes. This photo shows a mated pair of red-crowned cranes giving a unison call. (b) This tree illustrates a hypothesis for how the unison call evolved, based on the assumption that simpler displays originated earlier and more complex displays arose later. (c) This tree shows the evolutionary relationships of cranes. EXERCISE The text claims that the two trees are "remarkably similar." Do you agree?

Some of the concepts discussed in this chapter—including altruism, Hamilton's rule, kin selection, and natural selection—may seem a little abstract at first. Yet Martin Daly and Margo Wilson have shown that they can be enormously important tools for understanding certain aspects of human behavior.

Daly and Wilson study the "dark side" of human behavior—homicide, domestic violence, and adultery—from a biological perspective. They try to determine whether some of

Can we study the "dark side" of human behavior?

these events are consistent with the types of actions favored by natural selection.

For example, let's consider data that Daly and Wilson have collected on child abuse. They hypothesized that natural selection should favor parents who invest resources in biological children, but not in stepchildren—with whom they have no genetic relationship. Based on this hypothesis, they predicted that child abuse should be much more common in households containing a stepparent than it is in homes containing only biological parents. Further, infants should be most at risk if stepparents choose to abuse their stepchildren because very young children demand the most time and resources and are least able to defend themselves.

Are the data consistent with the prediction? Daly and Wilson have analyzed the most extreme form of child abuse, which is the killing of children by parents. Using a database on all

homicides reported in Canada between 1974 and 1983, they found 341 cases in which a child was killed by a biological parent and 67 in which the perpetrator was a stepparent. Because households containing only biological parents were much more common, however, Daly and Wilson realized that they needed to compare the rate of violence in the two types of households, rather than the absolute number of incidents.

When they expressed the data as a rate—specifically, as the number of children killed per million years by their parents—the histograms in **Figure 1** resulted. The pattern is striking. Children who live with a stepparent are at much higher risk of abuse than children who live with biological parents. Kids who are less than 2 years old are, in fact, 70 times more likely to be killed. To appreciate the magnitude of this relative risk, consider that smokers are 11 times more likely to develop lung cancer than are nonsmokers.

The study points up the value of applying "selection thinking" to human behavior. It also has an urgent practical message. Society should be especially alert to indications of violence in households where very young stepchildren are present. Several points about the data are worth noting, however. It is *extremely* important to recognize that violence occurs among biological kin as well as non-kin, and that the vast majority of stepparents are solicitous and generous with their stepchildren. Further, the behavior is undoubtedly pathological rather than adaptive. Killing "stepcubs" may improve the reproductive success of male lions, but human perpetrators are jailed and treated as abhorrent. It is extremely unlikely, then, that the act of killing a stepchild improves the reproductive success of the murderer.

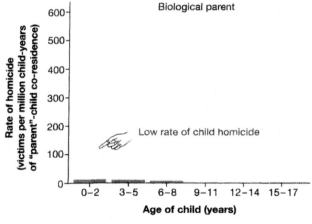
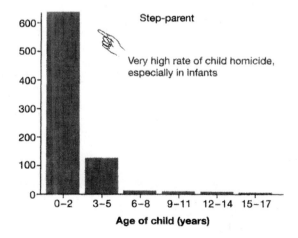

FIGURE 1 Rate of Child Homicide
Here, rates are expressed as victims per million child-years. A child-year is a year that a child of a particular age lived in a particular family situation. For example, the histogram to the left indicates that if a million children aged 0–2 years lived with their biological parents for one year, on average about 10 would be murdered.

Summary

Biologists study behavior at the proximate and ultimate levels. At the proximate level, experiments and observations focus on understanding how neurotransmission and hormonal signals cause behavior. At the ultimate level, researchers seek to understand the adaptive significance of behavior, or how it enables individuals to survive and reproduce. Studying the genes and alleles responsible for behavior provides an important link between proximate and ultimate levels of explanation, because different proximate mechanisms for behavior result from the presence of certain genes or alleles, and because alleles that affect behavior change in frequency over time in response to natural selection.

In the field of study called behavior genetics, cross-fostering experiments are an important technique for establishing that certain types of behavior have a genetic basis. Investigators can also examine the specific genes involved in behavior by identifying a variable behavioral phenotype, such as roving and sitting in fruit flies, and doing experiments designed to map and characterize the locus where the mutation occurred.

In virtually all cases, however, the presence of certain alleles only creates a predisposition for certain types of behavior rather than others. The actual expression of a behavior is contingent upon environmental conditions. For example, biologists study condition-dependent behavior like sex change in fish to explore how an individual's social environment affects its actions.

Proximate-level studies usually focus on the neuronal and hormonal mechanisms responsible for certain behavior. Studies of song centers in bird brains have revealed that some changes in behavior are associated with the generation of new neurons and new synaptic connections. In this case, the changes in neurons are instigated by the sex hormone testosterone, which in songbirds is produced in response to the long day lengths and warm temperatures that signal the onset of spring. Hormone release triggered by environmental change is also responsible for increased sexual activity in *Anolis* lizards. But in this case environmental cues are not sufficient for full expression of the behavior. Female lizards must also be stimulated by males, which exhibit their dewlaps in courtship display.

At the ultimate level of analysis, one fundamental question is whether animals choose among behavioral options in a way that maximizes their ability to survive and reproduce. In hummingbirds, for example, experiments have shown that individuals defend their territories with low-cost calls or visual displays when food resources on the territory are depleted, but with high-cost chases when food resources are plentiful.

Studies of phenomena like infanticide have helped convince biologists that individuals do not do things for the good of the species. But when close relatives benefit from a behavior, like alarm calling in prairie dogs, natural selection can favor individuals who act altruistically. To understand how certain types of behavior originated and changed through time, biologists examine phylogenies and analyze the sequence in which the behavior evolved.

By combining proximate and ultimate viewpoints and studying the genetic basis of behavior, biologists can seek a comprehensive understanding of how and why animals do what they do.

Questions

Content Review

1. What do proximate explanations of behavior focus on?
   a. how displays and other types of behavior have changed through time, or evolved
   b. the functional aspect of a behavior, or its "adaptive significance"
   c. neurological, hormonal, and skeletomuscular mechanisms of behavior
   d. psychological interpretations of behavior—especially motivation.

2. Why do cross-fostering experiments allow researchers to distinguish environmental and genetic influences on behavior?
   a. They keep environmental effects constant.
   b. They intensify environmental effects.
   c. They reduce environmental effects.
   d. They randomize environmental effects.

3. If a researcher starts a behavior genetic study by noticing a mutant phenotype and then doing experiments designed to identify the gene(s) associated with the behavior, what is the researcher pursuing?
   a. forward genetics
   b. reverse genetics
   c. a candidate gene approach
   d. a molecular genetic study

4. When researchers wanted to determine if cell division events had created new neurons in the song centers of bird brains, they used radioactive thymidine molecules as a marker for DNA synthesis. Why was thymidine an excellent choice?
   a. It is more stable than uracil.
   b. It is found only in DNA, not RNA.
   c. It is cheaper and easier to work with than other nucleotides.
   d. Other nucleotides cannot be radioactively labeled.

5. Why are biologists convinced that the sex hormone testosterone is required for normal sexual activity in male *Anolis* lizards?
   a. Males with larger testes court females more vigorously.
   b. The molecule is not found in females.
   c. Males whose gonads had been removed did not develop dewlaps.
   d. Males whose gonads had been removed did not court females.

6. When is a behavioral trait adaptive?
   a. When it is favored by natural selection.
   b. When it makes individuals more likely to survive, relative to individuals without the trait.
   c. When it helps individuals produce more offspring than individuals without the trait.
   d. All of the above.

7. What does Hamilton's rule specify?
   a. Why "selfish" alleles spread at the expense of alleles that function "for the good of the species."
   b. Why infanticide is adaptive.
   c. When alleles that favor altruism increase in frequency.
   d. More complex behaviors evolve from simpler behaviors.

Conceptual Review

1. This chapter outlined four reasons why behavior is not determined by genes in the sense of "if you have this allele, you will act this way":

   • The transcription of genes is regulated, so expression of an allele is a function of action by hormones, neurotransmitters, and other signals.

   • Gene products function only in concert with many other gene products, so their effect varies with the amount and identity of these other molecules.

   • Individuals frequently have a large repertoire of different types of behavior; which behavior is used depends on the social environment and other types of conditions.

   • Genetic differences among individuals invariably produce statistical differences in behavior, not either-or responses.

   Using the data reviewed in this chapter, or other examples you are aware of, provide a case that illustrates each of these four points.

2. Compare and contrast proximate and ultimate explanations for behavior.

3. To study how displays or other types of behavior have changed through time, why must researchers know the phylogeny, or evolutionary history, of the species involved?

4. What data convinced researchers that *for* and *dg2* were the same gene? How might changes in the activity or amount of a protein kinase affect foraging behavior in fruit flies?

Applying Ideas

1. The data reviewed in section 47.1 suggest that the development of teen-onset alcoholism in boys does not depend on whether alcohol abuse occurs at home. Yet less than 17 percent of the boys in the study who were genetically predisposed to teen-onset alcoholism actually developed the illness. What other factors might be involved in the development of this behavior? How would you test your hypotheses?

2. In many species of songbirds native to the tropics, both females and males sing (often in duets). How would you expect the song centers in the brains of these female birds to change as the breeding season approaches? What molecule would you predict is responsible for causing these changes? Design experiments that can test your predictions.

3. Most tropical habitats are highly seasonal. But instead of alternating warm and cold seasons, there are alternating wet and dry seasons. Most animal species breed during the wet months. If you were studying a species of *Anolis* native to the tropics, what environmental cue would you simulate in the lab to bring them into breeding condition? How would you simulate this cue? Further, think about the sensory organs that lizards use to receive this cue. Are they the same or different than the receptors that *Anolis caro-linensis* uses to recognize that spring has arrived in the southeastern United States?

4. Biologists use the following terms to describe the four types of interactions that are possible between two individuals:

	Benefits Recipient	Costly to Recipient
Benefits actor	cooperative	selfish
Costly to actor	altruistic	spiteful

   This chapter discussed only altruism and selfishness, but cooperation and spite are also interesting. Can these types of behavior evolve? If so, would you expect them to be more or less common than selfishness and altruism? Why or why not?

5. A friend of yours argues that the unison call of cranes is genetically determined because it is stereotyped and completely uninfluenced by learning. Another friend argues it is a condition-dependent behavior, because only mated pairs do it and because the tendency to give unison calls varies among pairs (some pairs are more aggressive than others, and give unison calls more frequently in territorial contexts). Who's right?

CD-ROM and Web Connection

CD Activity 47.1: Proximate Causes of Behavior *(animation)*
(Estimated time for completion = 5 min)
Observe how the canary's seasonal breeding song is influenced by neurological and hormonal changes.

CD Activity 47.2: Observing Behavior: Homing in Digger Wasps *(tutorial)*
(Estimated time for completion = 10 min)
How does a wasp find its nest after returning from a foray for food?

At your **Companion Website** (http://www.prenhall.com/freeman/biology), you will find self-grading exams and links to the following research tools, online resources, and activities:

Behavioral Genetics
This article from *Science* Magazine discusses research on the genetics of behavior.

Behavior and the Judicial System
This provocative article addresses the ethical and sociological ramifications of scientific advances in behavioral genetics.

Seasonal Neuroplasticity
This article from *Nature* magazine discusses the ways in which hormonal development affects bird songs.

The Egotist and the Altruist
This article from *Nature* magazine reviews an attempt by Jacob Koella to understand behavior and its effect on evolution using computerized models.

Duplicitous Ducks
This article from *Scientific American* describes a relationship called "conspecific brood parasitism" within some duck species.

Additional Reading

Diamond, J. 1992. *The Third Chimpanzee* (New York: HarperCollins). An insightful look at adaptive aspects of human behavior.

Heinrich, B. 1989. *Ravens in Winter* (New York: Summit Books). Introduces how behavioral biologists do field observations and experiments.

Human Sexual Anatomy and Physiology

PHYSICAL

Female Sexual Anatomy and Physiology

- **Female Internal Sexual Organs**
  The internal sexual organs of the human female include the ovaries, fallopian tubes, uterus, and vagina.

- **Female External Sexual Organs**
  The external sexual organs of the human female include all of the parts of the vulva: the mons veneris, the labia, the vestibule, and the clitoris.

- **The Menstrual Cycle**
  The menstrual cycle, the preparation of the female reproductive system for pregnancy, occurs in women between puberty and menopause.

- **Menopause**
  Menopause, the permanent cessation of ovulation, is a life transition marked by a number of physiological changes.

- **Disorders of the Female Sexual Organs**
  The female sexual organs are subject to a number of disorders, including endometriosis, fibroids, cervical and ovarian cancers, ovarian cysts, and vaginitis.

- **Breasts**
  The primary function of female breasts is the production of milk. The most serious disease of the breast is breast cancer.

- **Diseases of the Breast**
  Both noncancerous and cancerous lumps may occur in the female breast. Breast self-examinations and mammograms are important in the early detection of breast cancer. Men also may develop breast cancer, though much less frequently than women.

SOCIAL

EMOTIONAL

SPIRITUAL

COGNITIVE

Taken from: *Human Sexuality,*
by Tina S. Miracle, Andrew W. Miracle, and Roy F. Baumeister

Male Sexual Anatomy and Physiology

- **Male Internal Sexual Organs**

  The internal sexual organs of the human male include the seminiferous tubules, epididymis, vas deferens, seminal vesicles, prostate gland, and Cowper's glands.

- **Male External Sexual Organs**

  The external sexual organs of the human male include the scrotum, testes, and penis.

- **Disorders of the Male Sexual Organs**

  The male sexual organs are subject to a number of disorders, including prostate and testicular cancers, testicular torsion, epididymitis, and Peyronie's disease.

As you learned in Chapter 1, human sexual anatomy and physiology evolved to enhance reproduction and promote the survival of the species. To ensure the successful adaptation and reproduction of the species, three objectives must be accomplished: fertilization of an egg by a sperm; successful development of a fetus resulting in live birth of a healthy individual; and survival of the offspring until physical maturity to reproduce another generation.

Our social interactions, emotional responses, and even our cultural institutions and values are inextricably linked to our physical sexual needs. Increased knowledge of the structure and function of your reproductive organs can improve your sexual health, increase your sexual pleasure, and cause you to be more responsible in your sexual behavior.

Although men and women sometimes glorify, vilify, or are mystified by one another's bodies, when you take a close look, they are remarkably similar. Female sexual organs and male sexual organs develop from similar tissue before birth. In Chapter 10 you will learn more about the **homologous,** or corresponding, nature of the male and female bodies and the amazing synchrony that is necessary for fertilization and the reproductive success of our species.

This chapter provides descriptions of both the structure (*anatomy*) and function (*physiology*) of the sexual organs of the human male and female bodies. Even when we are aware of our exteriors, most of us have no idea what our interior bodies are doing from one moment to the next. In this chapter you will gain a clearer understanding of the **genitals** (the external sexual organs) and the internal sex organs that make this "plumbing" work.

Female Sexual Anatomy and Physiology

Understanding the purpose and function of the parts of the body involved in female sexuality and reproduction is critical to maintaining sexual satisfaction and reproductive health. Not knowing the location and function of the clitoris, for example, may diminish sexual pleasure. Or, if a woman doesn't know the importance of regular pelvic exams and Pap tests, she may compromise her health.

Homologous: having the same basic structure

Anatomy: the form and structure of an organism

Physiology: the vital processes or normal functions in a living organism

Genitals: male and female sexual organs

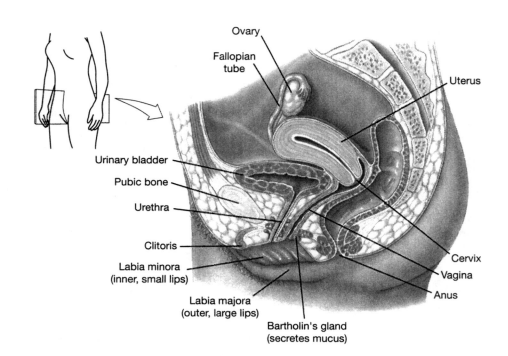

FIGURE 2.1   The Female Internal Sexual Organs. The internal sexual organs of the human female include the ovaries, fallopian tubes, uterus, and vagina.

Ovaries: female gonads that produce ova and sex hormones

Gonads: organs that produce the sex cells and sex hormones; testicles in males and ovaries in females

Estrogen: a hormone secreted by the ovary and responsible for typical female sex characteristics

Progesterone: a hormone produced in the ovary that prepares and maintains the uterus for pregnancy

Ova: egg cells

Ovulation: the discharge of a mature ovum from the ovary

Fertilize: to join male and female cells, sperm and ova, so that offspring develop

Fallopian Tubes: ducts that connect the ovaries to the uterus; oviducts

Oviducts: fallopian tubes

Fimbriae: the fingerlike projections at the end of the fallopian tube nearest the ovary that capture the egg and deliver it into the tube

FEMALE INTERNAL SEXUAL ORGANS

The internal sexual organs of the human female consist of the ovaries, fallopian tubes, uterus, and vagina (Figure 2.1). We will explain the functions of these various organs by tracing the pathway of an unfertilized egg from an ovary out of the body.

Ovaries

Each human female has two **ovaries** (Figure 2.2) about the size, shape, and texture of an irregular unshelled almond (though not almond-colored; the ovaries are a dull gray). Located at the ends of the fallopian tubes, one on each side of the uterus, the ovaries are attached to the uterus by ovarian ligaments, a type of connective tissue. The ovaries are **gonads** that perform two primary functions: the production of the female sex hormones **estrogen** and **progesterone,** and the production of mature **ova,** or egg cells. At birth, a female infant's ovaries contain about 400,000 immature ova, all of the eggs she will ever have. This is far more eggs than a woman will ever need; during her reproductive years only about four to five hundred ripened eggs will be released for possible fertilization. The *ovarian follicles* are small sacs containing ova. After maturing in the ovarian follicles, eggs are released (usually one at a time) during the process of **ovulation.** The released egg is gently drawn from the surface of the ovary into the fallopian tubes (the topic of the next section). This journey, which typically takes 3 or 4 days, is the period during which a woman is *fertile,* that is, the time when pregnancy may occur. If the egg is not **fertilized** during this time, it is expelled during menstruation.

Fallopian Tubes

The twin **fallopian tubes,** or **oviducts,** are hollow, muscular tubes approximately 10 centimeters or 4 inches long, attached one on each side of the uterus (see Figure 2.1). They extend outward from the uterus toward, but are not attached directly to, the ovaries. Each funnel-shaped fallopian tube fans out into fingerlike extensions called **fimbriae,** which drape over the ovary, but may not actually touch it. Hairlike cilia on the fimbriae become active during ovulation, coaxing the egg from the ovary and propelling it down the length of the tube toward the uterus. If sperm are present, the egg

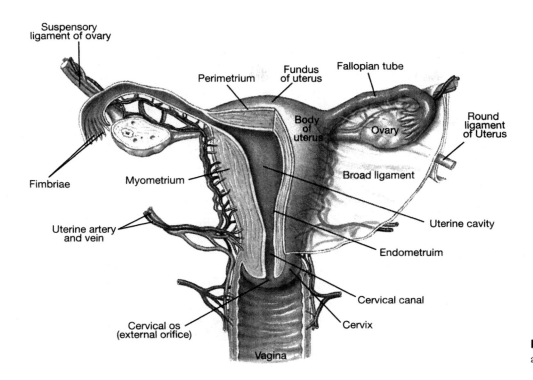

Suspensory
ligament of ovary

Perimetrium

Fundus
of uterus

Fallopian tube

Body
of
uterus

Ovary

Round
ligament
of Uterus

Fimbriae

Myometrium

Broad ligament

Uterine artery
and vein

Uterine cavity

Endometrium

Cervical canal

Cervical os
(external orifice)

Cervix

Vagina

FIGURE 2.2 The Ovaries and Uterus. Source: Martini, 2001.

may be fertilized while in the upper portion of the fallopian tube. If the fertilized egg does not precede all of the way to the uterus, an aptly named *tubal pregnancy* may result. (See Chapter 5 for more on this potentially dangerous condition.)

Uterus

The **uterus,** or **womb,** is a hollow, muscular organ shaped like an upside-down pear (see Figure 2.2) in which a fertilized egg implants and develops into a fetus. The uterus is suspended in the pelvic cavity by a number of flexible ligaments. Usually the uterus is positioned so that the top slants forward toward the abdomen (*antroverted*), although in about 10 percent of women the uterus tips backward toward the spine (*retroverted*). A retroverted uterus generally becomes antroverted spontaneously during the third month of pregnancy (Martini, 2001). If a woman has not given birth, the uterus is about 3 inches long, 3 inches wide, about an inch thick near the top, and weighs about 2 ounces. No organ undergoes the same kind of dramatic change in adulthood as the uterus. It grows to 2 pounds by the end of pregnancy, independent of the weight of the fetus or placenta, and then after pregnancy shrinks back almost (but not quite!) to its original size.

Nature seems to like to do things in groups of three. The uterus is divided into three major parts. The uppermost part of the uterus (the bottom of the pear) is the **fundus.** The central region of the uterus in which the fetus develops is called the **uterine body.** The **cervix,** the lower part of the uterus, projects down into the vagina and opens slightly for the release of menstrual blood and even more so for the birth of a baby. Viewed through the vagina, the cervix of a woman who has never been pregnant appears like a smooth, pink disk with a small hole, called the **os,** in the middle—some have described it as looking something like a glazed doughnut.

The uterine wall is composed of three layers. The innermost layer, the **endometrium,** is richly supplied with blood vessels and glands. It is the endometrial tissue that is expelled through the cervix and vagina during menstruation (see page 34). The middle, muscular layer, the **myometrium,** gives the uterus strength and flexibility and is the source of the contractions necessary for childbirth. The outermost layer, the **perimetrium,** provides an external cover for the uterus.

Uterus: hollow, muscular internal female organ in which the fertilized egg develops until birth

Womb: the uterus

Fundus: the uppermost part of the uterus

Uterine body: the central region of the uterus in which a fetus may develop

Cervix: small, lower end of the uterus that protrudes into the vagina

Os: opening in the middle of the cervix that leads to the interior of the uterus

Endometrium: tissue that lines the inside of the uterine walls

Myometrium: the smooth muscle layer of the uterine wall

Perimetrium: the thin membrane covering the outside of the uterus

What is the G Spot?

Ancient Indian texts from the 11th century refer to an area in the front part of the vagina that was later named after German gynecologist Ernest Gräfenberg, who described this sexually arousable spot in an article published in 1950. The **Gräfenberg spot,** sometimes referred to as the *G spot,* usually is described as a mass of tissue about the size of a bean that is located on the front wall of the vagina midway between the pubic bone and the cervix. See Figure 2.3. It has been reported that some women experience sexual arousal, orgasm, and even "ejaculation" when the G spot is stimulated (Darling, 1990; Davidson et al., 1989; Zaviacic & Whipple, 1993). There are those who think that the G spot is not a spot that can be touched with a finger but more accurately should be called the G zone to describe a fairly large area composed of the lower anterior wall of the vagina and the underlying urethra and surrounding glands (Alzate & Lodano, 1984; Heath, 1984).

If you can't find your G spot, don't be alarmed; one study reported that a tissue mass corresponding to the G spot was found in less than 10 percent of women examined (Masters, Johnson, & Kolodny, 1992). Other investigators have found no evidence for the existence of this area of heightened sensitivity (Goldberg et. al., 1983), or think it may be nothing more than a spot where the roots of the clitoris run deep into the vaginal wall (Angier, 1999).

FIGURE 2.3 How to Find the Grafenberg Spot. To locate the Grafenberg spot, use two fingers and press deeply into the anterior wall of the vagina.

Vagina

The **vagina** is an elastic, muscular tube that extends back and upward from the external vaginal opening to the cervix (see Figure 2.2). The vagina has three major functions: the receptacle for the penis during sexual intercourse, the passageway for menstrual flow, and the birth canal through which a **fetus** becomes a baby during childbirth. The vagina is a 3- to 5-inch-long passageway built of skin, muscle, and fibrous tissue that extend at a 45-degree angle from the labia to the cervix. You might think of the vagina as being something like a turtleneck sweater (see CROSS-CULTURAL PERSPECTIVES for other views of the vagina). At rest, the walls of the vagina lie against one another. During sexual arousal, the cervix lifts upward and the vagina expands in length to receive the penis. The width of the vagina is similarly flexible, to accommodate many dimensions, from an incoming penis or tampon to an outgoing baby.

CROSS-CULTURAL PERSPECTIVES

Genital Mythology

Many societies throughout the world have folklore about dangerous genitalia. Myths about vagina dentata, *vaginas with teeth that can kill men during intercourse, occur among American Indian groups north of Mexico as well as in* *South America, India, Siberia, Greenland, and the Pacific islands.* Penis dentatus, *the penis with teeth, is believed to be so powerful that it can eat, drink, and even cut down trees (Gregersen, 1994).*

The walls of the vagina consist of three layers. The inner lining, or *vaginal mucosa,* is a mucous membrane that is similar to the inside of the mouth. The cells of the vaginal mucosa are the source of vaginal lubrication that facilitates the insertion of a penis into the vagina during intercourse. As its name suggests, the *muscularis,* the middle

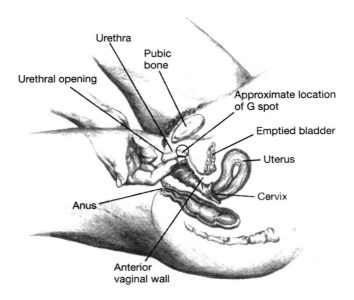

Urethra

Pubic bone

Urethral opening

Approximate location of G spot

Emptied bladder

Uterus

Cervix

Anus

Anterior vaginal wall

layer of the vaginal walls, is muscular; it is these muscles that contract during orgasm. The outer, fibrous layer connects the vagina to other pelvic structures. The vaginal walls are richly supplied with blood vessels throughout, but the sensory nerve endings are concentrated in the lower third of the vagina nearest the vaginal entrance.

FEMALE EXTERNAL SEXUAL ORGANS

The external sexual organs of the human female include all the parts of the vulva: the mons veneris, labia, vestibule, urethral opening, introitus, hymen, and clitoris (Figure 2.4).

Vulva

The external portion of the female reproductive system is collectively referred to as the **vulva.** The vulva includes the mons veneris, the labia, the urinary and vaginal openings, and the clitoris. The functions of the vulva are to protect the woman's internal sexual organs, to act as a source of her sexual pleasure, and to enhance the arousal of her partner. Beneath the hair, skin, and fatty pads of the vulva are a vast network of tissues and vessels that underlie the external sex organs. Two bundles of erectile tissue wrapped in muscle, the **vestibular bulbs,** are attached to the clitoris at the top and extend downward along the sides of the vaginal opening. During sexual arousal, the vestibular bulbs become engorged with blood, inflating the size of the clitoris and lengthening the vagina.

Mons Veneris

The **mons veneris** (Latin for "mound of Venus," named for the Roman goddess of love), also called the mons pubis, is the pad of fatty tissue that cushions the *pubic symphysis*, the slightly movable joint between the left and right pubic bones (see Figure 2.1). The pubic symphysis is relatively delicate and could be bruised by the impact of sexual intercourse (or riding a bicycle). The mons is supplied with a large number of nerve endings, and some women find manual stimulation of the mons to be pleasurable.

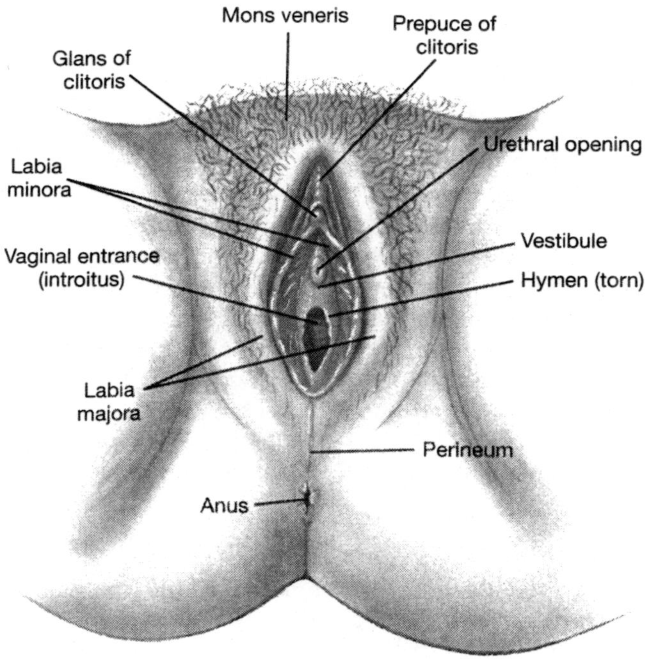

Vagina: the stretchable canal that extends from the external genital opening to the cervix

Fetus: the developing human organism from about 8 weeks after conception until birth

Gräfenberg Spot: a mass of tissue in the front wall of the vagina, claimed by some women to produce sexual arousal, orgasm, and an ejaculation of fluids when stimulated; also called **G spot**

Vulva: the external female genitals

Vestibular Bulbs: structures on each side of the vaginal opening that engorge with blood and swell during sexual arousal

Mons Veneris: mound of fatty tissue over the pubic bone above the vagina

Glans of clitoris
Mons veneris
Prepuce of clitoris
Urethral opening
Labia minora
Vestibule
Vaginal entrance (introitus)
Hymen (torn)
Labia majora
Perineum
Anus

FIGURE 2.4 The Female External Sexual Organs. SOURCE: Martini, 2001.

63

The appearance of external female genitalia vary considerably, as these three examples show.

Labia

Extending down from the mons, the vulva includes two prominent sets of skin folds, collectively referred to as the labia (Latin for "lips"): the **labia majora** (the big or outer lips) and the **labia minora** (the little or inner lips) (see Figure 2.4). With their vast network of nerve endings, the labia are an important source of sexual sensations for most women.

Beneath the outer folds of skin of the labia majora is a network of connective tissue and fat. Under the fat is erectile tissue that engorges with blood during sexual arousal. When they are not stimulated, the labia majora usually are folded together, to protect the urinary and vaginal openings. The fat of the labia, like that of the female breasts and hips, is sensitive to estrogen, the hormone of sexual maturity that will be discussed in more detail in Chapter 3. When estrogen surges through the female body during puberty, fatty deposits cause the labia to increase in size. Also during puberty, pubic hair grows on the outer sides of the labia majora. The skin of the outer sides of the labia majora usually is darker than the skin color of the thighs. The inner surfaces of the labia majora are hairless and lighter in color. The appearance of the labia majora can vary from thick and bulging to thin and flat. Within the tissue of the labia majora are smooth muscles, oil and fat glands, and nerve endings similar to those in the mons.

The labia minora, or inner lips, are the hairless inner folds of skin located within the labia majora that enfold and protect the vagina and nearby urethral opening. The labia minora contain oil glands (which can be felt through the thin skin as tiny bumps) and many nerve endings, so they are very sensitive to stimulation. Within the labia minora are small glands called **Bartholin's glands.** The function of these glands is something of a mystery. The few drops of fluid that they secrete during sexual arousal are not enough to effectively lubricate the vagina, though they may slightly moisten the labia. Additional functions of these glands are unknown. The labia minora are among the most variable part of female genitalia. They vary in size from one woman to another; in addition, the two may not be exactly symmetrical in the same woman, a cosmetic variation that is a cause for concern among some women (see CONSIDERATIONS box).

In some women the labia minora are hidden between the labia majora; in others, they may protrude. Like the labia majora, the labia minora swell with blood during sexual arousal, even doubling or tripling in size at peak arousal.

Vestibule

The area of the vulva inside the labia minora, the **vestibule** ("entranceway"), is rich in blood vessels and nerve endings, making it even more sensitive to the touch than the labia minora. At the front of the vestibule (toward the abdomen), the labia minora meet

Labia Majora: large folds of skin that form the outer lips of the vulva

Labia Minora: folds of skin located within the labia majora that form the inner lips of the vulva

Bartholin's Glands: small glands inside the vaginal opening that secrete a few drops of fluid during sexual arousal

Vestibule: the area of the vulva inside the labia minora

to form a fold or small hood of skin called the **prepuce,** or clitoral hood. Beneath the prepuce lies the clitoris. When the clitoris is erect and the labia minora spread, the vestibule become visible (see Figure 2.4).

Urethral Opening

The **urethral opening** is located below the clitoral glans and above the vaginal opening. Urine collected in the bladder passes through the **urethra,** a short tube connected to the bladder, and is excreted through the urethral opening. The urethral opening is not a reproductive organ. Although urine and semen both pass through the male penis, for women, urination and **coitus** do not occur through the same bodily opening.

Introitus and Hymen

The opening of the vagina, called the **introitus,** is located between the urethral opening and the **anus.** Partially covering the introitus is a fold of connective tissue called the **hymen,** a thin membrane containing a large number of blood vessels. The hymen may vary in shape and size (Figure 2.5) and may surround the vaginal opening (an annular hymen), form a bridge over it (a septate hymen), or appear as a sievelike covering (a cribriform hymen). Normally the hymen has an opening large enough to permit menstrual flow or the insertion of a tampon, but too small to permit entry of an erect penis without tearing.

   Although the function of the hymen is unknown, it has a great deal of cultural significance. In many societies, the presence of an intact hymen was historically considered proof that a woman had never had intercourse. But an intact hymen is not proof of virginity. Some girls are born with minimal or incomplete hymens; the hymen can also be ruptured by accident or by normal exercise. When an intact hymen is ruptured there may be no discomfort and only minimal bleeding. Although pain and bleeding can occur the first time a woman has intercourse, it may be related to muscular tension due to anxiety and not associated with the rupture of the hymen.

Clitoris

The **clitoris,** located in the vestibule at the top of the labia minora under the prepuce (see Figure 2.5), is a small body of spongy tissue that is highly sexually sensitive. The clitoris is a three-sectioned cylindrical structure. The head or **clitoral glans** (a glans is a small, round mass or tissue that can swell and harden) is the most visible external part of the clitoris. The glans is located at the top of the clitoral shaft, or body, which is partly visible, and then extends under the muscle tissue of the vulva and up toward the joint where the plates of the pubic bone meet. The clitoral shaft is surrounded by a capsule of *fibroelastic* tissue (the tube that you feel

FIGURE 2.5 Annular, Septate, and Cribriform Hymens.

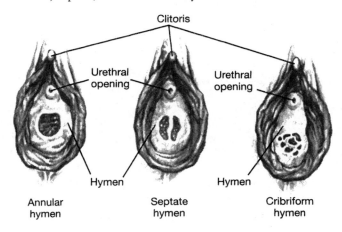

Are the clitoris and penis pretty much the same?

Although the clitoris and the penis are derived from the same embryonic tissue, they are not literal counterparts. An aroused clitoris is swollen but not rigid like an erect penis. Although it is usually much smaller than a penis, the clitoral glans has 8,000 nerve fibers, almost twice as many as the penis. In fact, the clitoris has the highest concentration of nerve fibers in the body. Unlike the penis, as a rule the clitoris of the female mammal has no secretory or excretory functions (the exception is the spotted hyena of Africa whose vagina and clitoris are one organ). The clitoris is the only sexual organ whose only purpose is pure pleasure.

■

Prepuce: a covering fold of skin

Urethral Opening: the duct through which urine is discharged from the bladder

Urethra: the tube through which urine from the bladder is expelled

Coitus: sexual intercourse

Introitus: the opening of the vagina

Anus: the opening through which solid waste is eliminated from the body

Hymen: membrane that partially covers the vaginal opening

Clitoris: highly sensitive female organ located above the urethral opening that's only known function is sexual pleasure

Clitoral Glans: the head of the clitoris, which has a large number of nerve endings

Private Proportions

Women's genitals vary in size, shape, and color. Just as women may be dissatisfied with the appearance of their noses, thighs, or breasts, there are those who are unhappy with the appearance of their genitals. Although it is less common than other types of plastic surgery, every year a few women undergo surgery to change the appearance of their genitals for aesthetic reasons or in hopes of improving their sex life. Although there are no precise statistics on the number of cosmetic procedures performed on female genitalia, the president of the American Society of Plastic and Reconstructive Surgery estimates that it is extremely rare (Schnur, 2000).

Labiaplasty is perhaps the most common female genital cosmetic procedure. In this procedure large, long, or asymmetrical labia minora are reconstructed by the surgical removal of excess skin. *Liposuction* can be used either to remove unwanted fat deposits from the mons,

or to plump up or reshape the labia. Vaginal tightening and *clitoroplasty*, removal of the clitoral shaft, purportedly result in heightened sensitivity. These surgeries are expensive and, because they are cosmetic, are generally not covered by insurance. Like all surgeries, there are risks, including infection, scarring, and excessive bleeding. There is no evidence that any of these procedures improve sexual satisfaction.

? ***Can you think of a good reason to undergo this type of cosmetic surgery?***

> —*What type of research (experimental, case study, interview, etc.) would you do to discover whether the sexual satisfaction of women who undergo these procedures is improved?*
> —*Prepare an outline of your experimental procedure.*

---

under the flesh) and is attached to twin **crura,** or roots, internal wing-shaped structures that branch inward from each side of the clitoral shaft and attach to the pelvic bone. Unlike the clitoral glans, the shaft has relatively few nerves. It is threaded through with thousands of blood vessels, allowing it to swell during arousal and push the glans upward.

Because so much of the clitoris is beneath the skin, it's hard to get an accurate measurement. Most measurements of clitoral size concern the clitoral glans and shaft. The average size of the adult clitoris from base to glans is about 16 millimeters, approximately the diameter of a dime (Verkauf et al., 1992). Like all body parts, there is considerable individual variation in size and shape (see CONSIDERATIONS box).

THE MENSTRUAL CYCLE

The sexual and reproductive lives of a woman are interwoven with **menstruation,** the sloughing off of uterine lining that takes place if conception has not occurred. But menstruation is only one part of the **menstrual cycle,** the series of events that occurs each month during a woman's reproductive years. The words *menstruation* and *menstrual* are derived from the Latin *mensis,* "month," because the human menstrual cycle averages 28 days, or about a month. Every month from her first menstrual cycle (**menarche**) as a preteen or teenager to her last (**menopause**) in her 40s or 50s, a woman's uterine lining prepares for the fertilization of an egg cell. A woman who has two pregnancies will average about 500 menstrual cycles in her lifetime. Although usually referred to as blood, menstrual fluid is actually a mix of blood, mucus, and cells from the endometrium, the lining of the uterus. If fertilization does not occur, the uterine lining sheds or sloughs off and is discharged as menstrual flow.

Menarche

The first menstrual cycle, which signals the start of puberty in young women, is called menarche. In the United States the average age at menarche is about 12 years (Herman-Giddens et al., 1997). The average age at first menstruation has decreased by 4 months every decade since 1830 (Welch, 1992) but has remained fairly stable for the last 30 years (Dann, 1996). One hundred years ago, the average age of menarche was 16 years. As we will discuss in Chapter 9, scientists have offered several possible explanations for

Crura: two trunks of the clitoris that separate and join at the pubic arch and attach the clitoris to the pubic bone

Menstruation: the sloughing off of built-up uterine lining that recurs in nonpregnant women from menarche to menopause

Menstrual Cycle: the time from the beginning of one menstrual period to the beginning of the next; typically 28 days

Menarche: the initial onset of menstruation in life

Menopause: the cessation of menstruation in life

this change. There is a wide variation in the age of onset of menstruation. Numerous factors are involved in the timing of the first menstrual period, including genetics, diet, climate, stress, and emotional interaction (Frayser, 1985). In some societies menarche is celebrated as the time when a girl becomes a woman. We will discuss the social implications of menarche and menstruation in more detail in Chapter 8.

Length and Frequency of the Menstrual Cycle

The menstrual cycle is measured from the first day of menstrual flow to the day before the next flow begins. The length of the menstrual cycle ranges from 24 to 42 days (Belsey & Pinol, 1997), with an average length of 28 days. Some women's cycles are as regular as clockwork, while for others the lengths of the cycles vary widely. A woman's period may arrive a few days earlier or later than usual for a number of reasons. Travel to a different time zone, sleep deprivation, stress, or changes in diet and exercise can delay or accelerate menstruation. There can also be variations in the amount of flow; sometimes the menstrual flow is heavy and other times it is light. A single absent or particularly heavy period is no reason to panic, but significant changes in your period can be an early-warning sign of a possible health problem (see "Menstrual Problems" later in this chapter).

Hormonal Regulation of the Menstrual Cycle

Have you ever heard the expression "raging hormones"? This phrase is commonly used to describe feelings experienced during the menstrual cycle, although it can also be used to refer to teenagers undergoing the dramatic changes of puberty. Biologically, **hormones** are chemicals that are released at one location in the body and sent to act on another. A number of different organs distributed throughout your body, collectively called the **endocrine system,** act together to regulate hormone levels. The endocrine system is a form of chemical communication. The chemical messengers sent on these errands are the hormones, and the circulatory system (the blood) is the path they take to accomplish their mission, whether it is sexual arousal, initiating the changes of puberty, or delivering a baby.

The **hypothalamus** and **pituitary gland** in the brain, various endocrine glands, and activity of the ovaries and uterus all play roles in the regulation of the menstrual cycle (Figure 2.6). The hypothalamus, sometimes called the "master gland," oversees this process via a mechanism called *negative feedback*. When the hypothalamus detects decreased hormone levels in the bloodstream, it stimulates the other players to increase the levels of these hormones. Once hormones reach a certain level, the hypothalamus orders a decrease in hormone production. More details about the raging of the hormones appear in the following discussion of the phases of the menstrual cycle.

Phases of the Menstrual Cycle

While several models of the menstrual cycle have been suggested, the menstrual cycle is most easily understood as consisting of three phases: *menstrual, proliferative,* and *luteal.* Complex ovary and uterine changes characterize each of these phases (see Figure 2.6).

The Menstrual Phase While the **menstrual phase** actually signifies the end of the cycle (if a cycle can be said to have a beginning and an end!), it is the easiest place to begin since it is marked by the onset of menstruation, the only visible sign of the menstrual cycle. As you have already learned, the menstrual phase consists of the sloughing off and discharge of the endometrium, the inner lining of the uterus. This process may take 3 to 6 days. Menstruation is the result of falling levels of estrogen and progesterone in the blood (see the "Luteal Phase" later). Without these hormones to sustain it, the endometrium disintegrates, and the dead cells along with small amounts of blood are discharged through the cervix and vagina. Typically 1 to 2 fluid ounces (i.e., 2–3 Tbs) of menstrual flow occur with each menstrual period.

"[W]e bleed to rid the uterus of potentially dangerous pathogens that might have hitched a ride inside on the backs of sperm. Think of it. The uterus is a luxurious city just waiting to be sacked, and sperm are the ideal Trojan horse."

(ANGIER, 1999, P. 116)

Hormones: chemicals produced by one tissue and conveyed by the bloodstream to another to effect physiological activity

Endocrine System: the body system of ductless glands that produce and secrete hormones directly into the bloodstream

Hypothalamus: brain structure that plays a major role in controlling the production of sex hormones and regulates many sexual responses

Pituitary Gland: small gland in the base of the brain that receives instructions from the hypothalamus and secretes hormones

Menstrual Phase: the phase of the menstrual cycle during which the lining of the uterus is shed

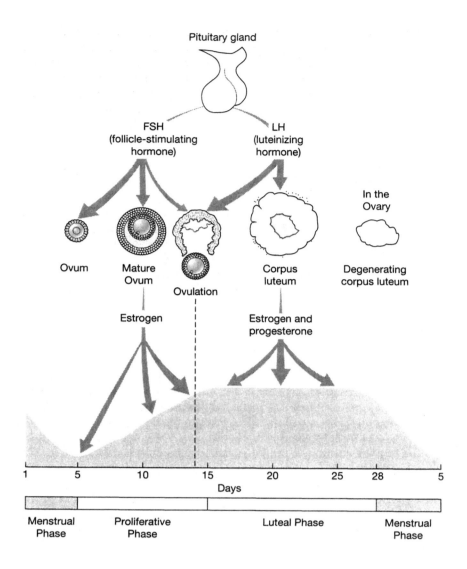

FIGURE 2.6 The Menstrual Cycle.

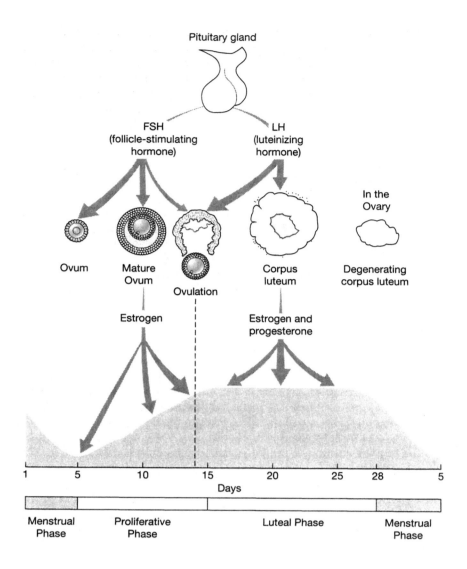

Within the figure:
Pituitary gland

FSH
(follicle-stimulating hormone)

LH
(luteinizing hormone)

In the Ovary

Ovum

Mature Ovum

Ovulation

Corpus luteum

Degenerating corpus luteum

Estrogen

Estrogen and progesterone

Days

1 5 10 15 20 25 28 5

Menstrual Phase   Proliferative Phase   Luteal Phase   Menstrual Phase

Proliferative Phase: the phase of the menstrual cycle in which the ovarian follicles mature

Gonadotropins: hormones that stimulate the activity of the function of the gonads (ovaries and testicles)

Gonadotropin-Releasing Hormone (Gn-RH): hormone produced and released in a pulsating manner by the hypothalamus; controls the pituitary gland's production and release of gonadotropins

Follicle-Stimulating Hormone (FSH): pituitary hormone that stimulates the development of the ovarian follicles (eggs) and the release of estrogen in women

The Proliferative Phase During the **proliferative phase,** the lining of the uterus proliferates or expands as the pituitary gland increases production of **gonadotropins,** hormones that stimulate activity in the ovaries (and in testes, which we will discuss later in this chapter). The low level of estrogen at menstruation signals the hypothalamus to release a hormone called **gonadotropin-releasing hormone (Gn-RH),** which then stimulates the pituitary to produce two other hormones, **follicle-stimulating hormone (FSH)** and **luteinizing hormone (LH).** FSH causes the ovaries to increase secretion of estrogen, which initiates a new proliferative phase. LH causes the ovary to release a mature ovum and stimulates the development of the **corpus luteum,** the mass of cells left in the ovary after the follicle ruptures and an egg is released.

During the proliferative phase, ovarian **follicles** mature as the ovaries prepare for ovulation, and the endometrium changes in order to allow a fertilized ovum to implant. Midway through the proliferative phase, estrogen production by the ovaries increases. The estrogen and other hormones prepare the developing follicle for ovulation. When the estrogen level peaks, the pituitary gland decreases the release of FSH and stimulates LH production. In response to the increased levels of LH in the bloodstream, the mature follicle ruptures and releases an ovum.

Ovulation, the release of the mature ovum from the ovary, marks the transition from the proliferative phase to the luteal phase. Immediately following ovulation is the time during the cycle when a woman is most likely to become pregnant. As many as 10

or 20 ova (eggs) may begin to ripen, but usually a single ovum is released from the surface of the ovary; the other ova degenerate. Ovulation typically occurs at midcycle, approximately day 14 of a typical 28-day menstrual cycle. However, it may occur from day 9 to day 19, and in some cycles there may be no ovulation (Masters & Johnson, 1966; Masters, Johnson, & Kolodny, 1992). **Anovulatory cycles,** cycles during which no egg is released, occur most frequently in the years just after menarche.

At ovulation, increases in estrogen cause the endometrium to thicken, due to the growth of tissue and blood vessels. As endometrial cells grow, the uterine lining expands up to 10 times its normal thickness. Increases in estrogen also cause cervical mucus secretions to increase. The mucus changes consistency, becoming clear, slippery, and stretchy. The pH of the mucus also becomes more alkaline, which contributes to sperm motility and longevity.

A woman's *basal body temperature* drops slightly at ovulation and then rises about 1 degree Fahrenheit the following day. A woman who wishes to become or not to become pregnant may use this information to help her determine the day of ovulation. However, changes in body temperature also may result from factors unrelated to ovulation so, as we discuss in Chapter 6, this may not be a reliable method of birth control. Some women experience cramping during ovulation called *mittelschmerz* (German for "middle pain," reflecting the fact that it occurs in the middle of menstrual cycles). The pain occurs on the same side of the abdomen as the ovary releasing an ovum.

The Luteal Phase   The **luteal phase** (also referred to as the postovulatory or secretory phase) begins immediately after ovulation and lasts until menstrual flow begins again. Luteal refers to the *corpus luteum*, which is formed during this phase. The corpus luteum produces large amounts of progesterone. Progesterone, along with estrogen produced by the ovaries, causes the uterus to prepare for the possible implantation of a fertilized egg and serves to regulate the production and release of other hormones in the woman's body.

If **implantation** of a fertilized ovum does not occur, the pituitary gland responds to high estrogen and progesterone levels by decreasing production of LH and FSH; this causes the corpus luteum to degenerate (10 to 12 days after ovulation) and estrogen and progesterone production to drop abruptly. The reduction of hormone levels causes endometrial cells to die, initiating the menstrual phase (Masters, Johnson, & Kolodny, 1992). So we're back to the "beginning" of the cycle.

Menstrual Synchrony

In 1971 biologist Martha McClintock presented data on **menstrual synchrony** after looking at the menstrual cycles of several groups of college roommates. The roommates began the semester with menstrual cycles randomly distributed throughout the month. Over the course of the school year, the roommates' cycles gradually converged until after 7 months the dates of onset of menstruation among the roommates were 33 percent closer than they had been at the beginning of the school year. Among a control group of women who did not share a room, there were no signs of menstrual synchrony. However, in a review of the menstrual synchrony studies published over the past 25 years, 16 were found to have statistically significant evidence of synchrony and 10 had no evidence of statistically meaningful patterns. A few studies have found evidence of asynchrony—as the months passed women who lived together became less harmonized in their periods rather than more (Weller & Weller, 1993). Menstrual synchrony was not found for 30 cohabiting lesbian couples (living together an average of 35 months) from whom 3 months of menstrual data were collected (Weller & Weller, 1998).

There is evidence that menstrual synchrony is affected by the release of **pheromones,** airborne chemicals released into the environment by certain animals, which affect the behavior of other animals of the same species. The pheromones affecting the length of the human menstrual cycle may be detected by the sense of smell,

Luteinizing Hormone (LH): hormone secreted by the pituitary gland that triggers ovulation and helps prepare the uterine lining for implantation

Corpus Luteum: the mass of cells left in the ovary by the ruptured follicle during ovulation, releasing an egg; subsequently it produces progesterone and estrogen

Follicle: small sac in the ovary that contains a developing egg

Anovulatory Cycles: cycles without ovulation

Luteal Phase: phase of the menstrual cycle in which the corpus luteum is formed and the uterus is prepared to nourish a fertilized egg

Implantation: attachment of the fertilized egg to the uterine lining

Menstrual Synchrony: the development of congruent menstrual cycles that sometimes occur among women who live together

Pheromones: airborne chemical substances secreted externally by some animals that convey information or produce specific responses in other members of the same species

Pads or tampons?

Dealing with menstrual discharge has been a concern for thousands of years. The women of ancient Egypt fashioned tampons from rolls of softened papyrus leaves. The ancient Japanese used paper, and Romans used wads of wool. The first disposable sanitary napkin was marketed in the late 1800s, but sanitary napkins did not become popular until after World War II. In 1933 Dr. Earle Cleveland Haas patented the internally worn tampon.

Today sanitary napkins (pads) and tampons are the most popular products. However, the federal Food and Drug Administration (FDA) has approved a number of new products in recent years. A product called Instead, a disposable cup, is inserted into the upper vagina, under the cervix; it rests against the rear wall of the vagina and behind the pubic pone. Instead, which is made of flexible, medical-grade plastic, softens with body heat to mold to a woman's individual anatomy. It collects, not absorbs, menstrual flow and can be worn about twice as long as a tampon. The Keeper, a reusable cup, also is worn internally. This soft rubber cup is inserted into the lower vagina to collect menstrual flow. The device is held in place by suction and, unlike Instead, The Keeper can be reused each month for up to 10 years.

Various methods of dealing with menstrual discharge include the use of sanitary napkins (pads), tampons, Instead, and The Keeper.

but at such low levels that they cannot be consciously detected. The phases of the woman's cycle are either lengthened or shortened, depending on which phase of the menstrual cycle she was in when she was exposed to the pheromones. Pheromones from women in the menstrual phase tend to shorten the cycle of women exposed to them, while pheromones from women in the proliferative phase lengthen the recipient's menstrual cycle. Secretions taken from women during the luteal phase of the cycle have no detectable impact on the timing of other women's periods (Stern & McClintock, 1996).

Sexual Activity and the Menstrual Cycle

In most animal species females are more interested in sex around the time of ovulation, which as you have already learned is when fertilization is most likely to occur. Although human females can engage in sexual behavior any time during the menstrual cycle, a number of studies have investigated the possibility that female sexual desire is linked to the hormonal changes associated with the phases of the menstrual cycle. While some research suggests that women tend to have more erotic interests around the time of ovulation (Dennerstein et al., 1994, Regan, 1996), other studies have found little or no difference in arousability at the different phases of the menstrual cycle (Morrell et al., 1984; Meuwissen & Over, 1992). The effect of hormones on sexual desire will be discussed more thoroughly in Chapter 3.

While there is no medical reason to avoid intercourse during the menstrual phase, some couples prefer to abstain from coitus during this time (Barnhart et al., 1995). One reason for avoiding intercourse is the reduction in the woman's sexual desire due to uncomfortable symptoms of menstruation (see "Dysmenorrhea" in the next section). However, sexual activity (orgasm) may actually help relieve these symptoms (Choi, 1992). People may also avoid sex during menstruation because of religious beliefs, cultural taboos (see CROSS-CULTURAL PERSPECTIVES box), or a dislike of messiness. As we will discuss in Chapter 6, having intercourse during a woman's menstrual period is not a reliable form of birth control.

Menstrual Problems

While many women have some physical or mood changes during the menstrual cycles (McFarlane & Williams, 1994), several conditions associated with menstruation require special attention. See Table 2.1 for a summary of symptoms and possible causes.

Dysmenorrhea   **Dysmenorrhea** is the medical term for painful menstruation. Symptoms may include pelvic or lower abdominal cramping, backache, and a feeling of being bloated, sometimes accompanied by diarrhea, nausea, or vomiting. Most women have experienced some degree of dysmenorrhea at one time or another. Symptoms usually begin approximately 24 hours before menstrual flow starts and continue for 2 to 3 days.

Dysmenorrhea is classified into two types, depending upon the onset and cause of the discomfort. If no pelvic abnormalities are present or the condition is present from the onset of menses, the condition is called *primary dysmenorrhea.* Primary dysmenorrhea is caused by an excessive release of *prostaglandin,* a hormonelike substance produced by many tissues of the body, including the lining of the uterus. Various medications, such as aspirin, naproxen sodium, and ibuprofen can provide symptom relief. Birth control pills are 90 percent effective in relieving the discomfort of dysmenorrhea. As we have already noted, being orgasmic also may reduce the symptoms (Masters & Johnson, 1966). *Secondary*

CROSS-CULTURAL PERSPECTIVES

Curses

The idea that menstrual blood is toxic is found in many cultures. Menstruating women have been said to make meat go bad, wine turn sour, bread dough fall, mirrors darken, and knives become dull. Some anthropologists have suggested that hunting societies have been particularly stringent in keeping women quarantined when they are menstruating, in part because of fears that menstrual odor attracts animals (Angier, 1999). Many societies that associate menstruation with impurity or regard the menstrual flow as dangerous to others isolate menstruating women to protect the community. Magical precautions and purification rites are also undertaken in a vast number of cultures. In many New Guinea societies men consider menstrual blood so poisonous that they take extraordinary measures to avoid coming into contact with it (Meigs, 1984).

There are at least 12 societies in the world where people believe menstruation is caused by sexual intercourse. This belief might be explained by the fact that most girls in these societies either marry or are allowed to have sex before puberty (Gregersen, 1994). Other cultures be-

In many indigenous societies in North and South America, as well as other areas of the world, menstruating women were segregated in special living quarters.

lieve that menstrual blood is therapeutic or endows special powers on women. Moroccans have used menstrual blood in dressings for sores and wounds, while among the Yurok of northern California, women traditionally believed that a menstruating woman should isolate herself because this is the time when she is at the height of her powers. Thus, her time should not be wasted on mundane tasks or social distractions, nor should her concentration be broken by concerns with the opposite sex. Rather, all of her energies should be applied in concentrated meditation on her life. The menstrual shelter, or room, was seen as a place where women go to make themselves stronger (Buckley, 1982).

---

dysmenorrhea is diagnosed when a specific physical condition, for example, endometriosis, pelvic inflammatory disease, ovarian **cysts,** or **tumors,** accompanies the menstrual pain. To obtain relief from secondary dysmenorrhea the underlying condition must be treated.

Menorrhagia   If a woman experiences excessively heavy or prolonged menstrual bleeding (soaking through at least one pad or tampon every hour for several consecutive hours), she may have **menorrhagia.** Hormone imbalances or a variety of medical disorders may cause this abnormal uterine bleeding.

In a normal menstrual cycle there is a balance between estrogen and progesterone. If this balance is disrupted, the endometrium continues to build up during the proliferative phase. When it sheds during the menstrual phase, heavy bleeding results. If a hormone imbalance is responsible for menorrhagia, *hormone therapy,* treatment that prevents cancer cells from getting the hormones they need to grow, may be recommended. Another common cause of menorrhagia is the presence of uterine **fibroids** (discussed in "Disorders of the Female Sexual Organs"). In some cases endometrial **cancer** (cancer of the lining of the uterus), inflammation or infection of a reproductive organ, polyps, thyroid conditions, or other diseases may be responsible for the excessive bleeding. In order to alleviate menorrhagia in such cases, the underlying medical condition must be treated.

Dysmenorrhea: pain or discomfort before or during menstruation

Cyst: membranous sac containing a gaseous, liquid, or semisolid substance

Tumor: an abnormal mass of tissue

Menorrhagia: excessive menstrual discharge

Fibroids: benign smooth muscle tumors of the uterus that may cause pain, irregular bleeding, and an enlarged uterus

Cancer: disease in which cells in body grow without control

TABLE 2.1	
Menstrual Problems	
Problem	**Possible Cause**
Absent or Infrequent Periods	Pregnancy Menopause Hormone imbalance Low body fat Stress
Spotting	Ovulation Breakthrough bleeding Thyroid imbalance Cervical polyps Cervical cancer Drug reaction Infection
Prolonged and Heavy Periods	Fibroids Endometrial polyps Perimenopause
Short and Light Periods	Hormonal imbalance

Amenorrhea Amenorrhea is the complete absence of menses for more than 6 months. *Primary amenorrhea* is the failure to begin to menstruate at puberty. This may be caused by problems with the reproductive organs, hormonal imbalances, or poor health. *Secondary amenorrhea* is the absence of menstrual periods in women who have had regular periods in the past. There are a number of causes of secondary amenorrhea. For most sexually active women in their reproductive years, amenorrhea is a signal of possible pregnancy. In older women, it may mean that menopause is approaching. In both cases, amenorrhea is perfectly normal. However, for nonpregnant women in their reproductive years, amenorrhea is usually a sign of a disturbance in the secretion of ovarian hormones. Other causes include defects in or absence of the uterus or vagina (see CONSIDERATIONS box for another cause).

When body fat falls below 5 percent, the body stops producing estrogen and ovulation ceases. Women with eating disorders such as *anorexia nervosa* and *bulimia* (Schweiger, 1991), as well as female athletes such as long-distance runners, can experience estrogen shutdown (Prior & Vigna, 1991; Shangold, 1985). When these women gain some body fat, they usually resume normal menstrual cycles.

Amenorrhea: the absence of menstruation for more than 6 months

Eliminating "The Curse"

Since some hormone-based contraceptives, especially Depo-Provera, make it simple, safe, and relatively inexpensive to eliminate menstruation, having a period can be optional. Certainly some women consider menstruating a pain—both in terms of the physical discomfort and the nuisance factor. Some might view menstruation as unnecessary and even dangerous since it is the cause

of so many health problems for women. Others feel that no matter how inconvenient it may be menstruation is an essential part of being a woman.

 If you had the opportunity, would you eliminate menstruation? Why or why not?

Toxic Shock Syndrome   **Toxic shock syndrome** is a rare but sometimes fatal bacterial disease among menstruating women that was first recognized in the late 1970s. The toxin-secreting bacteria (certain strains of staphylococcus aureus and group 4 streptococci) that cause toxic shock are usually already present in the body in harmless numbers. If these bacteria proliferate in the vagina, the toxins may cause high fever, a rapid drop of blood pressure, a rash followed by peeling skin on the palms of the hands and the soles of the feet, nausea, vomiting, diarrhea, and aching muscles (Vastag, 2001).

Toxic shock syndrome appears to be linked to tampon use, particularly the use of superabsorbent tampons. Tampons left in the vagina for 6 hours or more may provide an environment conducive to overgrowth of toxin-producing bacteria. As a precaution, it is recommended that a woman use the least absorbent tampon needed for her flow; she should also change tampons every 2 to 4 hours, and use sanitary pads during the night.

Premenstrual Syndrome (PMS)   **Premenstrual syndrome (PMS)** usually is defined by a set of symptoms including tension, irritability, sluggishness, impatience, dizziness, nervousness, depression, indecisiveness, breast tenderness, constipation, headache, or a bloated feeling that appear beginning 2 or 3 days before the onset of menstrual flow (Stewart & Tooley, 1992) (see CAMPUS CONFIDENTIAL box). One study found that approximately half of the 40 to 50 percent of North American women who crave chocolate or sweets do so principally in the premenstrual part of their cycle (Michene et al., 1999). Severe PMS symptoms may afflict 10 to 20 percent of women of childbearing age (Woods et al., 1987) and can interfere with the ability to function socially or at work (Mortola, 1998). Women diagnosed with PMS do not necessarily have all of these symptoms, and it is not clear how many women actually suffer from some degree of PMS. Premenstrual syndrome should not be confused with *Premenstrual Dysphoric Disorder (PMDD)*, a psychiatric disorder characterized by more severe mood changes that interfere with normal activities and relationships in the luteal phase of the menstrual cycle (APA, 1994). Advertisements for antidepressant medication to treat PMDD may lead to greater recognition and improved treatment of PMDD, but also may lead to greater confusion and concern.

The cause or causes of PMS are not known, and it remains a controversial diagnosis (Olasov & Jackson, 1987; Robinson, 1989). According to one study, a majority of the women who report symptoms of PMS to their physicians have other medical or psychiatric disorders (Korzekwa & Steiner, 1999). Women seeking help for PMS have been reported to have significantly higher levels of depression and anxiety (Hunter et al., 1995). In addition, there is some evidence that attitudes toward menstruation and premenstrual experience are associated with exposure to messages about menstruation during adolescence (Anson, 1999): negative messages may result in negative experiences. Not everyone agrees that symptoms of PMS are necessarily negative. There is other research that suggests that the premenstrual phase of the cycle is accompanied by heightened activity, intellectual clarity, and feelings of well-being, happiness, and sexual desire (Nicholson, 1995).

Rather than being a matter of "raging hormones," that is, excess or deficiencies of hormones, in one study women with severe PMS were found to respond differently to normal hormone levels (Schmidt et al., 1998). In other words, they were more sensitive to the normal hormone fluctuations of the menstrual cycle. PMS is most likely the result of a complex interaction between ovarian hormones and central nervous system neurotransmitters such as serotonin (Mortola, 1998).

Many of the symptoms of PMS can be minimized by lifestyle adjustments. Simple measures that can reduce PMS symptoms include a well-balanced diet, not smoking, aerobic exercise, and relaxation techniques (Frackiewicz & Shiovitz, 2001). Limiting caffeine intake may also help. For more severe cases, drugs that have been shown to be effective include the antidepressant medications Prozac and Zoloft, which belong to a class of medications known as selective serotonin reuptake inhibitors (SSRIs).

CAMPUS CONFIDENTIAL

"For about 5 days every month, I have raging PMS. Irritable doesn't even begin to describe my mood. It's way beyond irritable to have a major temper tantrum because someone moved my stapler. And talk about moody . . . a soppy TV commercial can make me bawl like a baby.

"I know my irrational behavior affects my relationships, but when I'm PMS-ing I don't really care. What I really hate is when someone tells me that PMS is all in my head. I don't think I have any abnormal hang-ups about being a woman or think of my period as a "curse." But no matter how hard I try, right before my period I get bloated and achy, I have difficulty concentrating, and the smallest thing can set me off. Hormones are real, menstruation is real, and PMS is real, too." ●

Toxic Shock Syndrome: disease that occurs most often in menstruating females using tampons in which an overgrowth of bacteria may cause fever, vomiting, diarrhea, and often shock

Premenstrual Syndrome (PMS): physical and emotional symptoms of discomfort that occur in some women prior to menstruation

MENOPAUSE

Since men do not have a menstrual cycle, strictly speaking they cannot undergo menopause. A sudden arrest of gonadal functions and fertility does not occur in middle-aged men as it does in middle-aged women. However, there are some who believe that male menopause (sometimes referred to as **viropause** or **andropause**) does exist. Proponents of this view claim that male menopause affects men ages 45 to 60 and causes symptoms including irritability, depression, indecisiveness, memory loss, weight gain, reduced endurance, a lower sex drive, and increased difficulty with **erections**. As they age, men typically produce less testosterone, the hormone primarily responsible for characteristics such as hair growth and sex drive. However, the decline in testosterone production is not great. Two thirds of men over age 65 produce as much or more testosterone than healthy 20-year-olds. Health problems such as cancer, heart disease, and diabetes, as well as drinking and smoking, can lower testosterone levels. For some men, testosterone pills, injections, or patches can be helpful, although there may be risk factors including prostate enlargement and prostate cancer.

■

Viropause/Andropause: male menopause; period when testosterone levels may decrease

Erection: firm and enlarged condition of a body organ or part when surrounding erectile tissue becomes engorged with blood; especially such a condition of the penis or clitoris

Some young women look forward to their first menstrual period and others dread it. Similarly, some women think that menopause, sometimes referred to as "the change of life" or simply "the change," means the loss of their youth, attractiveness, and femininity while others eagerly anticipate a new lease on life—physically, emotionally, sexually, and spiritually.

Menopause, the permanent cessation of menstruation, is a life transition, not a disease. It is one of the physiological changes of the *climacteric*, the time period of a woman's natural transition from fertility to infertility. The climacteric generally lasts for about 15 years, approximately from age 45 to 60. The cessation of menstruation is about a 2-year process beginning at around age 50.

Until the last 200 years or so, most women never experienced menopause because they didn't live that long. Today, the average life expectancy for a woman in Western societies is approaching 80 years. This means that the average woman can expect to live about one third to half of her adult life after menopause (Beck, 1992).

The period before menstruation completely stops is called **perimenopause**. Beginning about age 35, the menstrual cycles of many women begin to shorten, to about 23 days on average by the mid-40s (Whitbourne, 1985). By her late 40s, a woman's cycles often become erratic. Another early sign of menopause is "gushing," the sudden heavy flow of menstrual blood that may be dark or clotted, and may seep through the normal tampon or sanitary napkin protection. Surgical menopause occurs if the ovaries are removed, or damaged so that they no longer produce hormones. In such cases menopause begins immediately with no perimenopausal period.

As a woman approaches age 50, the ovaries gradually stop producing progesterone and estrogen, so egg cells will no longer ripen. A decrease in progesterone lessens the possibility of embryo implantation in the uterus. The lowered levels of estrogen may result in unpleasant physical sensations such as night sweats, hot flashes, and alternating cold sweats. All of these symptoms result from the body's inability to dilate (expand) or to constrict (squeeze) blood vessels and thus to maintain an even body temperature. Other signs of estrogen deficiency include dizziness, headaches, joint pains, heart palpitations, difficulty sleeping, tingling, and burning or itchy skin. With less estrogen and elevated FSH levels, bones can become brittle (a condition known as *osteoporosis*), rates of heart disease can increase, the vagina becomes less moist, and the skin generally becomes dry and thin.

Some 10 to 15 percent of North American women experience no problems during menopause, while another 10 to 15 percent have severe symptoms. The remaining 70 to 80 percent have some symptoms that come and go over a period of years (Sheehy, 1992). Cross-cultural data indicate that while women in all societies experience some of the same symptoms, relatively few women have severe problems. Women in some non-Western societies report less severe symptoms than menopausal women in the West do (Sixth International Congress on the Menopause, Bangkok, 1990, in Sheehy, 1992).

While most women do not experience a loss of sex drive during or after menopause, perhaps as many as 30 percent do (Sheehy, 1992). However, as we shall discuss more fully in Chapter 9, a woman's sexual life does not end when menopause begins. Some women even report an increased sex drive after menopause often attributed to no longer worrying about unintended pregnancy. Four or 5 years after menopause, some women experience a decrease in the levels of testosterone, the most important hormone in the sexual function of men and women. Decreased testosterone is often correlated with a decrease in sexual appetite in both men and women. Vaginal dryness and the thinning of vaginal tissue can lead to discomfort during sexual intercourse and masturbation for some women.

Treatment Alternatives

As we have already stated, menopause is not a disease, it is a naturally occurring life transition. For some women the symptoms of menopause may be disruptive, but they are not dangerous. Some women find that a healthy diet, regular exercise, moderate alcohol use, not smoking, and stress-reduction provide all the help they need. Other women find alternative therapies, such as acupuncture, to be helpful. However, about 10 million women, approximately 20 percent of menopausal American women (Love, 1998), rely on **hormone replacement therapy (HRT),** including estrogen, **progestin,** and sometimes testosterone, to counter the estrogen deficiency that occurs in post-menopausal years.

In addition to being one of the most widely prescribed treatments in the United States, HRT is also one of the most controversial. You have already learned about estrogen's role in the menstrual cycle. Estrogen, which will be discussed more fully in the next chapter, also affects tissues throughout the body. This makes the decision of whether or not to use estrogen or any type of HRT a complicated one. Some research has shown that postmenopausal estrogens can reduce the risk of osteoporotic fractures (Willett et al., 2000). On the other hand, a recent study cautions that women should not decide to go on hormone replacement therapy because they think it will protect them against heart disease, as widely used HRT guidelines were developed before the results of randomized trials become available or the results are inconsistent and unclear (Manson & Martin, 2001). Furthermore, the long-term use of unopposed estrogen (estrogen used alone) may sharply increase a woman's risk of two deadly diseases, endometrial cancer and breast cancer (Grodstein et al., 1997).

DISORDERS OF THE FEMALE SEXUAL ORGANS

Endometriosis

Endometriosis is a non-life-threatening condition in which the tissue that normally lines the uterus grows in other areas of the body, causing pain, irregular bleeding, and sometimes infertility. Typically the tissue growth occurs in the pelvic area, on the outside of the ovaries, uterus, bowels, rectum, or bladder, or invading the delicate lining of the pelvis, but it can occur in other areas of the body as well.

What's Your Risk?   Endometriosis occurs in an estimated 10 to 20 percent of women during their reproductive years. The prevalence may be as high as 15 to 50 percent among infertile women. It is still not clear why endometriosis occurs. Some experts believe menstrual blood flows backward through the fallopian tubes, and then enters and become implanted on other parts of the body. Others believe that the lymph or blood systems carry endometrial tissue to different parts of the body. Although typically diagnosed in women between the ages of 25 and 35, endometriosis probably starts to develop about the time that regular menstrual periods begin. Genetics appears to play a role, as the risk for a woman who has a mother or sister with endometriosis is six times greater than that of the general population. Other risk factors include a menstrual cycle length of 27 days or less, early onset of menstruation, and periods lasting 7 or more days.

How Is It Detected?   Pain is the most common symptom of endometriosis, and can occur during menstruation, ovulation, or intercourse. Back pain and painful bowel movements also affect some women. The severity of the pain and the extent of the tissue invasion are not linked. Women with mild endometriosis may experience severe pain, while those with severe endometriosis may have little or no pain.

Women with endometriosis are likely to menstruate heavily, have *spotting* (bleeding between periods), and have irregular periods. A pelvic exam may reveal the presence of tender nodules with a lumpy consistency in the posterior vaginal wall or near the ovaries. In addition, the uterus may be fixed or retroverted, or there may be pain when the uterus is palpated. It can be difficult to diagnose endometriosis during a pelvic exam; *laparoscopy,* a procedure in which a long, narrow tube (a laparoscope) is inserted through an incision in the navel, permitting the visual inspection of organs in the pelvic cavity, may be required for a definitive diagnosis.

Perimenopause: period before menstruation completely stops at menopause

Hormone Replacement Therapy (HRT): use of synthetic hormones to replace estrogen no longer produced by the ovaries in postmenopausal years

Progestin: hormone of the corpus luteum from which progesterone can be isolated in pure form

Endometriosis: condition in which endometrial tissue grows in pelvic regions outside the uterus

How Is It Treated? Treatment usually depends on the extent of the disease, the woman's desire for childbearing, and the severity of the symptoms. If there are few, mild symptoms, "watchful waiting," or monitoring of the condition without intervention, may be recommended. Hormone therapy may be used to prevent ovulation or to interfere with the production of hormones. Surgical options include surgical removal of glandular tissue or scar tissue. In the most severe cases, **hysterectomy,** the surgical removal of the uterus, or *oophorectomy,* removal of the ovaries, may be advised.

SEXUAL HEALTH AND YOU

The Gynecological Exam

A pelvic exam is a visual and manual medical evaluation of a woman's reproductive system. The external genitals are examined first to determine if there is any swelling, irritation, discoloration, or abnormal discharge. Then there is a visual internal examination. The examiner inserts a *speculum* to spread the vaginal walls in order to check for cervical abnormalities. A Pap test (see text discussion) is performed, and the examiner then conducts a bimanual internal examination by inserting two gloved fingers into the vagina while pressing the other hand on the lower abdomen to check the uterus, ovaries, and fallopian tubes. Finally, a rectovaginal exam is performed in which a finger is inserted in the rectum and two fingers are inserted into the vagina for further examination of the internal pelvic organs and the rectum.

Pelvic exams can be the cause of much anxiety for some women. Females in our society are socialized to keep their pubic area covered, and even women who may feel comfortable with exposing their genitalia to their sexual partners can find a vaginal examination to be uncomfortable or even highly stressful.

A sociological study described the woman's transition from a person to a "pelvic" during a vaginal exam. The authors of the study note that the vagina is conceptualized as a sacred object. The following routines adopted by the mostly male medical profession are designed to ensure the continued sacredness of

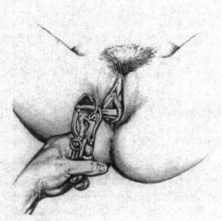

A pelvic exam.

the vagina and avoid any hint of personal violation (Henslin & Biggs, 1978):

The doctor is not present while the woman removes her clothing, which prohibits any suggestion of a striptease. The drape sheet placed over the patient keeps her genital area exposed, allowing that area to become an object separate from the rest of the woman's body. The drape sheet also keeps the woman from seeing her exposed genitals and the doctor's examination. A female nurse is present during the exam to act as a chaperon and to give assurance that no sexual acts will take place. After the exam, the doctor leaves the room so that the woman can dress in private. "[P]atients who have just had their genital area thoroughly examined both visually and tactilely by the doctor are concerned that the same man will see them in their underclothing" (Henslin & Biggs, 1978, p. 166).

Endometrial Cancer

Cancer originating in the lining of the uterus is called *endometrial cancer.* Nearly all of these life-threatening cancers occur in the form of adenocarcinomas (tumors of glandular cells). Endometrial cancer is the most common malignancy of the female reproductive organs.

What's Your Risk?   In the United States, white women are four times as likely to get endometrial cancer as African American women. The disease most often occurs in women between the ages of 55 and 75 (Miller et al., 1996). Women who develop endometrial cancer before age 45 usually have a history of infrequent or absent menstrual periods.

Estrogen is the major risk factor for the most common type of endometrial cancer. Estrogen-related exposures that have been shown to increase the risk include estrogen replacement therapy for treatment of menopausal symptoms (discussed earlier), use of Tamoxifen (a drug used in the treatment of breast cancer), early menarche (before age 12), late menopause (after age 52), never having been pregnant, and a history of failure to ovulate. Research has not implicated estrogen exposure in the development of other, more aggressive types of endometrial cancer, which have a poorer prognosis. The use of progesterone plus estrogen rather than the exclusive use of estrogen is believed to offset the increased risk associated with estrogen replacement therapy. Other risk factors include infertility, diabetes, gallbladder disease, hypertension, obesity, family history, previous breast or ovarian cancer, and prior pelvic radiotherapy. Pregnancy and the use of oral contraceptives appear to provide protection against endometrial cancer.

How Is It Detected?   Abnormal bleeding from the uterus is the primary symptom of endometrial cancer. About 90 percent of patients diagnosed with endometrial cancer complain of post-menopausal bleeding or irregular vaginal bleeding. In about 10 percent of cases, the discharge associated with endometrial cancer is white rather than blood-tinged. In later stages of the disease women may experience pelvic pain, a pelvic mass, or weight loss. At this time there is no recommended screening test or examination that can reliably detect most endometrial cancers in asymptomatic women. Endometrial biopsy is sometimes recommended at menopause and periodically thereafter for women at very high risk of developing this type of cancer (American Cancer Society, 2001).

How Is It Treated?   There are four basic types of treatment for women with endometrial cancer. Treatment of endometrial cancer is usually twofold. In most cases a hysterectomy is performed immediately. Due to the danger of *metastasis*, the spread of cancer cells to other areas of the body, surgery may be followed by a course of *radiation* (the use of high-energy rays to kill cancer cells and stop them from growing), *hormonal therapy* to keep cancer cells from getting the hormones they need to grow, or *chemotherapy*, the use of drugs to kill cancer cells. The 1-year survival rate for endometrial cancer is 93 percent. If the cancer is detected at an early stage, the 5-year survival rate is 95 percent; this drops to 64 percent if it is not diagnosed until a later stage.

Uterine Fibroids

Fibroids are balls of solid tissue that can grow inside the uterus, within the uterine wall, or outside the uterine wall. Fibroids can range in size from a grain of rice to a basketball. Fibroids frequently occur in groups or clumps, which tend to enlarge and distort the uterus. Fibroids are almost always **benign**, becoming cancerous in less than 1 percent of cases.

What's Your Risk?   Fibroid tumors are very common, affecting up to 25 percent of women over age 30, and 20 to 40 percent of all women of reproductive age. African American women are three to nine times more likely to be affected by uterine fibroids

Benign: noncancerous; does not invade nearby tissue or spread to other parts of the body

than white women. Sometimes fibroids worsen during pregnancy, when larger amounts of estrogen are produced, or in menopausal women using hormone replacement therapy. Fibroids are often found in women with endometriosis.

How Is It Detected?   The majority of women with uterine fibroids have no symptoms. However, some women have excessive menstrual bleeding, longer menstrual periods, spotting, menstrual pain, pain in the abdomen or lower back, constipation, and frequent or difficult urination. Fibroids are usually discovered during a pelvic exam. Sometimes diagnosis is difficult, especially in obese women. Fibroid tumors have been mistaken for ovarian tumors, pelvic inflammatory disease, and pregnancy. A transvaginal or pelvic ultrasound may be used to confirm the diagnosis. Dilation and curettage (D and C), a procedure in which the cervix is widened and the uterine lining scraped, may be necessary to rule out other potentially **malignant** conditions.

How Is It Treated?   The method of treatment of uterine fibroids depends on the severity of symptoms, age, pregnancy status, desire for future pregnancies, general health, and characteristics of the fibroids. If fibroids are not causing pain, bleeding, or discomfort, many physicians recommend leaving them alone and monitoring them for growth and complications. The decrease in estrogen levels at menopause may lead to shrinkage of fibroids and relief of symptoms.

If fibroids are large or are causing symptoms, there are a number of treatment options. *Endometrial ablation*, "washing" the uterine lining, does not treat the fibroids themselves, but alleviates the symptom of heavy bleeding. Ablation is used to treat excessive bleeding from other noncancerous conditions and is not the preferred option for women who want to have children. In a new version of this procedure a balloon is placed in the uterine cavity via a catheter, and then inflated with a hot liquid. Hormone therapy may be used alone, or in conjunction with surgery, to shrink fibroids. The surgical options include one of three types of *myomectomy*, a procedure that removes the fibroids but leaves the uterus intact.

In a new, less invasive technique called *fibroid embolization*, a catheter is inserted through a tiny incision in the groin into the femoral artery and then fed into the uterine artery. The catheter is used to inject tiny plastic particles that block the blood vessels feeding the fibroids, causing them to shrink. Because of the risk of damage to the ovaries, embolization is usually restricted to women who are not planning a pregnancy.

Cervical Cancer

Cervical cancer, cancer of the lower portion of the uterus, begins in the lining of the cervix and does not form suddenly. There is a gradual change from a normal cervix to precancer to cancer. Some women with *precancerous* changes of the cervix will develop *malignant* cancer. This usually takes several years, but sometimes can happen more rapidly.

What's Your Risk?   The risk of cervical cancer is very low among girls in their early teen years; the risk increases between the ages of 15 and 35. Although the risk of cervical cancer does not increase significantly after age 50, the average age of women newly diagnosed with cervical cancer is between 50 and 55 years. The risk of cervical cancer is closely linked to sexual behavior and to infection with certain types of **human papilloma virus (HPV),** a sexually transmitted infection we will discuss in Chapter 7. Most of the more than 80 types of HPV are benign and cause genital warts at worst. But persistent infection with any one of 13 types of HPV is responsible for at least 95 percent of cervical cancer (American Cancer Society, 2000b).

How Is It Detected?   Women with cervical precancers and early cancers are usually symptom-free; typically it is only in later stages, after the disease becomes invasive, that symptoms develop. Unusual vaginal discharge, abnormal vaginal bleeding, and spotting are

Malignant: cancerous; a growth that invades nearby tissue or spreads to other parts of the body

Human Papilloma Virus (HPV): a sexually transmitted infection that causes genital warts

some of the symptoms of advanced cervical cancer. Pain during intercourse or bleeding following intercourse is also common. However, each of these signs may be caused by other conditions; professional medical testing is the only way to ensure an accurate diagnosis.

Cancer of the cervix can usually be found early by having a Pap test as part of the pelvic exam (see SEXUAL HEALTH AND YOU box). The Pap test is a simple procedure in which a small sample of cells is swabbed from the cervix, transferred to a slide, and examined under a microscope. It is currently the only screening test that can be used to prevent cancer, by picking up cellular changes before they become cancerous. The American Cancer Society recommends that all women begin yearly Pap tests at age 18 or when they first become sexually active. However, more than half of the women diagnosed as having cervical cancer in the United States have not been screened with a Pap test within the past 3 years, and many women in developing countries are unable to get the test. Studies show that a new test that can be done by doctors or by women themselves could greatly increase the number of women who can be tested worldwide. The test, a vaginal swab for HPV/DNA, is just as sensitive as a Pap smear for detecting cervical cancer and precancerous changes; scientists predict that eventually it will become a primary screening test (Schiffman et al., 2000; Wright et al., 2000).

It is important to note that the Pap test is a screening test, not a diagnostic test. While the Pap test rarely fails to detect full-blown cervical cancer, as many as 20 percent of precancerous conditions may be missed. Women who have abnormal Pap test results usually will undergo a *colposcopy*, a procedure in which the cervix is viewed through an instrument with magnifying lenses that makes it possible to see the surface of the cervix closely and clearly. If an abnormal area is seen, a *biopsy*, the removal of a sample of tissue to check for cancer cells, is the only way to determine if the cells are precancerous or cancerous.

How Is It Treated?   Treatment options largely depend on the stage of the disease. If an area of abnormal cells is detected during colposcopy or upon biopsy, the abnormal tissue can be removed using LEEP (loop electrosurgical excision procedure), in which tissue is removed with a wire that is heated by electrical currents, or the cold knife cone biopsy, which uses a surgical scalpel rather than a heated wire to remove tissue. Other techniques for tissue removal include cryosurgery or laser surgery. During cryosurgery

SEXUAL HEALTH AND YOU

There Are No Stupid Questions

It is important to be able to talk with your physician about cancer care. No question is too trivial. In addition, if you are unsure about your doctor's recommendations, you should not be afraid to get a second opinion. Some questions to consider:

- What type of cancer do I have?
- Has the cancer spread to lymph nodes or internal organs?
- What is the stage of my cancer and how does it affect treatment options and prognosis?

- What treatments are appropriate for me, what do you recommend and why?
- What are the risks and side effects that I should expect? If I want children, will the treatment affect my fertility?
- What should I do to get ready for treatment?
- What are the chances for recurrence?

a metal probe cooled with liquid nitrogen is used to kill the abnormal cells by freezing them. Laser surgery uses a focused beam of high-energy light to vaporize the abnormal tissue. Other surgical options include a simple hysterectomy (removal of the uterus) or a radical hysterectomy and pelvic lymph node dissection (removal of the uterus, tissues next to the uterus, and lymph nodes from the pelvis). In the most severe cases, a pelvic exenteration (removal of uterus, tissues next to the uterus, pelvic lymph nodes, the bladder, vagina, rectum, and part of the colon) may be necessary. Radiation or chemotherapy may be recommended in addition to surgery.

Eighty-nine percent of cervical cancer patients survive 1 year after diagnosis and 70 percent survive 5 years. When detected at an early stage, invasive cervical cancer is one of the most successfully treatable cancers with a 5-year survival rate of 91 percent for localized cancers.

Ovarian Cysts

Ovarian cysts are balloonlike swellings of fluid contained within an envelope of ovarian tissue. Most types of ovarian cysts are harmless and will go away without any treatment. The most common type of ovarian cyst is called a *functional ovarian cyst*. Recall that, during ovulation, a follicle forms inside the ovary and ruptures when an egg is released. If pregnancy does not occur, the empty follicle usually dissolves and is reabsorbed. Sometimes the follicle does not dissolve, but instead becomes a fluid-filled cyst. Functional ovarian cysts may occur as the result of abnormal hormonal signals, stress, or illness, or simply because the surface of the ovary tends to become thickened and scarred after years of ovulation. These cysts will often shrink and disappear within two or three menstrual cycles.

There are several types of *nonfunctional ovarian cysts*. For example, endometrioma can form when tissue from the uterine lining becomes attached to an ovary in women with endometriosis. Cystadenomas develop from ovarian tissue; some are filled with watery fluid and others with a gelatin-like material. Dermoid cysts contain skin and other tissue such as hair, bone, or even teeth; these cysts develop from ovarian germ cells—the cells that produce human eggs.

What's Your Risk?   Any woman who ovulates may develop an ovarian cyst, and women who have had one cyst are at an increased risk for additional cysts. About 20 percent of women have a condition called *polycystic ovary syndrome (PCOS)* that causes many tiny, harmless cysts to form on the ovaries. Women taking fertility drugs and women with higher-than-normal levels of testosterone are especially at risk for developing this condition.

How Is It Detected?   The majority of ovarian cysts don't cause any symptoms. Some women experience low levels of pain or pressure in the lower abdomen. Intense pain and nausea can occur if cysts become twisted or rupture. Pain during intercourse, constipation, and a need to urinate frequently are additional signs of ovarian cysts. Ovarian cysts can be discovered during a pelvic exam.

How Is It Treated?   If there are no symptoms or if the cysts are small, the doctor may recommend that the cysts be monitored for two or three menstrual cycles without treatment. Birth control pills are sometimes used to prevent ovulation in women with functional cysts, causing the cysts to shrink and fewer new cysts to form. Surgical treatment may be required for cysts in women past menopause, for very large cysts, or for cysts accompanied by severe symptoms. The type of operation will depend on how early the cyst is found, its size, the type of cyst, and the age of the woman. Laparoscopy, removal of an ovary, or removal of both ovaries and the uterus are possible types of surgery.

Ovarian Cancer

The most common *ovarian cancer* in women age 55 to 80 is *adenocarcinoma*, cancer that develops in the lining of the inner surface. Malignant ovarian tumors in women under age 30 will usually be germ cell tumors, which can be some of the most aggressive cancers known.

What's Your Risk?   Each year more than 26,000 women in the United States are diagnosed with ovarian cancer; approximately 1 in 70 women will develop the disease (American Cancer Society, 2000c). While ovarian cancer ranks fifth in cancer incidence among women, it causes more deaths than any other cancer of the female reproductive system. Overall incidence rates are highest among Native American women, followed by whites, Vietnamese, Hispanic, and Native Hawaiian women. Rates are lowest among Korean, Chinese, and Native Alaskan women. Mortality patterns differ from the incidence rates of ovarian cancer; white women have the highest mortality rates in each age group (Miller et al., 1996).

The risk of ovarian cancer increases with age and is highest among women over 60. Women who have never had children are twice as likely to develop ovarian cancer as women who have had children; women who have previously been diagnosed with breast, intestinal, or rectal cancer are also twice as likely to develop the disease (American Cancer Society, 2000c). The most important risk factor for ovarian cancer is a family history of a first-degree relative (mother, daughter, or sister) with the disease. Women with two or more first-degree relatives who have had ovarian cancer are at the highest risk (Piver et al., 1996).

How Is It Detected?   Often there are no symptoms in the early stages of ovarian cancer. The cancer may grow for some time before it causes pressure, pain, or other problems; even when symptoms do appear, they may be so vague that they are ignored. As an ovarian tumor grows, it can cause fluid to build up in the abdomen, resulting in swelling, bloating, or general discomfort. Loss of appetite, indigestion, nausea, and weight loss are other possible symptoms. In addition to the fluid buildup in the abdomen, in some cases fluid may also collect around the lungs, causing shortness of breath. Some women with the disease may experience vaginal bleeding, and as the tumor grows it may press on the bowels or bladder, causing diarrhea, constipation, or frequent urination.

A thorough pelvic examination is essential to the detection of ovarian cancer. If the physician discovers irregularities, a transvaginal ultrasound, CT (or CAT) scan, or X-ray exam may be able to differentiate healthy tissue, fluid-filled cysts, and tumors. Although an ovarian cancer blood antigen, CA-125, has been identified, it is not always present in women who have early-stage ovarian cancer and may be found in some women with benign gynecologic diseases. Research data suggest that a small extracellular phospholipid (lyphosphatidic acid or LPA) may be a more sensitive marker for ovarian cancer than CA-125 (Xu et al., 1998). However, at the present time, the only sure way to diagnose the disease is to have a biopsy examined by a pathologist.

How Is It Treated?   Treatment for ovarian cancer depends on a number of individual factors, including the stage of the disease, the woman's age, and her general health. Surgical intervention is the initial treatment in the majority of cases. Usually the surgeon will perform a hysterectomy with bilateral salpingo-oophorectomy. This impressive-sounding procedure involves the removal of the ovaries, the uterus, and the fallopian tubes. If the cancer is detected early, especially in younger women, it is possible to limit surgery to the cancerous ovary. Surgery may be followed by chemotherapy, or less often by radiation therapy, to kill any remaining cancer cells, or to prevent recurrence.

When detected in its early stages, the 5-year survival rate for ovarian cancer is 93 percent. However, only about 24 percent of all ovarian cancers are identified at this stage (Friedrich, 1999). Because of the absence of symptoms or reluctance to obtain treatment, women are not usually diagnosed until the cancer has spread, causing the overall 5-year survival rate to plunge to 46 percent.

Vulvar Cancer

Cancer of the vulva, or *vulvar cancer*, is a malignancy that can occur on any part of the female external reproductive system but most often affects the inner edges of the labia majora or the labia minora. Less often, vulvar cancer occurs on the clitoris or the Bartholin's glands. Over 90 percent of cancers of the vulva are *squamous* cell carcinomas, a type of skin cancer that occurs in squamous cells, the main cell type of the skin. The second most common type of vulvar cancer (about 4 percent) is melanoma, the deadliest type of skin cancer.

What's Your Risk?   In the United States, vulvar cancer accounts for 4 percent of all cancers of the female reproductive organs and $\frac{1}{2}$ percent of all cancers in women. The American Cancer Society (2000f) estimates that about 3,200 cancers of the vulva will be diagnosed each year.

Age is an important risk factor. Of the women who develop vulvar cancer, 75 percent are over age 50 and two thirds are over 70. However, the number of vulvar cancer patients under age 40 is increasing.

Infection by HPV is thought to be responsible for about 30 to 50 percent of vulvar cancers. Of the more than 80 types of HPV that have been identified, some, including HPV 16, 19, and 31, are considered "high-risk" types. Smoking, other genital cancers, and chronic vulvar inflammation caused by infections and poor hygiene have also been suggested as risk factors for vulvar cancer.

How Is It Detected?   The most common early symptom of cancer of the vulva is persistent itching that does not improve. Because several less serious conditions, such as a yeast infection (see the upcoming discussion of vaginitis), can cause this symptom, many women fail to recognize the potential seriousness of their problem. As the disease progresses, a distinct tumor may emerge in the form of a red, pink, or white bump or bumps with a wartlike or raw surface. An area of the vulva may appear white and feel tough. Some women complain of pain, burning, painful urination, bleeding, and discharge. The appearance of a darkly pigmented lesion or a change in a mole that has been present for many years may indicate vulvar melanoma.

CONSIDERATIONS

Clinical Trials

To learn more about promising new and experimental types of treatment, researchers conduct studies known as clinical trials. The researchers use these trials to answer the following questions: Is the proposed treatment effective? Does it work better than existing treatments? What are the side effects? Do the benefits of the treatment outweigh the risks involved? Which patients is the treatment most likely to help? Most clinical trials involve a control group given a **placebo,** a "sugar pill" or dummy medication, so the researchers can compare the progress of the treated group with that of the untreated group. In most cases, patients do not know whether they are taking the experimental treatment or the placebo.

If your physician discusses the possibility of enrolling you in a clinical trial, you should be well informed about the proposed course of treatment. Enrollment in a clinical trial is strictly voluntary. Before agreeing to participate in a clinical trial you should find out what side effects you might expect, how long the study will last, what will happen if you are harmed by the research, and what type of long-term follow-up care is part of the study.

 Would you enroll in a clinical trial?

—*What if you found out you were a member of the control group?*

—*Should clinical trials of treatment for a life-threatening illness such as ovarian cancer be conducted with or without a control group?*

If vulvar cancer is suspected, a physician will usually conduct a visual and manual inspection. To make a final diagnosis, a biopsy is performed.

How Is It Treated?   As with other cancers, options for treating vulvar cancer depend on the stage of the disease and include surgery, radiation, and chemotherapy. Laser surgery to vaporize the layer of skin containing abnormal cells is not used for treating invasive cancer. Excision involves removing the cancer and about ½ inch of the surrounding skin. In a complete radical vulvectomy, the entire vulva along with deep tissues including the clitoris is removed. When vulvar cancer is detected early it is highly curable. The overall 5-year survival rate when the lymph nodes are not involved is 90 percent. However, when cancer has spread to the lymph nodes the 5-year survival rate drops to 50 to 60 percent.

Vaginitis

Vaginitis is an inflammation of a woman's vagina that may be due to infection by bacteria, fungi, viruses, or parasites, a lack of estrogen, or a chemical imbalance. The vulval area secretes sebum, a blend of oils, waxes, fats, cholesterol, and cellular debris that serves as a waterproofing against bacteria that might otherwise be harmful. When conditions are healthy, the bacteria in the vagina aren't harmful. Each vaginal cell contains large quantities of glycogen, a stored sugar molecule. Protective bacteria use glycogen as their energy source. The slightly acidic environment of the vagina helps foster the growth of these bacteria. When the pH balance of the vagina is disrupted, one or more types of organisms can begin to thrive, resulting in vaginitis.

There are three primary types of vaginitis. The two that are spread by sexual contact, bacterial vaginosis and trichomoniasis, will be discussed in Chapter 7. The most common type of non-sexually contracted vaginitis is a yeast infection caused by *Candida albicans*, a fungus that regularly exists harmlessly on the vagina, the mouth, and the digestive tract. As described previously, a yeast infection develops when the pH of the vagina is altered, causing it to become less acidic. The decreased acidity results in an overgrowth of Candida organisms, causing the uncomfortable symptoms of a yeast infection.

What's Your Risk?   Diabetes and hormone imbalance are two causes of the overgrowth of the Candida fungus. Hormonal fluctuations that occur during pregnancy, at various times during the menstrual cycle, or with the use of oral contraceptives can all upset the vaginal environment. Prolonged use of antibiotics, or use of a strong antibiotic, can also upset the balance of vaginal flora; if a woman eats yogurt or takes acidophilis when on antibiotics, the risk of a yeast infection is reduced.

How Is It Detected?   The most common symptoms of a yeast infection are itching, burning, and redness in the vagina and the vulva. Some women also experience vaginal discharge, pain, and/or a burning sensation during intercourse. The vaginal discharge, which is generally white, may have a faint, sweet, yeasty smell and a texture resembling cottage cheese.

The symptoms overlap with those of a number of other disorders, so accurate diagnosis requires an examination by a health-care practitioner, particularly for a first bout of the problem. The National Vaginitis Association (2001) recommends testing a sample of vaginal discharge in addition to having a visual pelvic examination.

How Is It Treated?   The usual treatment for yeast infections is nonprescription antifungal creams or suppositories. Treatment with a nonprescription medication is recommended only for those who are sure they have a yeast infection and not some other type of vaginitis or sexually transmitted infection. Chronic yeast infections may require treatment with a prescription antifungal medication.

Placebo: an inactive substance or preparation given to reinforce a patient's expectation to get well, as a control in an experiment, or to test the effectiveness of a medicine

Vaginitis: inflammation of the vagina, typically caused by bacteria or yeast infection

Secondary Sex Characteristics: physical characteristics, other than the genitals, that indicate sexual maturity and distinguish males from females

Mammary Glands: glands found in female mammals that produce milk

Nipple: protuberance through which milk is drawn from the breast

Areola: area of dark-colored skin on the breast that surrounds the nipple

BREASTS

Breasts are one of a number of human **secondary sex characteristics,** traits other than the genitals that distinguish males from females and indicate sexual maturity. Unlike the internal and external sex organs you have just learned about (the primary sex characteristics), secondary sex characteristics play no direct role in reproduction. Other secondary sex characteristics include the distribution of body hair and fat, body size and muscle mass, and the deepening of the male voice. While both males and females have breasts, the structure and size of the breasts tends to distinguish males and females.

In a physically mature female, each breast consists of 15 to 20 subdivided lobes of glandular tissue called mammary or milk glands surrounded by fatty and fibrous tissue (Figure 2.7). While the popular media and adolescent bathroom discussion may suggest otherwise, the primary function of female breasts is to produce milk for infants. The **mammary glands** secrete milk that a new mother can use to nurse her infant. A milk duct that opens on the surface of the **nipple** drains each lobe in response to the sucking of an infant. Breast size is determined by the amount of fatty tissue in the breast; there is little variation among women in the amount of glandular tissue present. Thus the size of a woman's breasts has no bearing on the amount of milk produced after childbirth.

The nipple of the breast consists mostly of smooth muscle fibers along with many nerve endings. The dark textured skin of the nipple extends 1 or 2 centimeters onto the surface of the breast to form a circular patch called the **areola.** The areola is permeated by a set of modified sweat glands, the little "goosebumps," called *Montgomery's glands.* The nipple and areola are highly sensitive to touch and temperature. The nerve and muscle fibers of the areola can cause the nipple to stiffen and become erect in response to direct or indirect stimulation. Not all women have sensitive breasts, nor do they all enjoy having their breasts fondled. Although generally less sensitive to touch than the female breast (Robinson & Short, 1977), many men have sensitive nipples and obtain sexual pleasure when their breasts are stroked or licked.

FIGURE 2.7 The Structure of the Female Breast. SOURCE: Martini, 2001.

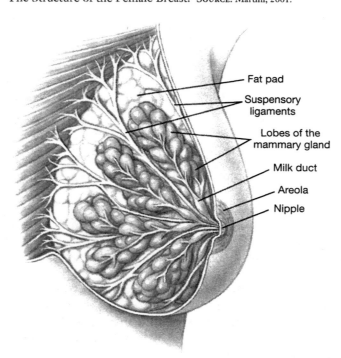

"These protuberances around the mammary glands seem poorly placed. They bobble painfully when a woman runs. They flop forward to block vision when she leans over to collect food. And they can suffocate a suckling child. Moreover, breasts (of any size) are sensitive to touch. Why?"

(FISHER, 1992, P. 180)

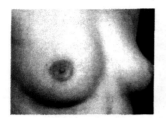 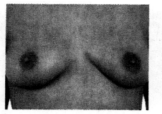 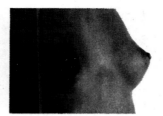

Breast size and shape vary in adult women.

Male breasts differ from female breasts principally in having little glandular or fatty tissues. Lack of glandular tissue means male breasts cannot produce milk. Sometimes males' breasts can become enlarged, a condition known as *gynecomastia*. A significant number of adolescent boys (40 to 60 percent) are troubled by gynecomastia; during puberty, as they begin to develop an increase in the amount of glandular tissue around their breasts, breast size may increase as a result of a surge in estrogen. Although it may be a symptom of liver or thyroid disease or a sign of drug use, for the most part it is just a variation of male adolescent development that usually resolves itself within a year or two.

DISEASES OF THE BREAST

Three types of lumps can occur in the breasts. The most common of these are *cysts*, fluid-filled sacs, and *fibroadenomas*, solid rounded tumors. Both of these types of lumps are noncancerous and easily treated, and together account for 80 percent of breast lumps. The third type of lump is a sign of the most common form of cancer among women in the United States: breast cancer.

Breast Cancer

The rates of breast cancer in the United States have remained stable for decades (Kolata, 1993). However, increased awareness and advances in detection and treatment have led to increased rates of survival. Indeed, early detection and treatment are essential to preventing the spread of the cancer to other parts of the body where it may become deadly.

What's Your Risk? Breast cancer represents 30 percent of all female cancers, affecting approximately 110 women per 100,000. It is not the cancer of the breast that is fatal. If untreated, the cancer may metastasize or spread to other vital body parts such as the brain, bone, or lungs.

In the United States the odds for a woman to develop breast cancer by age 85 are not insignificant. For younger women the chance is much smaller, however, the cumulative risk for all women is estimated at one in eight. (See Table 2.2.)

No specific cause of breast cancer is known. However certain risk factors that predispose a woman to breast cancer have been identified. Some risk factors can't be changed. Simply being a woman is the main risk factor for developing breast cancer. Genetic factors, a mother or sister with breast cancer history, aging, early menarche, and the late onset of menopause are known risk factors.

Lifestyle-related risk factors include smoking, alcohol consumption, not breastfeeding, never bearing children, or bearing a first child at a late age. Diet-related factors, especially fat intake, have been correlated with breast cancer rates on an international level, but a causal link has not been firmly established. Possible additional factors currently being studied include the use of oral contraceptives, exposure to toxic chemicals, and physical inactivity (American Cancer Society, 2000a).

FAQ:

Why is there such a variation in the size of women's breasts?

We don't know why there is such a wide variety of breast sizes, or what exactly controls the growth of the breast, particularly the fatty tissue that give the human breast its bulk. Breast size says little or nothing about a woman's health, fertility, or ability to breastfeed. As we stated earlier, breast size is primarily due to the amount of fatty tissue that is distributed around the glands. Breasts represent only a small fraction of the body's total fat mass, about 4 percent on average, and their size generally changes less in proportion to a woman's weight gain or loss than other body fat. Common variations in breasts include having one breast larger than the other (usually the left), an inverted nipple (a congenital condition in which the nipple does not protrude), and extra or false (nonfunctional) nipples. None of these is a health issue, although inverted nipples may make it more difficult to breastfeed an infant. Among adult females there is considerable variation in breast shape and size. There is no relationship between breast size and sexual responsiveness.

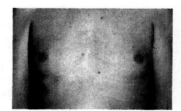

Gynecomastia.

TABLE 2.2

Odds for Developing Breast Cancer by Age

Problem	Possible Cause
From age 30 to age 40	1 out of 257
From age 40 to age 50	1 out of 67
From age 50 to age 60	1 out of 36
From age 60 to age 70	1 out of 28
From age 70 to age 80	1 out of 24
Ever	1 out of 8

SOURCE: American Cancer Society, 2001

Mammogram: X-ray exam of the breast to detect cancerous tumors

One study found that 75 percent of women who develop breast cancer have no identifiable risk factor other than gender and age (Hortobagvi, McClelland, & Reed, 1990). Breast size and cancer risk are not directly related, although large breasts can make discovery of small lumps more difficult. No evidence has been found that breast implants cause breast cancer.

How Is It Detected? Breast changes such as a lump, thickening, swelling, dimpling, tenderness of the nipple, and nipple discharge are among the symptoms of breast cancer in both men and women. However there are often no symptoms, particularly during the early stages of the disease, a fact that underscores the importance of early detection by self-examination and mammography. The most important factor in survival is early detection; 90 percent of cancerous lumps are first discovered by breast self-examination (see SEXUAL HEALTH AND YOU box).

Mammograms. A screening **mammogram** is the best tool currently available for finding breast cancer before a tumor is large enough to be felt in a BSE. The procedure consists of an X-ray of each breast while compressed in a device that flattens the breast so accurate pictures can be taken. The benefits of mammography greatly outweigh any potential risk from the low dose of radiation used. Most women report little or no discomfort with the procedure. To assure less discomfort, schedule a mammogram right after a menstrual period when the breasts are less sensitive.

Although mammograms are the best way to find breast cancer early, they do have some limitations. A mammogram may miss some cancers that are present (false negative) or may find things that turn out not be cancerous (false positive). Approximately 10 to 15 percent of tumors don't show up on a mammogram. Mammography is considered to be even less reliable with younger women who have denser breast tissue; the error rate is approximately 40 percent in women younger than 40 years.

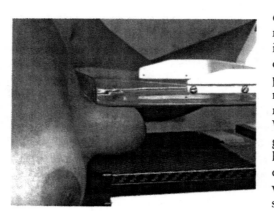

A mammogram is key to early detection of breast cancer.

Another procedure that is used to detect breast cancer is magnetic resonance imaging (MRI). This procedure is thought to be better at early detection of a tumor, but is considerably more expensive than a mammogram. Digital mammograms, computerized breast X-rays, were approved by the FDA in 2000. While sonograms and digital mammograms appear to be no better than regular mammograms in detecting breast cancer, the new technology does away with film exposure problems, as well as storage and loss issues.

⟨www⟩ ⫼S⫼EXUAL HEALTH AND YOU

Breast Self-Examination

All women are advised to examine their breasts for unusual lumps every month. In that way they can become familiar with what is normal for their own breasts and increase the chances of early detection. Many women don't do regular breast self-examinations (BSE). They may forget, not think they're at risk, or be afraid of what they might find. Be afraid of *not* doing a BSE. If you do discover a lump, don't panic! Most lumps are not cancerous: For every malignant lump found in young women, 12 benign lumps are detected.

The best time to do a BSE is about a week after your menstrual period ends, when your breasts are less likely to be tender or swollen and least influenced by hormones. For those women who don't have regular periods, it's helpful to do a BSE about the same time every month. Regular inspection will give you confidence in what is normal for you and alert you to any changes.

There are three parts to a thorough BSE:

1. Examine your breasts in the shower or bath. Keeping your fingers flat and gently move the finger pads over every part of each breast, checking for any lumps, hard knots, or thickening. Use your right hand to examine your left breast and reverse the procedure to examine your right breast.

2. Inspect your breast before a mirror with your arms at your sides. Next, raise your arms overhead looking for changes in the contour of each breast, a swelling, dimpling of skin, or changes in the nipple. Then rest your palms on your hips and press down firmly to flex your chest muscles.

3. Lying down, put a pillow or folded towel under your right shoulder to examine your right breast (Figure 2.8). Place your right hand behind your head to distribute breast tissue more evenly on the chest. Use your left hand with fingers flat to press gently in small circular motions around an imaginary clock face. Begin at 12 o'clock, the outermost top of your right breast, and so on around the circle back to 12. A ridge of firm tissue in the lower curve of the breast is normal. Then move in an inch toward the nipple. Keep circling to examine every part of your breast, including the nipple. Then slowly repeat the procedure by placing the pillow under your left shoulder, raising the left arm and using the fingers on your right hand to examine your left breast. Finally, gently squeeze the nipple of each breast to check for discharge.

Can men get breast cancer?

Although breast cancer is 100 times more common among women, the American Cancer Society (2000a) estimates some 1,600 new cases of invasive breast cancer will be diagnosed among men in the United States each year. The average male breast cancer patient is 59 years old. Because the disease is so rarely found in men there have been few studies of the risk factors. It is thought that hormones and the environment play a role; however, about half of men who get breast cancer have no known risk factors. One reason that men have few breast cancers is simply that they have less breast tissue. In men, the only tissue that resembles the milk ducts in women is located directly beneath the nipple—and that is where most male breast cancers occur.

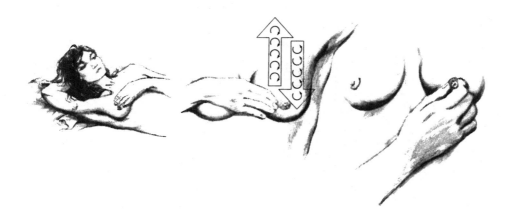

FIGURE 2.8 Breast Self-Examination.

The American Cancer Society recommends that beginning at age 40 women should have an annual mammogram. Women who have a first-degree relative with the disease (mother, sister, or daughter) should have their first mammogram 10 years before the age at which the relative was diagnosed; for example, if your mother was 42 when she was diagnosed, you should have your first mammogram at age 32. If a suspicious lump is found, diagnosis is made by a biopsy, i.e., removal and examination of a small amount of tissue from the suspected area or the surgical removal of all or part of the area in question.

How Is It Treated?   Treatment choices for breast cancer are complex and depend on a number of factors including age, general health, and the size, location, stage, and features of the tumor. Treatment options include surgery, radiation therapy, hormone therapy, and chemotherapy. Two or more methods may be used in conjunction.

There are several types of surgery used to treat breast cancer. In a **lumpectomy** only the lump in the breast is removed, although some surgeons also take out some of the lymph nodes under the arm. In a *segmental mastectomy* the cancer and a larger area of breast tissue are removed, occasionally including some of the lining over the chest muscles below the tumor, and possibly some lymph nodes under the arm. A total **mastectomy**, sometimes called a *simple mastectomy*, involves the surgical removal of the whole breast, and possibly some lymph nodes under the arm. A *modified radical mastectomy* involves the removal of the breast, most of the lymph nodes under the arm, and often the lining over the chest muscles; the smaller of the two chest muscles also is taken out to aid in the removal of the lymph nodes. In a *radical mastectomy*, the breast, the chest muscles, all of the lymph nodes under the arm, and some additional fat and skin are removed.

For many years the radical mastectomy was the operation of choice. Now it is used mainly when the tumor has spread to the chest muscles. Numerous studies have shown that for early-stage disease, long-term survival rates after lumpectomy followed by radiation therapy are similar to the survival rates for modified radical mastectomies. Lumpectomies leave the breast intact. When the breast is removed through a mastectomy, reconstruction is often an option either at the same time as the surgery or at a later date.

 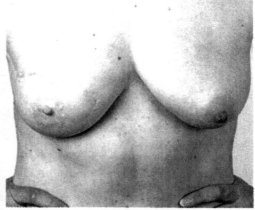

(a) A woman after a mastectomy without reconstructive surgery. (b) A woman with a reconstructed breast following a mastectomy.

Chemotherapy may be given orally or by injection in cycles, with each treatment period followed by a recovery period. Usually chemotherapy is administered on an outpatient basis. Another treatment option is hormonal therapy, which is used to keep cancer cells from getting the hormones they need to grow. This treatment may require the use of drugs, or surgery to remove the ovaries, which produce the majority of female hormones. Like chemotherapy, hormonal therapy is a systemic treatment affecting cells throughout the body.

Ninety-six percent of women with localized breast cancer survive at least 5 years after diagnosis. If the cancer has spread, the survival rate is about 75 percent. An increase in the survival rate is probably due to better and earlier detection, increased use of chemotherapy and radiation along with surgery, and better techniques for discovering metastases.

Semen: fluid containing sperm and secretions from the testicles, prostate, and seminal vesicles that is expelled from the penis during ejaculation; ejaculate

Ejaculate: semen

Sperm: male reproductive cell

Seminal Fluid: fluid from the prostate and other sex glands that helps transport semen out of a man's body during ejaculation

Spermatogenesis: the production of sperm cells

Male Sexual Anatomy and Physiology

Like the female sexual anatomy, the function of the male sexual organs is to ensure sexual arousal and reproduction. The penis and scrotum, which contains the testes, are the most observable parts of a man's sexual anatomy. However, the internal organs are essential to ensure that sexual functions, including erection, ejaculation, and fertilization (which will be discussed in Chapters 3 and 5) are possible. The male reproductive system is best understood by following the pathway of sperm from the site of production in the seminiferous tubules of the testes to ejaculation out the urethral meatus (or opening) of the penis.

MALE INTERNAL SEXUAL ORGANS

The primary function of the internal sexual organs of the human male (Figure 2.9) is the production of **semen**. Semen, sometimes referred to in clinical terms as **ejaculate,** is the **sperm**-containing **seminal fluid** ejaculated through the opening of the penis. A teaspoon

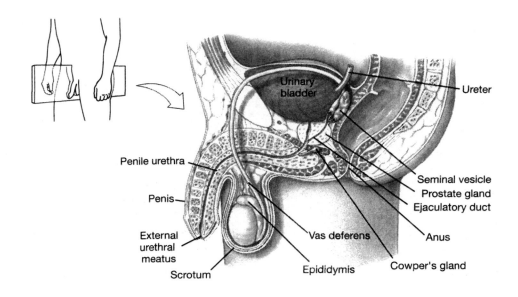

FIGURE 2.9 The Male Internal Sexual Organs.
Source: Martini, 2001.

When a man has an erection, the prostate gland squeezes shut the urethral duct to the bladder. This prevents urine from flowing down the urethra (and prevents semen from going up into the bladder). Thus normally, before a man with an erection can urinate, the pressure on the urethral duct must be released to allow passage of the urine down the urethra. Once this happens a man may urinate even though he may still have a partial erection. This is a common occurrence when a man awakens with a morning erection. (Contrary to popular opinion, the erection is caused by sexual arousal during the REM phase of sleep, not the need to urinate.) Usually by the time the bladder has been voided, the corpora cavernosa (see section on the penis) have disgorged the excess blood, leaving a flaccid or near flaccid penis. ■

of semen typically may contain between 200 and 500 million sperm, but a single sperm is all that is needed to fertilize an egg. Sperm are so small that they constitute only about 1 percent of the total volume of semen. The rest of the fluid is composed of ascorbic and citric acids, enzymes, fructose, water, and other substances. The amount of semen ejaculated by a male varies but averages roughly a teaspoonful. The volume of semen is also influenced by the length of time since the last ejaculation, the duration of arousal prior to ejaculation, and age (a man tends to produce less ejaculate as he gets older).

Seminiferous Tubules

Sometime after the onset of puberty, sperm production, called **spermatogenesis** (*genesis* = birth), takes place within the **seminiferous tubules.** Located within the testes (Figure 2.10) these thin, densely coiled sperm-bearing tubes are located inside the approximately 250 cone-shaped lobes of the interior of each testicle. Placed end to end, these tiny tubules would span the length of several football fields. Leydig's cells or interstitial cells, found between the seminiferous tubules, produce **androgens,** the hormones that promote the development of male genitals and secondary sex characteristics. The most important androgen is testosterone. (See Chapter 3 for a discussion of testosterone's role in sexual arousal.) The close proximity of Leydig's cells to blood vessels allows direct secretion of androgens into the bloodstream.

Epididymis

Sperm produced by the seminiferous tubules mature during storage in the C-shaped **epididymis** that is attached to the back and top surface of each testis (see Figures 2.9 and 2.10). Sperm may be stored in the epididymis for a period of several weeks. During this time the sperm cells continue to mature but are completely inactive.

Vas Deferens

Eventually the sperm stored in the epididymis move into the **vas deferens,** twin tubes that begin at each testis (see Figure 2.10). The vas deferens carries sperm up into the body cavity, where at the base of the bladder they form the ejaculatory ducts. The two

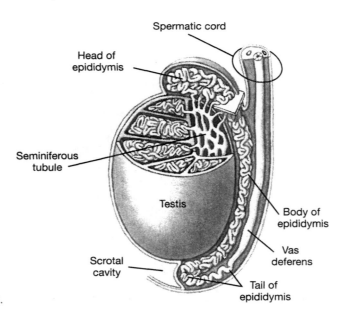

FIGURE 2.10 The Testes. Source: Martini, 2001.

ejaculatory ducts run through the prostate gland and connect to the urethra. The urethra is the common duct that also carries urine from the bladder to the opening of the penis where it is expelled from the body.

Seminal Vesicles

The **seminal vesicles** are two small glands located next to the ends of the vas deferens (see Figure 2.9). The excretory ducts of the seminal vesicles join the vas deferens to form the ejaculatory ducts. The seminal vesicles contribute to the production of seminal fluid, the viscous fluid ejaculated through the penis. The secretion of the seminal vesicles is high in fructose, a form of sugar. This sugar serves as a nutrient for the sperm, which require energy to make it to their destination. Once enriched by the secretions of the seminal vesicles, the sperm begin to propel themselves by the whiplike action of their tails.

Prostate Gland

Like the seminal vesicles, the **prostate gland** contributes ingredients to the seminal fluid soup. Secretions of the prostate gland constitute about 30 percent of the seminal fluid released during ejaculation; the other 70 percent is produced by the seminal vesicles. Both the ejaculatory ducts and the urethra pass through this gland, located at the base of the bladder and normally about the size and shape of a walnut (see Figure 2.9). It is composed of muscle as well as glandular tissue. During arousal, the muscular tissue of the prostate gland squeezes shut the urethral duct to the bladder, thus preventing urine from mixing with the semen and disturbing the chemical balance required by sperm. If the prostate gland becomes enlarged, as it often does as men age, the swelling can close off the ejaculatory ducts and urethra, making urination difficult and painful.

Seminiferous Tubules: thin coiled tubes located in the testicles in which sperm are produced

Androgens: hormones that promote the development of male sex characteristics

Epididymis: tightly coiled thin-walled tube where sperm maturation is completed

Vas Deferens: tubes that convey sperm from the testes to the ejaculatory duct of the penis

Seminal Vesicles: small glands that lie behind the bladder and secrete fluid that combines with sperm in the ejaculatory ducts

Prostate Gland: gland, which lies just below the bladder and surrounds the urethra, that produces about 30 percent of the seminal fluid released during ejaculation

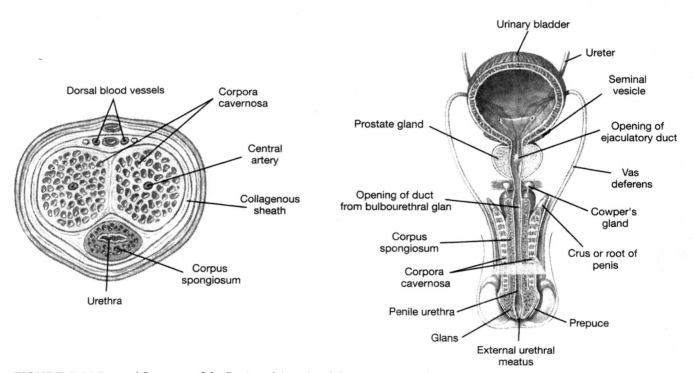

FIGURE 2.11 Internal Structure of the Penis and Associated Organs. Source: Martini, 2001.

Cowper's Glands

The **Cowper's glands,** also called the bulbourethral glands, are two small structures about the size of a pea located one on each side of the urethra just below the prostate gland (see Figure 2.11a). When a man is sexually aroused these glands may produce a fluid secretion called pre-ejaculate. Tiny ducts carry this secretion from the Cowper's glands to the urethra. It neutralizes the acidity of the urethra and also may help to lubricate the urethra and thus increase the flow of seminal fluid.

Some men notice the secretion of the Cowper's glands as soon as they get an erection; others rarely or never produce these droplets. For many men, however, this secretion appears just prior to ejaculation. While this fluid is not semen, it may contain healthy sperm if the man has not urinated since the last ejaculation. This is one reason why the withdrawal method of birth control (withdrawal of the penis from the vagina prior to ejaculation) is not highly effective.

MALE EXTERNAL SEXUAL ORGANS

The external sexual organs of the human male include the scrotum, testes, and penis (Figure 2.12).

Scrotum

The **scrotum** is a pouch of skin that normally hangs loosely from a man's abdominal wall directly beneath the penis (see Figures 2.9 and 2.12). This organ is also called the scrotal sac, reflecting its role in containing the **testes** or **testicles.** The scrotal sac consists of two layers. The outermost layer is a covering of thin skin that usually is a darker color than other body skin and becomes sparsely covered with pubic hair during adolescence. The second layer is composed of smooth muscle fibers and connective tissue. The scrotum's primary function is to maintain the temperature at which the testes most effectively produce sperm. The average scrotal temperature is lower than body temperature by approximately 3.1 degrees Centigrade (5.6 degrees Fahrenheit). Hanging the testes outside the body cavity is thus a way to keep them cool and to assure maximum sperm production. As the temperature of the testes rises, sperm production is reduced and may even cease. This is the reason that men are advised to wear

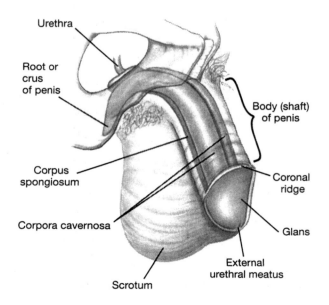

FIGURE 2.12 The Male External Sexual Organs.
SOURCE: Martini, 2001.

boxer shorts and loose clothing if they are having trouble conceiving a baby. There are relatively few nerve endings in the scrotum, so it is not highly sensitive, although some men find scrotal stimulation highly arousing. When a male is "kicked in the balls," the pain results from damage to the testes, not the scrotum.

Testes

Within the scrotal sac are two separate compartments or cavities, each of which houses a single testicle or *testis* (plural, testes). Each testis is suspended within the scrotum by the **spermatic cord** (see Figure 2.10). The spermatic cord contains the vas deferens (see section on Male Internal Sexual Organs), blood vessels, nerves, and fibers of the *cremasteric muscles.* The cremasteric muscles influence the position of the testicle in the scrotal sac and are affected by temperature and sexual stimulation; they can also be contracted voluntarily (try it!). Supposedly, some practitioners of Asian martial arts learn to retract the testes fully into the body cavity to protect them during combat.

The testes have two major functions: the secretion of sex hormones and the production of sperm. In most men the testes are asymmetrical, that is, they are not the exact same size and shape. The left testicle often hangs lower than the right since the left spermatic cord is longer than the right.

Penis

The **penis** has two functions: the passage of urine from the bladder to the exterior, and the passage of sperm from the testes to the exterior. It is divided into three major areas: the tip of the penis is called the *glans*, the body of the penis is called the *shaft*, and the portion of the shaft that extends internally and is attached to the pelvic bones is called the *root* (see Figure 2.12). The skin that covers the glans of an uncircumcised penis is the **prepuce** or **foreskin** (see Figure 2.11a). The shaft of the penis contains nerves, blood vessels, fibrous tissue, and three parallel cylinders of spongy tissue (Figure 2.11b). The cylinder on the underside of the shaft, which extends into the glans, is the **corpus spongiosum** (spongy body). The urethra runs through the middle of the corpus spongiosum. Urine and sperm pass through the urethra and exit at the *urethral meatus*, the urinary opening in the glans. Two cylindrical bodies called **corpora cavernosa** (cavernous bodies) run along the top of the shaft. To accomplish its second function, the penis must stiffen, or become erect. This is accomplished by a sudden influx of blood into the corpus spongiosum and the corpora cavernosa. At the root of the penis, the corpora cavernosa branch into tips called crura that are attached to the pelvic bones. Although an erect penis is sometimes referred to as a "boner," there are no bones in the human penis (but the walrus and other mammals do have penis bones that are associated with erections). There is an extensive network of muscles at the base of the penis, but the penis itself does not contain much muscle tissue.

Circumcision   Circumcision, the surgical removal of the prepuce or foreskin of the penis, is one of the oldest surgical procedures known to humans. For more than 3,000 years, Jewish families have been circumcising their newborn males on the eighth day after birth as a sign of their covenant with God. Most Jewish and Muslim families routinely choose to have their sons circumcised. You may have heard the term *female circumcision* used to refer to the ritual excision of the vulva, but this is a misnomer, as the vulva is not a foreskin (this topic, more correctly referred to as female genital mutilation, will be explored in detail in Chapter 8).

The National Center for Health Statistics estimates that about 60 percent of all male infants born in the United States are circumcised (Figure 2.13). This is in sharp contrast with other Western societies, in which circumcision is much less common. The medical value of neonatal circumcision is a subject of heated debate. The American Academy of Pediatrics has issued new circumcision policies three times in as many decades. In the 1970s, the academy's position was that there was no medical reason for circumcision, but in the 1980s it reported potential medical benefits.

What is the most sensitive area of the penis?

While the entire penis has many nerve endings, making it highly sensitive to touch, pressure, and temperature, the glans has the highest concentration of nerve endings. The *coronal ridge*, the aptly named ridge of tissue that rings the glans and forms the border between it and the shaft (*coronal* = crown; see Figure 2.12), is a particularly sensitive area. Another area that is highly responsive to manual and oral stimulation is the *frenulum*, a thin strip of skin on the underside of the penis that attaches the glans to the shaft.

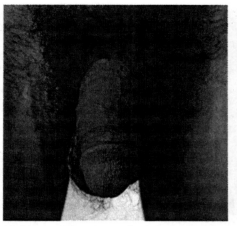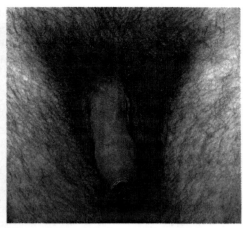

(a) A man with a circumcised penis. (b) A man with an uncircumcised penis, showing the prepuce, or foreskin.

In 1999 the Academy concluded that although there are potential benefits, the data are not significant enough to recommend routine circumcision (American Academy of Pediatrics, 1999). Although uncircumcised boys have four times the risk of getting urinary tract infections in their first year, the risk is still only 1 in 100 (Fergusson, Lawton, & Shannon, 1988; Herzog, 1989; Roberts, 1990). And, while uncircumcised men, particularly those with *phimosis* (the inability to retract the foreskin), have three times the risk of developing penile cancer, the risk is extremely low. Only nine out of a million American men are diagnosed with the disease annually (Harahap and Siregar, 1988; McAninch, 1990; Rotolo & Lynch, 1991). While there have been some claims that cervical cancer is more frequent in women who have sexual relations with uncircumcised partners, research has not supported this assertion (Brinton et al., 1989; Snyder, 1991; Wallerstein, 1980). Moreover, while some studies suggest that circumcised men have a reduced risk of contracting HIV, behavioral factors are more important risk factors than circumcision (Halperin & Bailey, 1999).

Although some of those opposed to circumcision claim that removal of the foreskin may reduce sexual pleasure, other reports indicate that circumcised men suffer less sexual dysfunction, especially those over age 45. The National Health and Social Life Survey asked men about their circumcision status, history of sexually transmitted infections, and experience of sexual dysfunction. There were no significant differences between circumcised and uncircumcised men in the contraction of sexually transmitted infections, but uncircumcised men were slightly more likely to experience sexual dysfunction, especially in later life (Laumann et al., 1997).

There are those who argue against routine circumcision, stating that the foreskin may serve an important but as yet un-

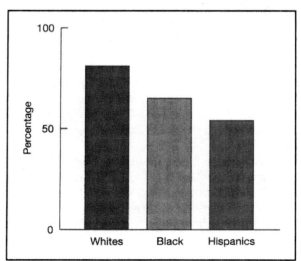

FIGURE 2.13 Who Gets Circumcised?
SOURCE: Data from Laumann, et al., 1994

known function. Others oppose what they see as an unnecessary, traumatic surgical procedure that poses possible complications including hemorrhage, infections, mutilation, shock, psychological trauma, and even death in rare cases (Chessare, 1992; Thompson, 1990).

Historically, circumcision is the only surgical procedure that is routinely performed without first administering analgesia or anesthesia (Wiswell, 1998). It was thought that newborns did not feel pain and that the risks involved in using anesthesia on infants were too high to justify its use. However, during circumcision boys were noted to be agitated, cry intensely, and have changes in facial expression indicating that the procedure was indeed painful (Williamson, 1997; Wiswell, 1998). Many physicians now use a local analgesic or a dorsal penile nerve block, a form of local anesthesia, to reduce circumcision pain and stress response (Holliday et al., 1999).

There is as much variation in the appearance of the external male genitalia as in the female vulva. Male genitalia reach adult proportions at approximately 15 years of age. Some people believe that you can predict penis length by a man's height or shoe size. Believe it or not, this idea has been researched, and it was found that neither body height nor foot size serve as practical estimators of penis length (Siminoski & Jerald, 1993). Compared to other species, the human penis is relatively large. A gorilla's erection might measure only 3 inches—though that of the blue whale, the world's largest mammal, may be 10 feet. Although the size of the male external sexual organs has been a source of pride (and concern) throughout history, these private proportions have little to do with sexual performance or satisfaction of either the male or the female partner (see CONSIDERATIONS box).

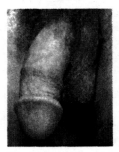

Natural variations in penis size and shape.

DISORDERS OF THE MALE SEXUAL ORGANS

Prostate Cancer

Prostate cancer, cancer of the prostate gland, is second only to skin cancer as a leading cancer killer among American men. Although it is estimated that over 180,000 new cases of prostate cancer are diagnosed annually in the United States and that one in six

CONSIDERATIONS

How Big Is Big Enough?

Cosmetic surgery to enlarge the penis, called *phalloplasty*, may not be as popular as breast augmentation, but in the past few years it has become increasingly popular. In 1996 men spent about $12 million on penile enlargements. Introduced in the United States in 1991, one penis-lengthening procedure involves severing the crura, the ligament that attaches the penis to the pubic bone; this allows the internal portion of the penis to drop down to the exterior. Another method combines this surgery with stretcher devices, specially designed weights that stretch the penis to prevent reabsorption of the internal portion into the abdomen. There have been no clinical studies of the results of penile augmentation. Individual surgeons claim the procedure may add ½ to 3 inches in length, though less than an inch seems to be common.

Thickening the penis (increasing its circumference) involves tissue grafts or injections of fat (extracted from the abdomen or other parts of the body) into the penis. Postsurgery increases of 1.1 to 2.1 centimeters (or approximately ½ to ¾ inches) in circumference have been reported, though there are claims of increases of 1 to 1½ inches in girth (Austoni & Guarneri, 1999).

If a man is born with an extremely small penis, penile enlargement may be a psychological if not medical necessity. However, most men who choose to undergo penile enlargement do not necessarily have smaller-than-average penises (Alexander, 1994). As with any surgery, there are potential risks. And many plastic surgeons report that the results are rarely impressive and can be disfiguring or even dangerous (Resnick, 1999).

Fat injection techniques may result in lumps, and because the body rejects a significant portion of the fat injection, the procedure may need to be repeated several times for a satisfactory result. Surgical techniques may result in scarring, loss of sensation, and other problems, including impotence. None of these penile augmentation procedures are endorsed by the American Urological Association or the American Society of Plastic and Reconstructive Surgeons.

 In what cases do you think the benefits of penile enlargement might outweigh the risks?

Can a man be "uncircumcised"?

Most men who seek to have their foreskin restored cite one of two reasons. The first is that they want to "regain . . . something taken from them without their consent" (Toppo, 1996, p. 21). The second reason is that some believe that restoration of the skin over the head of the penis restores a large amount of sensation, making for greater sexual pleasure. Surgical restoration of the foreskin is possible using skin grafts. Some men choose circumcision reversal without medical or surgical intervention. The process is time consuming, taking from 1 to 5 years of constant attention and care. Using stretching methods similar to those used to grow skin for skin grafts, some men use techniques that they claim eventually will permanently extend skin from the penile shaft over the penile glans.

American men will develop prostate cancer in his lifetime, many men have limited awareness of the symptoms, treatment, and consequences of the disease. Prostate cancer is curable if detected early. The 5-year survival rate for men whose tumors are diagnosed in the local and regional stages of the disease is 100 percent (American Cancer Society, 2000d).

What's Your Risk?   More than 80 percent of men with prostate cancer are over age 65; the median age is 72. Since 1970 the incidence of prostate cancer in the United States has risen 50 percent and deaths have risen 40 percent. The risk of prostate cancer increases as men age. As the life span of Americans increases, more and more men live to an age at which they are at high risk.

Men with high levels of the hormone insulin-like growth factor-1 (IGF-1) have four times the risk of prostate cancer as men with lower levels, though high levels do not mean that men are certain to develop the disease (Pollak, 1998). A high-fat diet is an environmental factor that has also been identified. In countries with a traditional low-fat diet, such as China and Japan, the incidence of prostate cancer is extremely low. Reflecting the flaws in the traditional American diet, prostate cancer rates for first- and second-generation Japanese Americans are considerably higher than those of their relatives in Japan. A large study found that men who consumed at least 2.5 servings of dairy products daily (not unusual in the traditional American diet) were about 30 percent more likely to develop prostate cancer than those who averaged less than half a serving a day (Chan et al., 1998).

How Is It Detected?   The average case of prostate cancer takes as long as a decade to develop. In its early stages, there are often no apparent symptoms. Later signs include urinary difficulties, blood in the urine, painful ejaculation, fatigue, weight loss, and bone pain in the lower back, hips, or pelvis. These symptoms may be attributed to other less serious health problems.

Exams and tests for prostate cancer include a digital rectal exam (see SEXUAL HEALTH AND YOU box later in this chapter), blood tests, a urine test, ultrasound, and X-rays. A physician may also perform a *cystoscopy*, a procedure in which the doctor looks into the urethra and bladder though a thin, lighted tube. If test results suggest that cancer may be present, the physician will perform a biopsy on the prostate tissue.

About 75 percent of men with prostate cancer have elevated levels of a protein called prostate-specific antigen (PSA). Testing blood for PSA has been a standard screening method for older men since about 1990. However other conditions, such as noncancerous prostate enlargement (see section on Prostatitis), can also elevate PSA levels, so doctors must perform needle biopsies, removing a sample of tissue with a needle, in order to determine whether or not the condition is malignant.

A blood test, approved by the FDA in 1998, has eliminated the need for many biopsies. While the traditional PSA test measures levels of PSA chemically bound to other proteins, the newer, free PSA test measures blood levels of "free" or unbound PSA in the blood serum. The newer test does not replace traditional PSA testing but is given as a follow-up when the traditional test yields uncertain results. A new urine test to detect prostate cancer in its earliest stages (years before it is clinically detectable) shows promise (Voeker, 2000).

Used routinely, traditional PSA testing alone could reduce deaths from prostate cancer by more than 66 percent. Researchers at the National Cancer Institute reported that in 1997 the prostate cancer death rate for white men under age 85 in the United States had fallen below what it had been in 1986, the first year the PSA test was used for screening. In men ages 60 to 79, the 1997 death rate was lower than any year since 1950. Yet none of these current research findings are proof that the PSA tests save lives. Many medical organizations and experts on prostate cancer don't agree about when or even if PSA screening should be done. The disagreement about whether the test is worthwhile stems from the age of the affected population; because of the long, slow progress of the disease, older men with prostate cancer are more likely to die from other, unrelated illnesses, and treatment can produce serious, debilitating side effects such as impotence and incontinence (Sung, Kabalin, & Terris, 2000). More definitive answers must await studies currently underway that compare the survival rates of men who get the blood tests and those who do not.

How Is It Treated?   The recommended treatments for prostate cancer include watchful waiting, surgical intervention, radiation, and hormone therapy (Table 2.3).

Watchful Waiting.   For those men whose prostate cancer is slow growing and found at an early stage, "watchful waiting" rather than treatment may be recommended, especially for older men and those with other serious medical problems, since the side effects of treatment might outweigh the possible benefits.

Surgical Intervention.   A standard early stage treatment is radical *prostatectomy*. This involves the surgical removal of the prostate without affecting the nerves essential for an erection. In *retropubic prostatectomy*, the prostate and nearby lymph nodes are removed through an incision in the abdomen. In *perineal prostatectomy*, the prostate is removed through an incision between the scrotum and the anus.

Radiation.   Another common treatment for prostate cancer is radiation therapy. In early-stage cancer, radiation can be used instead of surgery or it may be used after surgery to destroy any cancer cells that may have been missed.

Hormone Therapy.   Hormone therapy prevents the prostate cancer cells from receiving testosterone, the hormone they need for growth. There are several forms of hormone therapy. Because the testicles are the source of testosterone, one option is an *orchiectomy*, surgical removal of the testicles. One alternative to surgery is the use of a luteinizing hormone-releasing hormone (LH-RH) agonist to prevent the testicles from producing testosterone. Patients may also take the female hormone estrogen to prohibit testosterone production.

A study recently published in the *Journal of the American Medical Association* found that 60 percent of men who had their prostate gland removed suffered from erectile dysfunction (the inability to have an erection) and had some decline in urinary function 18 months after the surgery. Yet the researchers found that nearly 75 percent

TABLE 2.3

Treatment Options for Prostate Cancer

Treatment	Advantages	Disadvantages
Prostatectomy	100% cure rate for cancer limited to the prostate	Hospital stay and recovery Risk of erectile dysfunction and incontinence
Radiation Therapy (internal or external)	Can eliminate the need for surgery Outpatient procedure	Recurrence of cancer May be some pain at site of radiation Not appropriate for cancer that has spread beyond the prostate gland
Hormone Therapy	Outpatient procedure Temporary tumor shrinkage	Recurrence of cancer Sexual dysfunction
Watchful Waiting	No side effects or treatment risks	Risks the spread of cancer cells to other organs and tissue

said they were satisfied with the results (Stanford et al., 2000). Radical prostatectomy and external radiation patients showed comparable rates of improvement in sexual function during the first year after treatment. However, in the second year, the sexual function of radiation patients began to decline, while that of the surgery patients did not. After two years, men in each group had similar rates of erectile dysfunction (Litwin et al., 1999).

Prostate Cancer Vaccine. Researchers have recently developed a vaccine that helps strengthen the body's immune system against prostate cancer. The vaccine uses the patient's own cells, grown in his own plasma, to trigger the immune system to attack cancerous cells in the prostate. The results of the first human trials showed that the vaccine could trigger the immune system to fight cancer in the same way that it fights infection. While the researchers found the results to be promising, more research will be necessary to determine the effectiveness and safety of this approach before it becomes available to the general public (Simons et al., 2000).

Prostatitis

Prostatitis, inflammation of the prostate gland, is a common disorder that may occur in men of any age. There are two types of prostatitis: bacterial and nonbacterial. *Bacterial prostatitis* may occur as either an acute or chronic disorder. Acute cases often occur only once and respond to medical treatment. Chronic bacterial prostatitis is associated with an underlying defect in the prostate that becomes a focal point for the persistence of bacterial infection in the urinary tract; it is more difficult to treat than acute cases. Bacterial prostatitis causes fever and chills, pain in the lower back and genital area, body aches, painful urination, and the frequent and urgent need to urinate. *Nonbacterial prostatitis* has the symptoms of bacterial prostatitis but no evidence of a known infecting organism. *Prostatodynia* is a condition in which the symptoms and signs of prostatitis are present, without evidence of inflammation of the prostate or bacterial causes (Vastag, 2001).

What's Your Risk? Prostatitis accounts for up to 25 percent of all medical office visits by young and middle-aged men with genital and urinary symptoms. Nonbacterial prostatitis is eight times more common than bacterial prostatitis (MedicineNet.com, 2001).

How Is It Detected? Prostatitis is indicated by the presentation of symptoms mentioned earlier (fever and chills, pain, body aches, and painful or frequent urination). The evidence of white blood cells and bacteria in the urine can confirm bacterial prostatitis. The lack of bacteria in the urine indicates nonbacterial prostatitis.

How Is It Treated? Bacterial prostatitis is treated with antibiotics (Roberts et al., 1997). Chronic bacterial prostatitis may require 4 to 6 weeks of treatment due to the poor penetration of antibiotics into the prostate. Though nonbacterial prostatitis is the most common form, it also is the least understood. There is no treatment for nonbacterial prostatitis; symptoms may go away and then return without warning.

Benign Prostatic Hyperplasia (BPH)

It is not uncommon for the prostate gland to become enlarged as a man ages. *Benign prostatic hyperplasia (BPH)* is a noncancerous enlargement of the prostate. Though the prostate continues to grow during most of a man's life, enlargement does not usually cause problems until later in his life. As the prostate enlarges, the surrounding capsule (see Figure 2.11a) stops it from expanding, causing the gland to press against the urethra. In response to this pressure, the bladder wall becomes thicker; it also becomes irritable, or more easily stimulated, so the bladder begins to contract even when it contains small amounts of urine, causing more frequent urination. As the bladder weakens, it loses the ability to empty itself completely.

What's Your Risk?   By 60 years of age, 80 percent of men have an enlarged prostate and suffer some degree of urinary difficulty. This condition is considered a natural result of aging. The cause of BPH is not well understood. Studies done with animals have suggested that the increasing amounts of estrogen within the gland as a man ages intensify the activity of substances that promote cell growth.

How Is It Detected?   Many of the symptoms of BPH occur when the swollen prostate squeezes the urethra and blocks normal urine flow. The most common symptoms are a weak or hard to start urine stream, a feeling of incomplete bladder emptying, and waking during the night several times to urinate. BPH does not necessarily lead to cancer or impaired sexual functioning. In a small percentage of men there may be some damage to the bladder or kidneys. Diagnosis may be aided by a digital rectal exam, ultrasound, a urine flow study, or other tests. A check for BPH should be part of a regular physical examination for men over age 50.

How Is It Treated?   About one third of those afflicted with BPH opt for surgery, usually in cases of severe prostate enlargement. Men are often counseled to consider treatments other than surgery to relieve their symptoms, including, in some cases, no treatment at all. The standard surgical procedure for BPH is a *transurethral resection of the prostate (TURP)*. A tiny looped wire is inserted through the urethra and excess prostate tissue is trimmed away. Balloon dilation is another option; a balloon is inserted through the urethra and expanded to push back prostate tissue and widen the urinary path. Drugs, such as finasteride, may be used to shrink the prostate. In 1997 the FDA approved the use of the Prostatron, a computer-controlled device that shrinks the prostate through the use of heat. The Prostatron procedure takes about an hour and can be done on an outpatient basis with local anesthetic.

Testicular Cancer

Cancer of a testis usually can be discovered as a small lump before the cancer spreads to other parts of the body. However, relatively few men routinely perform a self-examination. (See SEXUAL HEALTH AND YOU box.)

What's Your Risk?   *Testicular cancer*, cancer of the testicles, comprises only 1 percent of all cancers in American males but is the most common malignancy in men ages 15 to 35 and is the second most common form of cancer among men under age 40. About 7,600 new cases occur in the United States each year. The incidence of testicular

▓**S**EXUAL HEALTH AND YOU

Digital Rectal Exam

Because of the proximity of the prostate gland to the rectum (see Figure 2.9), the digital rectal examination is the best way to detect changes that might indicate prostate cancer. To perform a digital rectal exam, the physician inserts a lubricated, gloved finger into the rectum. During the exam the patient bends forward over an examination table or lies on his side with legs bent while the physician feels the size, shape, and texture of the prostate gland. Some men may feel as though they have to urinate or defecate during the exam, or the probing may cause them to have an erection. This should not prevent men from undergoing this important procedure. If a hardened area, lump, or other irregularity is found, X-ray, biopsy, or other tests for cancer may be performed.

Going Nuts

Figure skater Scott Hamilton, Tour de France champion cyclist Lance Armstrong, and comedian and MTV host Tom Green might not seem to have much in common, but all three men are survivors of testicular cancer, a malignancy that can affect the tissue in one or both testicles. When Tom Green was diagnosed with testicular cancer at age 28, he found that laughter was still his best medicine. Green had TV cameras in the hospital when he underwent two surgeries, one to remove his right testicle and the second to take out the surrounding lymph nodes. Green created a charity, "Tom Green's Nuts Cancer Fund," and a theme song: "Hey, kids, feel your balls so you don't get cancer."

 Do you think that you would be able to keep as positive an attitude as Tom Green has?

—Do you think that his attitude helped him beat his cancer?

---

cancer has increased 56 percent in the United States since 1973. For unknown reasons, no rise in incidence has occurred among African American men, who account for only 5 percent of all cases in the United States (American Cancer Society, 2000e).

While the causes of testicular cancer are not known, studies show that several factors increase the likelihood of a man developing the disease. Men who have an undescended testicle are at higher risk of developing testicular cancer. There is some evidence that men whose mothers took DES (diethylstilbestrol) medication to prevent spontaneous abortion during pregnancy are at higher risk for reproductive tract abnormalities (Vastag, 2001). DES is no longer administered to pregnant women. Contrary to popular myth, there is no evidence that masturbation or other sexual activity increases the risk of testicular cancer. Sports activities do not appear to be related, despite the publicity given to the diagnoses of skater Scott Hamilton and cyclist Lance Armstrong.

How Is It Detected? Only half of those with testicular cancer report any pain in the early stages of illness. Men discover most cases of the disease during self-examination. It is critical for men, especially those ages 15 to 35, to perform regular testicular self-examinations to detect the presence of a tumor (see SEXUAL HEALTH AND YOU box). Men should seek medical care if they notice any of the following symptoms: a painless lump or swelling in either testicle, any enlargement of a testicle or change in the way it feels, a feeling of heaviness in the scrotum, a dull ache in the lower abdomen or groin, a sudden collection of fluid in the scrotum, or pain or discomfort in a testicle or in the scrotum.

To help find the cause of symptoms, a physician will perform a visual and manual examination of the testes and scrotum and may order an ultrasound or blood tests that measure the levels of substances that serve as tumor markers, such as alpha-fetoprotein (AFP), human chorionic gonadotropin (HCG), and lactase dehydrogenase (LDH). However, a biopsy of testicular tissue is the only sure way to know whether cancer is present.

How Is It Treated? The survival rate for testicular cancer detected in the early stages is about 96 percent. There are four types of treatment: surgery, radiation, chemotherapy, and bone marrow transplantation. Surgery to remove the testicle is a common treatment for most stages of testicular cancer. If only one testis is removed, the remaining testis will supply adequate amounts of hormones. If both testes must be removed, testosterone may be given to compensate for hormone loss; artificial testes implants are available for cosmetic purposes.

Testicular Torsion

Testicular torsion occurs when a testis is rotated, twisting the spermatic cord. This may cut off blood flow to the testicles and surrounding structures within the scrotum, resulting in permanent damage to the affected testis.

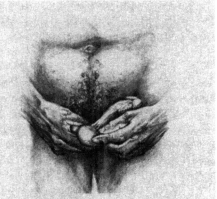

SEXUAL HEALTH AND YOU

Testicular Self-Exam

Isolate a testis and pull the skin of the scrotum tightly around it. Look for a pea-sized lump. Then carefully roll the testis between the thumb and fingers, feeling for any lumps. Repeat this process with the other testis.

The presence of a lump is not necessarily an indication of cancer, but you should seek a physician's examination immediately.

FIGURE 2.14 Testicular Self-Examination.

What's Your Risk? Incidence of testicular torsion in males under age 25 is approximately 1 in 4,000. It is believed that some men may be predisposed to testicular torsion as a result of a lack of support, that is, inadequate connective tissue within the scrotum. However, the condition also can result from trauma or injury to the scrotum. Wearing an athletic supporter or cup when participating in contact sports may help to reduce injuries to the testes, including testicular torsion. Testicular torsion also may occur after strenuous exercise, or there may be no obvious cause. However, the incidence is higher during infancy and between the ages of 12 and 18 years when the testicles are growing most rapidly.

How Is It Detected? Symptoms of testicular torsion include the sudden onset of severe pain in a testicle along with scrotal swelling and elevation of the affected testis. Additional symptoms are the presence of a testicular lump and blood in the semen.

How Is It Treated? Any acute scrotal pain should be evaluated immediately. Testicular torsion is considered a surgical emergency. Surgery to untangle the twisted spermatic cord involves an incision in the scrotum. The testicle is uncoiled and sutures are used to secure the testis and prevent it from rotating again. The unaffected testicle is secured by suture at the same time, because the unaffected testicle is at increased risk for torsion at a later date. In one study of emergency room patients of ages 4 months to 47 years, surgical intervention undertaken within 4 hours of symptom onset salvaged the testicle in 100 percent of the cases. The salvage rate dropped to 75 percent when surgery took place within 8 to 16 hours, and to 25 percent beyond 16 hours (Watkin et al., 1996).

Epididymitis

Recall that the epididymis is the C-shaped organ extending along the top of each testis that is responsible for storage of sperm produced by the seminiferous tubules (see Figures 2.9 and 2.10). When a man is experiencing scrotal pain, *epididymitis*, an inflammation of the epididymis, is by far the most common diagnosis. Although it was once widely believed that straining of the groin area was a contributing factor, infection is now considered the most common cause of this condition. Infection may become so severe that it spreads to the adjacent testicle. Such cases may cause fever and, rarely, abscess formation.

What's Your Risk? Bacterial organisms associated with urinary tract infections, sexually transmitted infections, and infection of the prostate, or surgical removal of the prostate typically causes epididymitis. Sexually active men who are not monogamous and do not use condoms are at increased risk. Men who have recently had prostate surgery or have a history of genitourinary tract problems also have higher-than-average incidence rates.

How Is It Detected?   The primary symptoms of epididymitis are scrotal pain and swelling. The pain or swelling may be mild or severe. At times the epididymis may become so inflamed that the patient is not able to walk. Tenderness is usually localized to a small area of the testicle where the epididymis is attached. Enlarged lymph nodes in the groin area and a discharge from the penis are additional symptoms; a rectal exam may reveal an enlarged prostate. Urinalysis and blood tests may be performed to screen for bacteria.

How Is It Treated?   For acute epididymitis, treatment with antibiotics, bed rest, scrotal support, and oral anti-inflammatory medication are effective. In chronic epididymitis, symptoms seem to persist even after the initial treatment. In these cases a second round of therapy may be helpful. Longer-term use of anti-inflammatory medication may be recommended. Surgical treatment is an uncommon last resort.

Penile Cancer

In *penile cancer*, cancer cells are found on the skin and in the tissues of the penis. This rare form of cancer accounts for less than $\frac{1}{2}$ percent of all malignancies in the United States. Most cases occur in men over 50 years of age.

What's Your Risk?   Although the definitive causes of penile cancer are not known, researchers have identified certain risk factors. The typical man diagnosed with cancer of the penis is over age 50, has had multiple sexual partners, and has had a sexually transmitted infection, especially HPV (genital warts). A long history of smoking increases a man's risk of developing penile cancer from 1 in 100,000 to 1 in 600 (Fair, Fuks, & Scher, 1993). Additional risk factors include not being circumcised. The risk of penile cancer is 3.2 times higher for uncircumcised men than for circumcised men. Researchers speculate that it takes more effort to keep an uncircumcised penis clean and free of *smegma*, a thick, cheeselike sebaceous secretion that collects beneath the foreskin, especially if the foreskin is difficult to pull back entirely (American Cancer Society, 1999).

How Is It Detected?   The cancer usually begins as a small, painless sore on the glans or the foreskin that won't heal. Symptoms like this are sometimes mistaken for a sexually transmitted infection. Tissue biopsy is the only way to make a definitive diagnosis.

How Is It Treated?   As with other cancers, surgery, radiation, and chemotherapy are standard methods of treating penile cancer. Surgical possibilities range from excision of the cancer and as little normal tissue as possible to a total *penectomy* (amputation of the entire penis). Usually only about one fourth of the length of the penis is amputated so the man may still be capable of orgasm and ejaculation. Although it is rare, penile cancer is deadly. Of the 1,300 men in the United States who develop penile cancer this year, only half will be alive 5 years from now. Early intervention is essential to survival. If the cancer is caught early and there is no lymph node involvement, the 5-year survival rate increases to nearly 90 percent.

Peyronie's Disease

Usually, a man's erect penis is straight. *Peyronie's disease* is a condition characterized by a bending or curving of the erect penis. The cause of Peyronie's disease is uncertain. However, many researchers believe it is caused by damage to the erectile bodies, the two long chambers within the penis that inflate with blood to cause an erection. When one of these bodies is stretched or bent during an erection, the damage can result in a thickened, inelastic scar on the outside of the erectile tissue, usually on the topside of the penis. It is the presence of this scar that causes the bending of the penis. Think of a long, thin balloon (the penis) with a piece of duct tape (the scar) stuck on one side. When you blow up the balloon, the duct tape prevents the area it covers from expanding properly, causing the inflated balloon to bend toward that side. A scar on the top of the penile shaft causes the penis to bend upward; a scar on the underside causes it to bend downward. In some cases, scars develop on both top and bottom, leading to indentation and shortening of the penis.

What's Your Risk?   When the distortion of the penis is severe, it may cause erectile dysfunction or pain during sexual intercourse (Vastag, 2001). While there are no precise figures, urologists who treat erection problems estimate it affects about 1 in 100 patients (National Institute of Health, 1995). Although it usually afflicts men in their 40s or 50s, both younger and older men can acquire this condition. As a result of aging, diminished elasticity near the point of attachment of connecting tissue might increase the chances of injury. Trauma explains some cases of Peyronie's disease, but most develop slowly and with no apparent traumatic event.

How Is It Detected?   We have already described the obvious structural symptoms of Peyronie's disease. These may occur without pain. Alternatively, intercourse may be painful and in severe cases, impossible. A physician should check any significant curve, bend, or unusual narrowing along the shaft of the penis, especially if it's accompanied by pain.

How Is It Treated?   Because the scar often shrinks or disappears without treatment, most medical experts suggest waiting 1 to 2 years or longer before attempting corrective surgery. There are two surgical options available. In the least intrusive, the Nesbit procedure, a small incision is made into the skin on the outside of the curve. The skin is then tightened on that side, counteracting the pull of the scar tissue and leaving the penis straighter. This procedure may shorten the penis a fraction of an inch or more. The second type of surgery involves removal of all or part of the scar tissue itself. Because the scar is located on the outside of the erectile tissue, any type of incision at that point may hinder erections. New treatments with less severe side effects are currently in development. These include laser surgery techniques and a calcium-blocker medication that may prevent the hardening of the scar. Table 2.4 provides information on other penile conditions.

TABLE 2.4			
Other Penile Conditions			
Condition	**Cause**	**Symptoms**	**Treatment**
Sclerosing Lymphangitis	Thrombotic vein probably due to trauma during intercourse	A hard, ropelike thickening that encircles the penile shaft	Will usually subside without treatment
Pearly Penile Papules	Common benign skin growths	Skin condition that looks like grains of sand dotting the corona	No treatment necessary
Fixed Drug Reaction	Rare localized allergy to a medication, often an oral antibiotic	Red, weeping rash the size of a quarter on the head of the penis	Medication change

■ R E V I E W

CHAPTER 2

CHAPTER 2

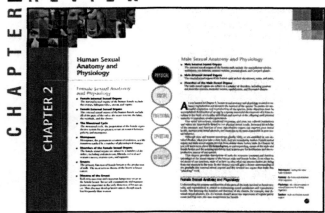

Human sexual anatomy and physiology evolved to enhance reproduction and promote survival of the species.

There are four female internal sexual organs. Eggs are produced by **1**_____ and carried down the **2**_____ (also called the oviducts) to the **3**_____. The lower end of the uterus extending into the vagina is the **4**_____. The wall of the uterus consists of three layers called the **5**_____, _____, and _____. A mature ovum may be fertilized by a sperm in the upper portion of a fallopian tube, but it should then become implanted in the lining of the **6**_____. The **7**_____ is the soft, muscular organ that leads from the uterus to the external surface of the female body. The hymen is a thin membrane stretched across the **8**_____ or opening at the lower end of the vagina.

The **9**_____ consists of the external female sex organs. The **10**_____ is the area over the pubic bone. The **11**_____ are the outer folds of skin that provide protection for the urethral opening and the introitus. The **12**_____ are the inner folds of skin at the front of the vestibule that form the prepuce or clitoral hood. The **13**_____ is the most sensitive area of female genitalia.

A female's first menses is called **14**_____. During the **15**_____ phase of the menstrual cycle, dead cells sloughed off the endometrium combined with small amounts of blood pass through the vagina, constituting the menstrual flow. **16**_____ is the release of an ovum from the ovary. The **17**_____ phase of the menstrual cycle begins immediately after ovulation and lasts until menstrual flow begins again.

18_____ is painful menstruation. **19**_____ is the absence of menstruation. Menopause is the permanent cessation of menstruation, part of the larger process of gradual decline in the reproductive capacity of the ovaries known as **20**_____.

21_____ cancer is the most common malignancy of the female reproductive organs. Uterine **22**_____ are balls of solid tissue that grow inside the uterus. A **23**_____ test can detect cervical caner, and should be performed annually. **24**_____ is an inflammation of the vagina that may be due to a number of causes, including bacteria, fungi, and viruses.

Breasts and pubic hair are examples of secondary sex characteristics. The human breasts are modified sweat glands called **25**_____ glands. The dark, sensitive skin surrounding the nipple is the **26**_____. Breast cancer is the most common form of cancer among women in the United States. Breast self-exams and **27**_____ are important in the early detection of breast cancers.

The **28**_____ or scrotal sac is the pouch that contains the testes. The testes produce **29**_____ and male sex hormones or **30**_____, the most important of which is testosterone. Developed sperm are moved from the seminiferous tubules in the testes to the **31**_____ and then into the vas deferens. A vas deferens joins the excretory duct of a seminal vesicle to form an ejaculatory duct. The two ejaculatory ducts, one from the vas deferens leading from each testis, run through the **32**_____ gland and connect to the urethra. The seminal vesicles contribute to the production of **33**_____ fluid. **34**_____ is the sperm-containing seminal fluid ejaculated through the urethral **35**_____ or opening of the penis. The tip of the penis is called the **36**_____, and the skin which covers it in an uncircumcised male is the **37**_____ or foreskin.

38_____ cancer is second only to skin cancer as a leading cancer killer among men in the United States. However, **39**_____ cancer is the most common malignancy in men ages 15 to 35.

SUGGESTED READINGS

Angier, N. (1999). *Woman: An Intimate Geography.* Boston: Houghton-Mifflin.

Angier, who calls her book "a celebration of the female body," describes the hormonal and neural underpinnings of sexual desire and challenges the insistence of evolutionary psychologists on the innate discordance between the strength of the male and female sex drives.

Barbach, L. (2000). *The Pause: Positive Approaches to Perimenopause and Menopause* (2nd Ed.). New York: Plume.

Dr. Barbach discusses the various natural physical and emotional changes that occur during menopause and presents traditional and alternative treatment approaches.

Ensler, E. (1998). *The Vagina Monologues.* New York: Villard Books.

Based on the play, *The Vagina Monologues*, this book contains meditations involving personal reminiscences and interviews with dozens of women whose attitudes range from fear to fascination.

Love, S. M., & Lindsey, K. (1995). *Dr. Susan Love's Breast Book.* New York: Addison-Wesley.

A breast surgeon and women's health advocate gives straightforward information about diseases of the breast and treatment options.

Paola, A. S. (1999). *Under the Fig Leaf: A Comprehensive Guide to the Care and Maintenance of the Penis, Prostate, and Related Organs.* Los Angeles: Health Information Press.

A comprehensive guide to men's health for consumers, this book covers prostate cancer, Viagra, circumcision, scrotal masses, and more.

Schulen, C. D. (2000). *The Change'll Do You Good: The Baby Boomer's Guide to Menopause.* Chicago: DCS Publishing.

The author dispels the common myths surrounding menopause and provides clear information to help understand what is happening to a woman's body during this time.

ANSWERS TO CHAPTER REVIEW:

1. ovaries; **2.** fallopian tubes; **3.** uterus; **4.** cervix; **5.** endometrium, myometrium, perimetrium; **6.** uterus; **7.** vagina; **8.** introitus; **9.** vulva; **10.** mons veneris; **11.** labia majora; **12.** labia minora; **13.** clitoris; **14.** menarche; **15.** menstrual; **16.** Ovulation; **17.** luteal; **18.** Dysmenorrhea; **19.** Amenorrhea; **20.** climacteric; **21.** Endometrial; **22.** fibroids; **23.** Pap; **24.** Vaginitis; **25.** mammary; **26.** areola; **27.** mammograms; **28.** scrotum; **29.** sperm; **30.** androgens; **31.** epididymis; **32.** prostate; **33.** seminal; **34.** Semen; **35.** meatus; **36.** glans; **37.** prepuce; **38.** Prostate; **39.** testicular;

Sexual Arousal and Response

PHYSICAL

SOCIAL

EMOTIONAL

SPIRITUAL

COGNITIVE

CHAPTER 5

- **One Advantage of Being *Homo sapiens***
  Unlike other mammals, human females are continuously responsive to and available for sexual activity, independent of ovulation.

- **Biological Foundations for Sexual Arousal and Response**
  The brain and central nervous system, including the five senses, play roles of varying importance in human sexual arousal and response.

- **Sex Hormones**
  The sex hormones, including testosterone, the estrogens, progesterone, oxytocin, and vasopressin, play crucial roles in regulating sexuality.

- **The Sexual Response Cycle**
  There are a number of theories regarding the events of sexual arousal and response, including Masters and Johnson's EPOR model; Kaplan's model of desire, excitement, and orgasm; and Reed's ESP model.

- **Orgasm**
  Men and women experience orgasm, the peak of sexual arousal, somewhat differently. The events and frequency of female orgasm vary more than those of male orgasm.

- **Sexuality and Disabilities**
  Although they may interfere with sexual arousal and response, physical and psychological disabilities don't necessarily preclude sexual expression.

Taken from: *Human Sexuality*, by Tina S. Miracle, Andrew W. Miracle, and Roy F. Baumeister

Sexual arousal, a heightened state of sexual interest and excitement, has both psychological and physical bases. There is much more to sex than the physical process of intercourse. Without the subjective feeling of pleasure, physiological arousal will not occur. However, knowledge of the physical changes that occur during sexual arousal is essential to a complete understanding of human sexuality. Sexual arousal and response are influenced by a number of factors. Of course, what one person finds sexually arousing, another might not. The patterns we will describe in the following pages can vary from person to person, and even from experience to experience.

Other biological factors and sensory processes also play significant roles in the **sexual response cycle,** the series of physiological processes and events that occur during sexual activity. In this chapter we focus primarily on the biology of sexual response. Later chapters will describe the influences of our emotional, social, and cultural needs on our sexual experiences.

ONE ADVANTAGE OF BEING HOMO SAPIENS

Unlike most species, humans engage in a great deal of sexual behavior that is not reproductive. But how much of our sexual response is preprogrammed, or biological, and how much is learned, either through personal experience or cultural expectations? This question has particular significance in the discussion of individual variations in sexual arousal as well as the differences between males and females.

Is mating, even among animals other than humans, just about reproduction? The **estrous** cycle, sometimes referred to simply as *estrus*, is the periodic state of sexual excitement in the female of most mammals, excluding humans, that immediately precedes ovulation and during which the female is most receptive to mating.

The cycle may range in length from 18 to 35 days (Jolly, 1972), a period that is much longer than necessary simply for fertilization. It is unlikely that all of the behavior that occurs during this time is for the purpose of reproduction. For example, females mate with many more males than is necessary for fertilization (Hrdy, 1981). Furthermore, although estrus is usually absent during pregnancy, some mammals may continue sexual activity during this time.

We can be certain that no member of the genus *Homo* ever experienced estrus. However, we can only guess at whether any of our pre-*Homo* ancestors were ever "in heat." One sure sign that evolution is progress is the unique capability of human females for continuous response to and availability for sexual activity, independent of ovulation (see CONSIDERATIONS box).

BIOLOGICAL FOUNDATIONS FOR SEXUAL AROUSAL AND RESPONSE

Which body parts do you most closely associate with sex? Although vaginal lubrication and an erect penis are more obvious physical signs of sexual arousal, it is important to remember that the genitals are not the only organs involved in sexual arousal and response; many body systems contribute to this process.

Sexual Arousal: heightened state of sexual interest and excitement

Sexual Response Cycle: physiological processes and events that occur during sexual activity

Estrous: the cycle of most female nonprimate mammals when they are most sexually receptive to males

Prime Mates

Because *Homo sapiens* share about 98 percent of their genetic material with both chimpanzees and bonobos, studying these evolutionary relatives can be useful in our understanding of human behavior.

The bonobos were described by Frans de Waal in his 1997 book *Bonobo: The Forgotten Ape.* Unlike their chimpanzee cousins, who are known for violence, male domination, and sexual efficiency, bonobos are peaceful, egalitarian, and lead sex-filled lives in the tropical forests of the Republic of Congo in Central Africa. According to de Waal, bonobos, not humans, appear to be the most sexual primates. They are constantly having sex of every variety, both heterosexual and homosexual, and with partners of all ages.

Adult male bonobos grab and mouth each other's genitals. Females regularly have sex with each other by placing their pelvises together, either face-to-face or rear-to-rear, and rubbing each other rapidly. Juvenile male bonobos suck on each other's penises and allow adult males to fondle them. They also participate whenever adults have sex by poking fingers and toes into the adults' body parts. Male and female bonobos copulate in both the typical mammalian back-to-front position and the face-to-face position, either standing or lying down with either the male or female on top. Furthermore, bonobos manually stimulate themselves and each other.

What makes bonobo sexuality of interest to researchers is that they use sex not only for reproduction but also just for the fun of it. Bonobos suggest that our idealization of private, monogamous sexual behavior might be a relatively recent deviation from our evolutionary heritage. Like bonobos, our ancestors may have used sex on a daily basis to form alliances, trade goods and favors, establish friendships, and keep the peace (Small, 1995).

According to Frans de Waal, bonobos, not humans, appear to be the most sexual primates. They are constantly having sex of every variety, both heterosexual and homosexual, and with partners of all ages.

Why should we be interested in bonobo sexuality?

—Do you think that studying bonobos adds to our knowledge of human sexual behavior?
—Do you think that primates and humans are too different for us to learn much from them?

The Brain

Orgasm: the peak state of sexual excitement; it is marked by rhythmic contractions of the pelvic floor muscles

Cerebral Cortex: thin outer layer of the brain's cerebrum that is responsible for higher mental processes including perception, thought, and memory

Limbic System: a group of interconnected deep brain structures that especially influence motivation and emotion

We may talk about following our hearts, but it is actually our brains that direct a great deal of our sexual behavior. The male erection and female vaginal lubrication may be triggered by direct stimulation, but it is the brain that interprets the stimulation and begins the process of sexual arousal and response. Motivation, desire, and behavior also are part of the thinking brain, the "executive function" that exercises volition, choice, and self-control. Even when we think we're "behaving like animals," very little of our conduct is really automatic.

Fisher and Byrne (1978) tested the arousal value of sex films on both male and female participants. Half the viewers in their study saw soft-core films in which the actors and actresses kept their underwear on, while the rest saw hard-core films with full nudity and explicit sex. To the researchers' surprise, the participants were equally aroused regardless of how explicit the film was. In this same study, the researchers tested the role of the thought process in sexual arousal. Prior to viewing the film, viewers were given different story lines for the sex scenes they watched. Some were told that the people on the screen were newlyweds. Others were told they were a prostitute and a client. Still others were told the scene involved a young man and woman who had just met each other at a dance. The context had a great degree of influence on how aroused the subjects became. Both male and female viewers were more aroused when they thought they were watching sex between two people who had just met. The prostitution and newlywed themes elicited lower levels of arousal (on both self-report and physiological measures), even though viewers were seeing exactly the same video clip. In other words, arousal depended less on what people actually saw than on what they thought it meant.

While various parts of the brain are involved in sexual response and behavior, the two most important are the **cerebral cortex** and the **limbic system** (Figure 3.1). The upper part of the brain, the cerebral cortex, is the "thinking center" of the brain, and is the area of the brain responsible for sexual fantasies, desires, thoughts, and images (it is also responsible for nonsexual thought processes). When the brain receives arousing messages, the cerebral cortex interprets this sensory information and transmits messages through the spinal cord causing an increase in heartbeat and respiration (breathing), which can alter muscle tension (or myotonia), send blood to the genitals, and increase skin sensitivity. Your ability to consciously identify these physical changes can actually contribute to your sexual arousal.

The limbic system, located within the cerebrum in the area below the cortex, consists of the *thalamus*, the *hypothalamus*, and other structures important to sexual arousal. This complex group of structures controls our emotions, motivations, memories, and behavioral drives (Everitt, 1990). In 1939, Heinrich Klüver and Paul Buey first demonstrated the importance of the limbic system in regulating sexual behavior in animals. When they destroyed certain areas of the limbic system, it tamed wild monkeys, but also triggered an increase in the frequency, intensity, and ability to perform sexual behaviors.

Sex and the Senses

The five human senses—*touch, sight, smell, hearing,* and *taste*—all contribute to sexual arousal and to the sexual response cycle. However, the same sensory stimulation can evoke different responses in different people. In one study (Herz & Cahill, 1997), researchers asked men and women to rate the importance of olfactory (smell), visual (sight), auditory (sound), and tactile (touch) information on their sexual response. Males rated visual and olfactory information as equally important in the selection of a

Can you have an orgasm just by thinking about sex?

The brain has been called our most important sexual organ. Sexual sensations, including **orgasm,** may be triggered by sexual stimulation that originates in the brain in the form of thoughts, fantasies, or memories. We can become aroused by images, words, aromas, and sounds, or without any outside sensory stimulation whatsoever in the form of thoughts, fantasies, or memories. Your brain, glands, nervous system, circulatory system, and reproductive system are all involved in your sexual fantasies. The fact that many people become sexually aroused during sleep, sometimes even to the point of orgasm, is one important sign that the brain contains all the information necessary to produce sexual arousal (at least sometimes).

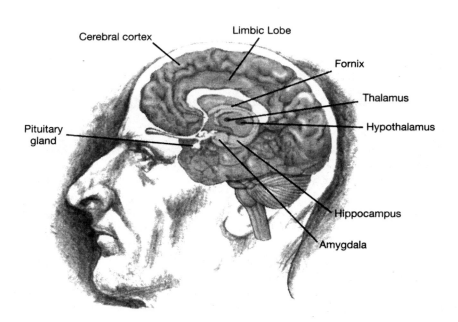

FIGURE 3.1 The limbic system of the brain, associated with emotion and motivation, is important in human sexual function.

109

What are erogenous zones?

Nerve endings are unevenly distributed throughout the body, causing some areas to be more sensitive to touch than others. Those body areas most sensitive to tactile stimulation are sometimes referred to as **erogenous zones**. The erogenous zones of the human body include the genitals, buttocks, anus, perineum, breasts, and inner surfaces of the thighs, neck, ears, navel, armpits, and mouth. As you have already learned, areas that may be extremely sensitive in one person may provoke no reaction, or even a negative reaction, in another. The only way to determine the location of your partner's erogenous zones is through experimentation. ∎

Erogenous Zones: parts of the body that are especially sensitive to stimulation

Touch is probably the most frequent method of sexual arousal and has the most direct effect on sexual response.

lover, while females considered olfactory information to be the single most important variable; in the words of an old television commercial, "If he stinks, forget it!" (The ad was for deodorant, of course!) When considering what sense had the most negative effect on sexual desire, females rated body odor highest; males regarded smells as being much more neutral stimuli for sexual arousal (Herz & Cahill, 1997).

Touch   The skin is the largest organ in the human body. Stimulating an area of the body by touch is probably the most frequent method of sexual arousal and has the most direct effect on sexual response. A soft kiss on the lips, a tender touch on the arm, or a gentle lick on the ear all can be highly arousing, as can stroking a penis or the brushing of lips across a nipple.

Sight   Visual information plays a major role in sexual arousal. The fashion, diet, and cosmetic industries, as well as the market for erotic photographs and movies, reflect the emphasis our society places on visual arousal. Animals other than humans also use visual cues to signal sexual attraction. The peacock's plumage and the lion's mane may be the animal kingdom's version of a low-cut blouse or skin-tight jeans.

Studies show that men and women respond differently to visual stimulation. In one study, 54 percent of the men but only 12 percent of women became erotically aroused when they were shown photos and drawings of nudes (Reinisch, 1991).

Smell   Recent research indicates that the sense of smell may control human sexual activity, compatibility, group behavior, and other social activity, just as it does in animals (Stern & McClintock 1998). In Chapter 2 we introduced pheromones, naturally produced chemicals that affect behavior through the sense of smell. The pheromones produced by a queen bee inhibit the sexual development in other females, who then become workers. Male mice use pheromones to promote the sexual development of nearby females, and if a sow or a cow in heat smells the pheromones contained in male urine she will take a mating stance (see CROSS-CULTURAL PERSPECTIVES box).

Only recently has the presence of human pheromones been confirmed. One study evaluated the effect of synthesized male pheromones placed in an aftershave lotion on six behaviors in men: petting, formal dates, informal dates, sleeping next to a romantic partner, sexual intercourse, and masturbation. Pheromone users had increased rates of intercourse, sleeping with romantic partners, petting, and informal dates; there was no effect on masturbation or formal dates (Cutler et al., 1998). Although the full extent to which pheromones influence human sexual behavior is unknown, researchers suspect that different pheromones may control different activities.

CROSS-CULTURAL PERSPECTIVES

Sex Scents

Olfactory preferences are determined in large part by culture. Women in some societies use their vaginal secretions as a perfume, rubbing some behind the ear or on the neck to attract and arouse sexual partners. Sweat is an almost universal ingredient in love potions throughout the world. In parts of the Balkans and Greece some *men carry handkerchiefs in their armpits during festivals and offer these as tokens to women they invite to dance. In contrast, in America, most people think that the smell of a moist vagina or sweaty armpit would not be appealing, and indeed many people regularly use deodorants to conceal these odors from a dating partner.*

Visual cues play a major role in sexual arousal.

Our sense of hearing influences sexual arousal and response. Sex and love have been the inspiration for music and music is often used to set a romantic mood.

FAQ:

What smells arouse men the most? What do women like best?

A research study measured changes in penile response and vaginal blood flow in response to different odors (Hirsch, 1998). In contrast to what the floral and perfume industries would have us believe, the study reported that the odors found most arousing were not flowers or cologne. The aromas that evoked the greatest response in men were pumpkin pie and lavender, while women were most stimulated by the smell of licorice coated candy (Good & Plenty), cucumbers, and baby powder. None of the odors tested was found to inhibit the sexual desire of men. However, smells that inhibited vaginal blood flow in women included cherries, charcoal-barbecued meat, and men's colognes. This same researcher theorized that odors might act directly on the link between the olfactory sense and the brain's limbic system (Hirsch, 1998).

Hearing Our sense of hearing also influences sexual arousal and response. For some, romantic music may set the mood (see CONSIDERATIONS box). Others may be sexually aroused when their lovers "talk dirty" or moan during lovemaking.

Tiny hair cells in the inner ear vibrate to transmit sounds. By examining these cells, researchers have found women's ears to be more sensitive than men's. Females hear high-pitched sounds better than males while men are more comfortable with louder sounds than women (Bloom, 1998).

In one study, male college students were shown 60-second erotic videos both with and without the accompanying audio. There was a significant positive correlation between male sexual arousal and sound, as measured by penile plethysmograph and self-report (Gaith & Plaud, 1997).

Another study found that a male partner's silence during lovemaking inhibited the female partner's sexual response (DeMartino, 1990). However, silence might be preferable to some other sounds, such as your partner burping during an embrace or the ringing of the phone. Many people find the sound of the words "I love you" to be the most arousing of all.

Taste The role of taste in human sexual arousal has not been fully investigated. Some individuals may be sexually aroused by the taste of vaginal secretions or seminal fluid. It is possible that genital secretions contain chemicals that have an arousing effect, or it may be the psychological association of the flavors with past sexual pleasure that cause the excitement.

Aural Sex

CONSIDERATIONS

Whether it is Ravel's "Bolero" or Barry White, music can simulate or stimulate sexual activity. Sounds of ecstasy have been a staple of pop music since the 1960s. Songs that contain sounds of female orgasm include: Marvin Gaye's "You Sure Love to Ball" (1973), Donna Summer's "Love to Love You Baby" (1975), Duran Duran's "Hungry Like the Wolf" (1982), Prince's "If The Kid Can't Make You Come" (1984), and Prince's "Orgasm" (1995). Sounds of male sexual pleasure are rarely heard in music. Perhaps this is because sound may be the only indication that some men have of women's orgasm, whereas women have more obvious physical evidence of a male partner's climax (Corbett & Kapsalis, 1996). The disembodied female vocalist

"oohing" and "aahing" herself into the throes of ecstasy "may stand as the most prominent signifier of female pleasure in the absence of other more visual assurances. Sounds of pleasure . . . seem almost to flout the realist function of anchoring body to image, halfway becoming aural fetishes of the female pleasures we cannot see" (Wiliams, 1989, pp. 122–123).

 Is there a song that almost always puts you in the mood for love?

—*What sounds, or words, do you like most, and least, to hear when making love?*
—*Can you think of a sound that would be an absolute turnoff?*

Chocolate, which contains phenylethylamine (PEA), a chemical believed to produce a lovelike sensation, is a very appropriate Valentine's Day gift.

In a 1980 study, Farb and Armelagos noted that the tradition of giving a box of chocolates on Valentine's Day might have arisen because chocolate contains phenylethylamine (PEA), a chemical believed to produce a lovelike sensation. Then again, foods such as salami and cheddar cheese have even higher levels of PEA—although few people would consider a deli sandwich an appropriate romantic gift. Chocolate also contains cannabinoids, the compound responsible for marijuana's high, although the amount isn't remotely close to that found in marijuana. In addition, the stimulants caffeine and theobromine are hidden in those delicious chocolate bars. The fat and sugar in chocolate candies are also likely to increase the volume of the brain chemical serotonin, which among other functions is responsible for making us feel good.

SEX HORMONES

The word *hormone* comes from the Greek *horman*, which means to arouse, to excite, to urge—which is exactly what our hormones do. Hormones, chemical substances secreted by your endocrine system (Table 3.1) arouse, excite, and influence your sexuality throughout your life. The endocrine system is a separate control system for the body, apart from the nervous system, and is comprised of ductless glands that release secretions directly into the bloodstream. There are several different types of hormones. For example, if you are in a stressful situation, hormones are deposited into the bloodstream by the adrenal, pituitary, thyroid, and other glands, resulting in an increase in heart rate, muscle tension, blood pressure, and perspiration. Sexual arousal works in a similar way. When you are aroused by a sexual stimulus, your endocrine system is activated, hormones are secreted, and changes occur in your body. Although androgens (from the Greek *andros*, for male) are commonly referred to as male sex hormones and estrogen (from the Greek *oistros*, for gadfly or frenzy) as the female sex hormone, neither hormone is gender exclusive. The difference is how much hormone circulates in the bloodstream.

Testosterone

Testosterone, the most important androgen, is secreted in small amounts by the adrenal glands in both males and females and in much larger amounts by the testes (Figure 3.2 on page 82). On average, men have at least 10 times more testosterone than women do (Worthman, 1999). Women produce testosterone in their ovaries and adrenal glands. The brain can convert testosterone into estradiol (a form of estrogen) so that the so-called male hormone becomes the so-called female hormone. In women, testosterone increases the flow of estrogen to the center of the brain that controls sexual motivation and drive. Each of us inherits a certain baseline level of testosterone, but testosterone levels are not constant; they fluctuate on a daily cycle and in response to daily events. Research has shown that testosterone levels change in response to physical, emotional, and intellectual challenges (Booth et al., 1992; Booth et al., 1995). On average, testosterone levels of U.S. males tend to go into a steady decline after age 20; the hormone's concentration in the blood decreases by about 30 percent by the time a male reaches 80.

In the developing human fetus, testosterone provides the early signal for the development of a male body, and it is responsible for the primary differences in male and female appearance. Even in adults, an imbalance in testosterone levels can alter body shape. It is clear that testosterone interacts with the nerve cells that make up the brain. We are not certain, however, what role the hormone plays in the development of personality and behavior (Blum, 1997).

A decrease in testosterone often is associated with a decline in male sexuality. In an attempt to restore their virility, in the 1920s physicians actually grafted monkey testes onto aging men (Blum, 1997). However, this pattern of hormone decline with aging is not universal. A cross-cultural study (Worthman, Beall, & Stallings, 1997) indicated that male subjects in Bolivia had a modest decrease in testosterone levels after

TABLE 3.1

Hormones of the Reproductive System

Hormone	Source	Regulation of secretion	Primary effects
Gonadotropin-releasing hormone (GnRH)	Hypothalamus	Males: inhibited by testosterone and possibly by inhibin. Females: GnRH pulse frequency increased by estrogens, decreased by progestins	Stimulates FSH secretion, LH synthesis
Follicle-stimulating hormone (FSH)	Anterior pituitary	Males: stimulated by GnRH, inhibited by inhibin. Females: stimulated by GnRH, inhibited by inhibin	Males: stimulates spermatogenesis through effects on sustentacular cells. Females: stimulates follicle development, estrogen production, and oocyte maturation
Luteinizing hormone (LH)	Anterior pituitary	Males: stimulated by GnRH. Females: production stimulated by GnRH, secretion by the combination of high GnRH pulse frequencies and high estrogen levels	Males: stimulates interstitial cells to secrete testosterone. Females: stimulates ovulation, formation of corpus luteum, and progestin secretion
Androgens (primarily testosterone and dihydrotestosterone)	Interstitial cells of testes	Stimulated by LH	Establish and maintain secondary sex characteristics and sexual behavior; promote maturation of spermatozoa; inhibit GnRH secretion
Estrogens (primarily estradiol)	Granulosa and thecal cells of developing follicles; corpus luteum	Stimulated by FSH	Stimulate LH secretion (at high levels); establish and maintain secondary sex characteristics and sexual behavior; stimulate repair and growth of endometrium; increase frequency of GnRH pulses
Progestins (primarily progesterone)	Granulosa cells from midcycle through functional life of corpus luteum	Stimulated by LH	Stimulate endometrial growth and glandular secretion; reduce frequency of GnRH pulses
Inhibin	Sustentacular cells of testes and granulosa cells of ovaries	Males: stimulated by factors released by developing spermatozoa. Females: stimulated by developing follicles	Inhibits secretion of FSH and possibly of GnRH

SOURCE: Martini, 2000, p. 1057.

age 30, with hormone levels remaining relatively stable after that time. On the other hand, testosterone levels in Tibetan males do not peak until the late 50s and then fall precipitously during the 60s and 70s. Neither the cause nor the possible significance of these variations is known.

There is as much controversy about the connection between blood levels of testosterone and measures of sexual desire, or **libido,** as there is about the connection

Libido: sexual desire

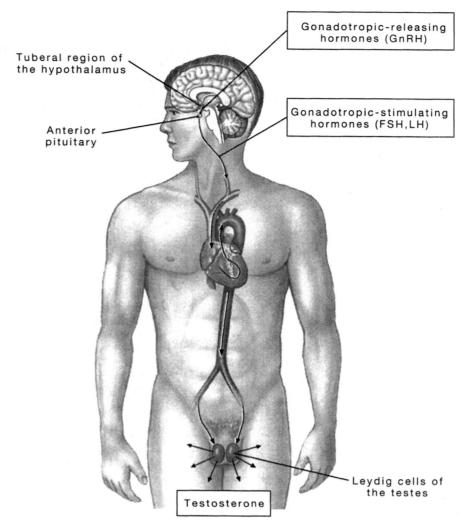

Gonadotropic-releasing hormones (GnRH)

Tuberal region of
the hypothalamus

Gonadotropic-stimulating hormones (FSH,LH)

Anterior
pituitary

Leydig cells of
the testes

Testosterone

FIGURE 3.2   The Production and Release of Testosterone in Males.   Stimulation of the tuberal region of the hypothalamus causes the release of gonadotropic-releasing factor, which causes the anterior pituitary to secrete luteinizing hormone (LH). LH then travels through the bloodstream to stimulate the Leydig cells of the testes to manufacture and release testosterone.

between testosterone and aggression (see CONSIDERATIONS box). Researchers at the Yerkes Primate Research Center at Emory University found that when male monkeys win a contest their T-levels increase for about 24 hours; the T-levels of the losers remain lower for even longer than a day. However, if the loser simply sees a sexually receptive female, his testosterone level shoots back up. "So now you know [what accounts for] the popularity of strip bars: they're where male losers go to get their T back up," claimed one of the Yerkes researchers (Wallen, 1997 quoted in Tierney, 1998, p. B1).

One of the best overviews of research on testosterone, *Heroes, Rogues, and Lovers* (Dabbs, 2000), portrays testosterone as a mixed blessing, with both good and bad features. According to Dabbs, high levels of testosterone (in both men and women) lead to more sexual activity, which of course helps make more babies. But it also leads people to become more fickle and restless, so they are less likely to stay around to nurture and support the children. Remarkably, nature seems to have instilled some mechanisms to make parents stick around. Dabbs reports that testosterone levels are high in single men, drop when the men get married, and drop even more when their wives

"Roid" Rage

When most people hear the word *steroid* they think of **anabolic steroids,** the drugs that bodybuilders and other athletes take in an effort to inflate their strength and bulk. These drugs usually are a synthetic version of testosterone. When scientists first created synthetic testosterone it was thought to be a "wonder drug" that would keep men young and strong well into old age. We now know better.

People, usually athletes, take anabolic steroids to improve their physical appearance and their performance. Steroids can also cause heart attacks, strokes, liver injury, damage to the reproductive system, and personality changes (Todd, 1987). It has been reported that steroid use in adolescents causes premature closing of the epiphyseal growth plates in the skeletal system, leading to shorter stature (Yesalis, Wright, & Bahrke, 1989).

Steroids also have a reputation for making men violent and aggressive. Violent criminals tend to have higher-than-average levels of testosterone. Separate studies in men's and women's prisons have found that murderers have higher levels of testosterone than other convicts, and, more generally, violent criminals have higher testosterone levels than nonviolent convicts. Although several studies have linked high testosterone levels (T-levels) to aggressive behavior in both animals and humans, others question the link between testosterone and aggression. Only three studies have reported a link between aggression or adverse overt behavior and anabolic steroid use (Bahrke, Yesalis, & Wright, 1997). Studies administering moderate doses of testosterone for clinical purposes reveal essentially no adverse effects on male sexual and aggressive behavior (Ibid., 1997).

Anabolic steroids, taken by some men to improve their physical appearance and performance, can cause heart attacks, strokes, liver injury, damage to the reproductive system, and personality changes.

Other studies look to psychosocial factors that may bring about the aggression attributed to steroids (Sharp & Collins, 1998). For example, the effects of previous psychiatric history, environmental and peer influence, and individual expectations remain unclear. One researcher hypothesizes that behavior we sometimes attribute to steroid abuse is actually the "nasty personality of some athletes reinforced by a sports culture that glorifies the physical response" (Yesalis, 1997).

> **?** *Do you know anyone who uses anabolic steroids?*
>
> *—Have you ever used or considered using steroids?*

have babies. In one study, expectant fathers who held a baby doll wrapped in a blanket experienced a statistically significant drop in testosterone within just half an hour (Storey et al., 2000). Men who remain single throughout life have high testosterone levels (but not as high as those who marry and then divorce). In general, men with high levels of testosterone are more likely to seek out sex and aggression, but are less reliable providers for their wives and children. In numerous species (including our own), males with low testosterone levels live longer (Worthman, 1999). Testosterone level also affects the workplace—or is it the other way around? (See CONSIDERATIONS box).

There may also be a link between T-levels and libido in women (Crenshaw, 1996; Hutchinson, 1995; Rako, 1996). At the onset of menopause, a woman's ovaries and adrenal glands begin to produce less testosterone and other androgens. As a result, the amount of testosterone circulating in the body is reduced by at least half. While some women may react to this change by experiencing a noticeable drop in sexual desire, others may not notice any difference. One study showed a decrease in sexual desire among premenopausal women whose ovaries were surgically removed

Anabolic Steroids: synthetic derivative of testosterone

High "T"

In a survey of various occupations, Dabbs found that testosterone levels varied widely. Comparing T-levels of nonlawyers, attorneys, and trial lawyers, Dabbs (1998) found that although the testosterone levels of attorneys matched those of doctors and similar professionals, they lagged behind those of construction workers and others in blue-collar jobs. However, trial lawyers had testosterone levels that were about 30 percent higher than other lawyers. And it wasn't just the men. Female trial attorneys had higher testosterone levels than those who didn't go to court. Farmers and white-collar workers such as office workers had low levels of testosterone, and ministers had the lowest of all occupations tested. Blue-collar workers had high levels of testosterone, and actors—especially ones favoring outrageous roles—had the highest, outranking even professional football players on the testosterone scale.

One study (Urdy, Morris, & Kovonock, 1995) found that women who choose a professional career tended to have higher T-levels than women who stayed home to raise their children. The high-T women were less likely to have children and less interested in becoming parents. When they did have children, their daughters also tended to have high testosterone levels. It is unknown if these results reflect a genetic predisposition for high testosterone, or if the high-testosterone mothers treated their daughters differently than mothers with lower T-levels.

Dabbs (2000) found that testosterone levels were high among the chronically unemployed, probably because their inclination to adventure made them poor prospects for steady work. On the other hand, losing a job may cause a decrease in testosterone, because many men experience that as a blow to their masculinity. People with low testosterone tend to get better grades in school, and enter into higher-status occupations (although within many competitive areas, high-testosterone people seem more likely to fight their way to the top). Low-testosterone men have happier

Both the male and female trial attorneys on *Ally McBeal* might be expected to have high testosterone levels.

marriages, feel closer to their friends and families, and smile more genuinely than high-testosterone men. Dabbs quoted various observers about the smiles of men with high testosterone. One described that smile as "wolfish," having a kind of dangerous or predatory aspect. Another, the political observer Myra MacPherson, said the high-testosterone smile is "a politician's smile—the kind that never reaches the eyes" (Dabbs, 2000, p. 156).

 What other professions do you think might have high testosterone levels?

—What professions do you think might have low testosterone levels?
—Do you think that that a male with a low-T-level job is less masculine or a woman in a high-T-level job is less feminine?

during a hysterectomy. When these women received estrogen and testosterone therapy, there was a significant increase in libido (Sherwin, 1996). However, there is more to libido than hormones. As we will discuss in Chapter 4, a lack of sexual desire may have a number of causes.

Estrogens

Estrogens are present in both men and women, but they circulate at the highest levels in women. The male testes and the female ovaries produce the estrogens. Men make estradiol while women make other estrogens as well. Early in female adolescence, the brain begins secreting regular bursts of hormones that stimulate the

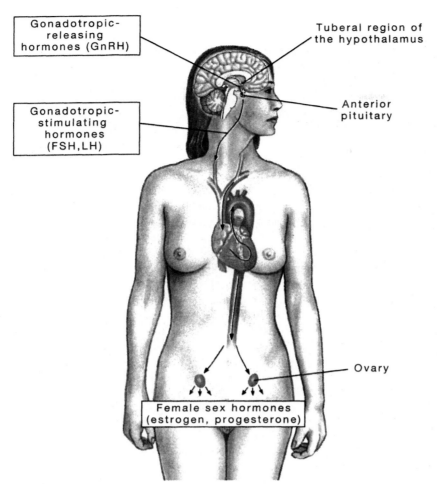

FIGURE 3.3 **The Production and Release of Female Sex Hormones.** Stimulation of the tuberal region of the hypothalamus causes the release of gonadotropic-releasing factor, which causes the anterior pituitary to secrete gonadotropic-stimulating hormones. The gonadotropic-stimulating hormones then travel through the bloodstream to the ovaries, stimulating the production and release of the female sex hormones.

ovaries (Figure 3.3). The ovaries in turn discharge estrogen, which encourages the development of the adult female body and regulates the menstrual cycle. At one time it was believed that the ovaries were a source of female weakness; one historical treatment for moodiness was removal of a woman's ovaries (Blum, 1997). Today it is known that, rather than a source of problems, the estrogens have beneficial effects in both men and women. As a matter of fact, the estrogens, especially estradiol, appear more directly necessary to survival than the androgens.

To make estrogen, the body needs an enzyme called **aromatase.** With aromatase, a tissue of the body can transform a precursor hormone into estrogen. The precursor may be testosterone (which women make in their ovaries, adrenal glands, and possibly in the uterus and the brain) or another androgen. The ovaries produce aromatase as well as testosterone, so the androgen can instantly be converted into estrogen. Other tissues that contain aromatase include fat, bones, muscle, blood vessels, and the brain. Give any of these tissues a bit of precursor hormone, and they'll convert it to estrogen.

There are at least 60 forms of estrogen in the body, the most important of which are *estradiol, estriol,* and *estrone.* Generally, different tissues of the body produce

Aromatase: an enzyme that converts androgen to estrogen

117

the different estrogens, though there is a lot of overlap, redundancy, and unknowns. **Estradiol,** the principal estrogen of women's reproductive years, is the product of the ovaries. It flows out of the cells of the follicles and from the corpus luteum. In men, the testes produce estradiol. Estradiol is considered the most potent of the three estrogens. Estradiol production in girls begins to rise slowly at about age 8 and continues its ascent until the onset of puberty, at which point it levels off. It remains dominant until menopause, except during pregnancy when estradiol production shuts down. **Estriol** is generated by the placenta, and, to a lesser extent, by the liver. It is the major "pregnancy estrogen," the source of many of the symptoms of gestation such as morning sickness. Estriol levels remain high until after childbirth, when estradiol kicks back in. **Estrone** is the primary estrogen of menopause. As the ovaries stop producing estradiol at menopause, the fat cells start making estrone. As we discussed in the previous chapter, it is the decreased level of estrogen that is thought to cause health problems in some postmenopausal women.

Estradiol appears to stimulate the immune system and direct the immune response to where it is needed (Morrell, 1995). Estradiol is also essential to a healthy heart. It seems to make blood platelets slightly less active, which makes them less prone to clumping and clotting the arteries (USDA, 1995). Researchers at Johns Hopkins University have found that a form of estrogen compound increased the blood flow to the heart in men with coronary artery disease by nearly one third (Blumenthal et al., 1997). Researchers investigating estradiol's effects on brain function have found evidence that estradiol may protect against Alzheimer's disease. The discovery of a specific structure on the estrogen molecule responsible for estrogen's ability to protect nerve cells from death may prove useful in treating and preventing Alzheimer's disease (Gordon et al., 1997).

While estrogen performs many valuable functions, there can be too much of a good thing. Excess estrogen in men can result in erectile difficulties and enlargement of the breasts. Hormonal fluctuations, which can aggravate endometriosis and uterine fibroid tumors (disorders discussed in Chapter 2), can increase with excess estrogen. In addition, evidence is accumulating that high levels of estrogen may increase the risk of breast cancer.

The Link Between Estrogen and Female Sex Drive

A female mouse can't mate if she is not in estrus. Unless she is in estrus, her ovaries do not secrete estrogen and progesterone, and without hormonal stimulation, the mouse can't assume the mating position (lordosis) in which she arches her back and flicks aside her tail, which makes her vagina accessible to the male mouse's penis. But, as you learned in Chapter 2, human females, and other female primates, have been freed from hormonal control and can have sex throughout the menstrual cycle. Researchers have long wondered whether the hormonal process that regulates the menstrual cycle affects female sexual behavior as the estrus cycle affects the behavior of other mammals.

Stanislaw and Rice (1988) found that in any given menstrual cycle, sexual desire was usually first experienced a few days before the basal body temperature (BBT) shift, around the date of expected ovulation. These events are correlated with changing hormone levels. While these results suggested that hormonal factors do in fact contribute to sexual desire, other studies have found no association between rates of intercourse and where a woman is in her ovulatory cycle (Wilcox et al., 1995).

The endocrine system plays an important role in human sexual behavior, but the effects of hormones and their relationship to the various sexual behaviors is not yet fully understood. We do know that hormones are necessary to maintain a satisfying human libido, but we also know that hormones alone are not enough. In women, estrogens prime the central nervous system and sensory organs for sex (Graziottin, 1998), but there are other as yet unknown factors that contribute to the female libido as well.

Estradiol: principal estrogen produced by the ovary during a woman's reproductive years

Estriol: an estrogen hormone found in the urine during pregnancy

Estrone: a weaker estrogen found in urine and placental tissues during pregnancy

Progesterone

Estrogens tend to work in concert with another set of hormones, the **progestins.** These hormones essentially wait to perform their function until pregnancy, when they are responsible for all kinds of managerial functions. The best-known progestin is **progesterone,** the so-called hormone of pregnancy that prepares the endometrium for implantation of the fertilized ovum; and later is used by the placenta to prevent rejection of the developing embryo and fetus. Progesterone promotes weight gain and nutrition storage and helps stimulate the breasts for milk production. By inducing the growth of muscle cells around capillaries in the uterus they protect women from the dangers of hemorrhage when pregnancy does not occur and the fertilized egg is washed away in the menstrual cycle. It is the progestins that are responsible for the complaints of swollen ankles and puffiness; inducing fluid retention increases the volume of blood circulating in the body to ensure that mother and baby both get enough blood and oxygen.

Oxytocin and Vasopressin

When you think of sexual behavior, romantic love and parental love, the first words you think of are probably *not* **oxytocin** and **vasopressin.** But scientists believe that these sex hormones have a great deal of influence on our sexual and romantic experiences. Both males and females possess these "love hormones," but oxytocin plays a stronger role in females and vasopressin has more influence in males. It is unknown why the sexes might need two different hormones to achieve the same purpose. Oxytocin and vasopressin are both produced in the hypothalamus and are **peptide hormones,** as opposed to **steroid hormones** like estrogen or testosterone. Steroid hormones slip back and forth from the brain to the bloodstream and back to the brain, but peptide hormones move only from brain to blood. We do not understand the roles of oxytocin and vasopressin completely, partly because each of them serves a number of different functions.

Oxytocin has been found to cause uterine contractions during orgasm and labor, increase sexual receptivity, speed ejaculation, and increase penile sensitivity (Newton, 1978; Pedersen, 1992). Oxytocin is released by the pituitary gland, and is present in a range of nerve cells throughout the brain. The concentration of oxytocin is highest in the limbic system but it is also found in the brain stem and spinal cord. Through its association with the sense of smell, oxytocin also orchestrates the body's response to pheromones.

In mammals, oxytocin in combination with estrogen increases sensitivity to touch and encourages mating, grooming, and cuddling in both sexes. Infusing oxytocin into the brains of nonpregnant female rats rapidly induced maternal behavior toward young pups (Pedersen et al., 1992). Similar findings have been reported in ewes, which usually are hostile to offspring other than their own (Kendrick et al., 1987). Furthermore, it appears that oxytocin not only fosters the bond between mothers and children, but it may also increase sexual activity. When oxytocin was infused into the brains of female rats, which are not very sexually receptive when not in estrus, their sexual activity increased considerably (Caldwell et al., 1984). It has been suggested that oxytocin can stimulate sexual behavior in humans (Anderson-Hunt & Dennerstein, 1994). In one study, women were asked to masturbate to climax, and their blood levels of oxytocin were measured before and after orgasm. The concentration of oxytocin climbed slightly, but measurably, with climax, and the greater the increase, the more pleasurable the women reported their orgasm to be (Pedersen et al., 1992).

Vasopressin is secreted from the brain's posterior pituitary and causes the contraction of vascular and other smooth muscles. While vasopressin resembles oxytocin in its chemical structure, in most respects it opposes the influence of oxytocin. Vasopressin acts as an antidiuretic, which prevents water and salt depletion, stimulates

Progestin: generic term for any substance, natural or synthetic, that effects some or all of the biological changes produced by progesterone

Progesterone: an antiestrogenic steroid produced by the corpus luteum and placenta or prepared synthetically that stimulates proliferation of the endometrium and is involved in the regulation of the menstrual cycle

Oxytocin: pituitary hormone that stimulates uterine contractions during labor and facilitates the secretion of milk during nursing

Vasopressin: a pituitary hormone that causes blood vessels and smooth muscles to contract

Peptide Hormones: group of hormones such as oxytocin and vasopressin that are produced in the hypothalamus

Steroid Hormones: group of hormones that include estrogen and testosterone

blood vessel constriction, and helps control blood pressure. In men, vasopressin levels increase when arousal occurs. Some researchers believe that vasopressin enhances mental alertness and moderates emotional response, allowing us to notice and respond to subtle sexual cues such as a glance or a gesture (Beckwith et al., 1990; deWied et al., 1989).

THE SEXUAL RESPONSE CYCLE

The cycle of human sexual response, the series of physiological processes and events that occur during sexual activity, is as complex and varied as the people who participate. However, it is useful to have models that describe common physiological changes and patterns in order to determine whether our experiences fall within the expected range (not to worry—almost everyone's do). Through their research, Masters and Johnson (1966), Helen Singer Kaplan (1979), and David Reed (1998) have come up with three ways of describing the events that occur during a sexual encounter.

Masters and Johnson's EPOR Model

Masters and Johnson recorded more than 10,000 cycles of sexual arousal and orgasm over a period of 12 years to arrive at a model of sexual arousal and response. There are four successive physiological phases to the sexual response cycle in their model: excitement, plateau, orgasm, and resolution (EPOR) (Figure 3.4).

The **excitement phase** is the first phase of the EPOR model. Both males and females may experience erection of the nipples, and increases in **myotonia** (muscle tension, spasm, or rigidity), heart rate, and blood pressure. In males, the excitement phase also produces penile erection because of the increased flow of blood to the erectile tissues. The time between the onset of stimulation and erection may be much shorter in young males than in older men. Also during this phase, the skin of the scrotum thickens, the testes increase in size, and the testes and scrotum are pulled up next to the man's body. In females, vaginal lubrication may begin within 10 to 30 seconds after the onset of sexual stimulation. **Vasocongestion,** the engorgement of blood vessels in response to sexual arousal, swells the clitoris and the labia majora, causing the labia to spread apart. The labia minora also increase in size, and the walls of the inner two thirds of the vagina expand. As the vaginal walls thicken, the increase in blood flow causes the normally pink tissue to darken. The uterus also becomes engorged with blood and is elevated further up into the body cavity. The breasts enlarge and blood vessels near the skin's surface may become more pronounced.

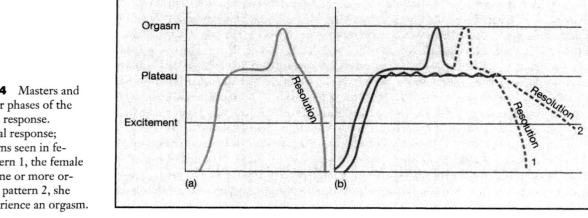

FIGURE 3.4 Masters and Johnson's four phases of the human sexual response. (a) Male sexual response; (b) two patterns seen in females; in pattern 1, the female experiences one or more orgasms, and in pattern 2, she does not experience an orgasm.

The **plateau phase** is an advanced state of arousal that precedes orgasm. By this phase a reddish rash called the **sex flush** may appear on the chest or breasts in about one fourth of males and three fourths of females. Myotonia may cause spasms in the hands and feet, as well as facial grimaces. Breathing becomes rapid, and the heart rate and blood pressure continue to rise. Males show a slight increase in the circumference of the coronal ridge of the penis and the glans turns purplish as a result of vasocongestion. The testes are pulled further in toward the man's body and may swell to $1\frac{1}{2}$ times their previous size. At this time a few drops of fluid from the Cowper's glands may appear at the tip of the penis. Vasocongestion swells the outer third of the female's vagina, producing the **orgasmic platform.** The inner part of the vagina expands fully and the uterus becomes fully elevated. The clitoris shortens and withdraws beneath the clitoral hood. The labia minora become redder; this is sometimes referred to as the **sex skin.** The areolas become so engorged with blood they may swell around the nipples. A mucuslike fluid is secreted from the Bartholin's glands on either side of the vaginal opening.

If an individual does not reach orgasm, myotonia and vasocongestion may take an hour or more to disappear. Continuing vasocongestion may cause a feeling of pelvic discomfort or fullness known as "blue balls" in males, a harmless condition that can be relieved by masturbation or by the passage of time (but time may appear to move very slowly to someone who is experiencing this condition). A woman who becomes highly stimulated but does not get sexual release may experience similar sensations, which can also be relieved by masturbation or the passage of time (Barbach, 1975).

In the **orgasmic phase,** rhythmic muscle contractions begin throughout the body in both males and females, while blood pressure, respiration, and heart rate continue to increase. The man experiences two stages of muscle contractions, sometimes referred to as the emission expulsion stage. In the first, the vas deferens, the seminal vesicles, the ejaculatory duct, and the prostate gland cause seminal fluid to collect in the urethral bulb, which expands to accommodate the fluid. The internal sphincter muscle of the bladder contracts to prevent seminal fluid from entering the bladder and urine from being ejaculated with the semen; if this muscle malfunctions, seminal fluid may enter the bladder rather than be ejaculated, an uncommon but harmless event called a *retrograde ejaculation.* At this time the man may experience a subjective feeling of impending ejaculation. In the second stage of the male orgasmic phase the external sphincter muscle of the bladder relaxes to allow the passage of semen. The muscles surrounding the urethra, the urethral bulb, and the base of the penis then contract rhythmically to propel the ejaculate out of the body and produce the pleasurable sensations associated with orgasm.

Female orgasm is marked by contractions of the pelvic muscles surrounding the vagina and release of vasocongestion that alleviates the muscle tension built up during the previous phases and produces a subjective feeling of release. Females also experience rhythmic contractions of the uterus and the anal sphincter during this phase. However, it should be noted that not all females enjoy orgasm with every experience of coitus.

The **resolution phase** follows orgasm. During this phase the body returns to its prearousal state. In both males and females myotonia decreases within a few minutes after orgasm, and blood pressure, heart rate, and respiration return to normal levels. Many individuals find their bodies covered in sweat and experience a general feeling of relaxation and satisfaction.

After ejaculation a male loses his erection in two stages. Within a minute, half the size of the erection is lost as blood from the corpora cavernosa, the tissues that engorge with blood, recedes. Then the remaining swelling subsides as the blood in the corpus spongiosum, a chamber on the underside of the penis, decreases. At this point the testes and scrotum return to their relaxed forms and positions. In females, swelling of the areolas and nipples decrease, and the sex flush rapidly disappears. The clitoris, vagina, uterus, and labia return to their relaxed states, and the "sex skin" returns to its prearousal coloration.

Plateau Phase: the second phase of Masters and Johnson's sexual response cycle in which muscle tension, heart rate, and vasocongestion increase

Sex Flush: rash that appears on the chest or breasts of some individuals during the sexual response cycle

Orgasmic Platform: the thickening of the walls of the outer third of the vagina that occurs during the plateau phase due to vasocongestion

Sex Skin: reddening of the labia minora that occurs during the plateau phase

Orgasmic Phase: the third phase of Masters and Johnson's sexual response cycle in which orgasm occurs

Resolution Phase: the fourth phase of Masters and Johnson's sexual response cycle during which the body gradually returns to its prearoused state

After resolution males enter what Masters and Johnson call a **refractory period** during which they are physiologically incapable of another orgasm or ejaculation. This period may last from a few minutes in adolescent males to a much longer period for older men. Females do not experience a refractory period. They may be restimulated quickly to the orgasmic phase.

Kaplan's Model of Sexual Response

In contrast to the four phases in the Masters and Johnson model, over many years of research sex therapist Helen Singer Kaplan (1974, 1979, 1987) developed a model of sexual response consisting of three independent components: desire, excitement and orgasm (Figure 3.5).

Desire is the most important element of Kaplan's model; it demonstrates the role of psychological and cognitive needs in the human sexual response cycle. Excitement and orgasm are described as primarily physiological components. The *excitement* phase consists of initial vasocongestion of the genitals, resulting in erection in the male and vaginal lubrication in the female. The *orgasm* phase is marked by pelvic muscle contractions in males and females, and ejaculation in males. In Kaplan's model, these three components are independent and not entirely sequential. For example, an individual might experience sexual excitement and perhaps orgasm without much desire. Other individuals may find that excitement stimulates sexual desire.

This model is useful for therapists precisely because it distinguishes desire as an independent component of the sexual response cycle, and, as you will discover in Chapter 4, lack of sexual desire is the most common problem clients bring to sex therapists. As we will discuss more fully in Chapter 4, an individual who lacks desire may not seek sexual stimulation or be able to respond when it is present.

Reed's ESP Model

David Reed's *Erotic Stimulus Pathway (ESP)* theory (1998) divides the sexual response cycle into four phases that contain elements of both Kaplan's and Masters and Johnson's models (Figure 3.6) as well as elements of the five basic needs discussed in Chapter 1. The first phase of Reed's model is *seduction*, the phase when an individual learns how to attract someone sexually. A seduction translates into memories and rituals. As a teenager you might have gone through a series of grooming rituals before going on a date. These rituals may have helped you feel you look good, which can translate into feeling good about yourself. The better you feel about yourself, the better you are at attracting others. These positive feelings are translated into sexual desire and arousal; the seductive techniques are stored in memory and can be activated at a later time.

In the *sensation phase*, the senses enhance sexual excitement extending it into a plateau phase, which makes us want to continue the pleasurable moment over a longer period of time. According to Reed, these seduction and sensation experiences are the psychological input to the physiology of sexual response.

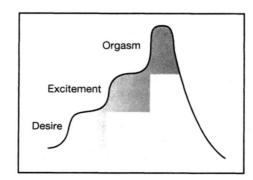

In the *surrender phase*, orgasm occurs. Reed's theory purports that people with orgasmic dysfunction (which will be discussed in Chapter 4) may be in a power struggle with themselves or with their partners or with the messages received from society about sex. Overcontrol or undercontrol can affect orgasmic potential and the ability to allow all of our passion to be expressed.

The final phase of Reed's model is the *reflection phase* where meaning is brought

FIGURE 3.5 Kaplan's three-stage model of the sexual response cycle. This model is distinguished by its identification of desire as a prelude to sexual response.

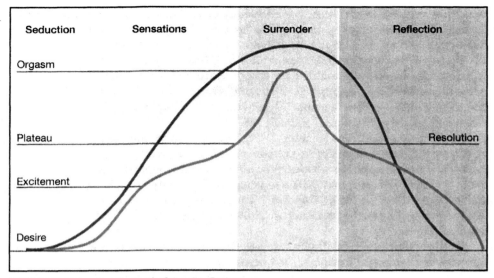

FIGURE 3.6 Reed's Erotic Stimulus Pathway.

to a sexual experience. Whether the experience is interpreted as positive or negative may determine the desire for subsequent sexual activity or under the same specific circumstances.

ORGASM

Why does the psychobiological experience of orgasm warrant so much attention? Our view is that orgasm is a complex response to a wide variety of social, physical, and mental stimuli. The differences in the behavioral expression of orgasm and the reported changes in consciousness and involuntary movements associated with orgasm in some individuals once led people to worry about its potential for harm both morally and biologically. During the 19th century, some medical professionals were so worried about the "dangers" of orgasm that they debated who should have orgasms and how often (Laumann et al., 1994).

The roots of the word *orgasm* include the Greek word *orgasmos*, meaning to grow ripe, swell, and be lustful, and the Sanskrit *urja*, meaning nourishment and power. From an evolutionary perspective, the importance of sex is reproduction, and while male orgasm is inextricably linked to reproduction, females don't have to have an orgasm to procreate. If you're trying to have a baby, male orgasm may be important to you, but for most of us, the importance of orgasm is pleasure, not procreation.

Studies comparing the orgasms of males and females indicate that they are more similar than you would think; there is more variation among individuals than between males and females (Proctor, Wagner, & Butler, 1974; Vance & Wagner, 1976; Wiest, 1987). Both women and men experience pleasurable sensations—orgasms "feel good." Both men and women describe the approach to a level of excitement beyond which it becomes progressively difficult to maintain voluntary control—the "point of no return." Other sensory perceptions may fade in the heat of the moment; people may experience some numbness in their senses and may not be very sensitive to painful stimuli (Katchadourian & Lunde, 1975).

Young men in adolescence and their early 20s report more frequent orgasms than older men do, while women generally experience their highest number of orgasms from their mid-20s to their mid-40s. However, these statistics do not reflect how often a man or woman would like to have sex or how much they are enjoying it. One reason for this possible orgasmic difference between men and women is that as

women become older they learn more about their sexuality and may feel more secure in their relationships, but as men age the lengths of their arousal, response, and refractory periods increase (Reinisch, 1991).

Biologist Stephen Jay Gould has argued that female orgasm is simply a byproduct of human development. Recall that the clitoris develops from the same tissue that produces the penis. Gould argues that the female orgasm exists because the clitoris is the homologue of the penis—"the same organ, endowed with the same anatomical organization and capacity of response" (Gould, 1987, p. 16).

Anthropologist Melvin Konner (1990) believes that female orgasm is the result of gender differences in selective pressures during the evolution of our species. For males in many mammalian species, reproduction is as simple as inseminating a female. For most females, mammalian reproduction inevitably entails gestation, labor, and nursing. Thus, in an evolutionary sense, males are rewarded for copulation, while females do best by choosing carefully among suitors and trying to sustain a bond with one.

Anthropologist Helen Fisher believes that human female orgasm does have a reproductive purpose. "I think female orgasm evolved for genuine purposes: to encourage females to seek sex, to make an intimate connection with a reproductive mate or extra lover, to signal enjoyment to this partner, and to aid fertilization" (Fisher, 1992, p. 183). There is some common-sense appeal to the notion that females who enjoy sex will be more likely to do it, and hence more likely to reproduce, than other females.

Sarah Hrdy (1996) proposes that while the female orgasm is not currently adaptive, it might have provided motivation for our female primate ancestors to mate with a range of partners. Such behavior would confuse the issue of paternity and increase the likelihood that a female could extract food and protection for her offspring from a number of different males. Hrdy raises the depressing possibility that, because the female orgasm is no longer functional, it is on its way out in an evolutionary sense; if she's right, our descendants may never share this glorious experience!

Randy Thornhill and Steven W. Gangestad (1996) speculate that female orgasm is an *atavism*, a trait that occurs in an individual because it occurred in an ancient ancestor. However, these University of New Mexico scientists also have proposed a theory with a rather unscientific name, the "upsuck theory," that the muscle contractions of female orgasm help suck the sperm into the fallopian tubes. Popular wisdom has sometimes upheld the belief that a woman cannot get pregnant unless she has an orgasm—wrong! But it is plausible than an orgasm might facilitate the process of getting pregnant in some way.

Men rarely wonder whether or not they have had an orgasm because of the obvious physical signs of ejaculation. Although the terms are often used interchangeably, *ejaculation* and *male orgasm* are not synonyms, but related physical events. A man cannot ejaculate without experiencing an orgasm, but it is possible for him to have an orgasm without ejaculating, for example in men with disease of the prostate, those practicing Tantric sex, or in prepubescent boys.

The physical signs of orgasm are not as obvious in women, and vary to a much greater extent, so a woman (and/or her partner) may not even know whether she has experienced an orgasm (see CONSIDERATIONS box).

Variation in Female Orgasm

Female orgasm has assumed a more convoluted role in the scientific understanding of sexuality. In the early 1900s, Sigmund Freud (1905) theorized that there were two distinct types of orgasm, vaginal orgasm and clitoral orgasm. Moreover, he took what appeared to be the anatomical locus of an orgasm to be a measure of developmental maturity. According to Freud, orgasms caused by clitoral stimulation were immature; by the time a woman entered puberty and was physically ready to have intercourse with a man, her center of orgasm should be transferred to the vagina (see CAMPUS CONFIDENTIAL feature for one woman's perspective). This theory influenced

Faking It

The psychological goal of orgasm that is so pervasive in many cultures may pressure some people, almost always women, to pretend they are having an orgasm. One study (Elliott & Brantley, 1997) of college students found that 60 percent of heterosexual college women and 71 percent of lesbian or bisexual women had faked having an orgasm, while only 17 percent of heterosexual college men and 27 percent of gay or bisexual men had faked it.

The most common reason given by women for faking an orgasm was to avoid disappointing or hurting their partners (Darling & Davidson, 1986). Other factors related to faking orgasm may include poor communication, limited knowledge of sexual techniques, a need for partner approval, an attempt to conceal a deteriorating relationship, protection of a partner's ego, or having given up hope of changing the partner's behavior (Lauersen & Graes, 1984).

If you usually climax when you're with your partner, but every now and then for some reason it's just not happening and what you really want to do is go to sleep, occasionally faking an orgasm might not be a big deal. But feigning orgasm most or all of the time can be far more problematic. It is hard to tell your partner that you have been faking enjoyment, but your partner deserves to know what is really going on.

As anyone who has seen the 1989 movie *When Harry Met Sally* knows, some women can do a very effective job of faking orgasm.

? ***Can you think of a good reason why someone might want to continue faking orgasms?***

—*Can you always tell if a partner is faking?*
—*What are other reasons why someone might fake orgasms?*
—*What are some ways that you might approach talking with your partner about this problem?*

---

thought on female sexual response for decades. Women who did not reach orgasm by the movements of the penis in their vagina were considered physically or psychologically inferior or abnormal.

The research of Masters and Johnson (1966) was crucial in dispelling Freud's theory by showing that there is no measurable physiological difference between female orgasms resulting from clitoral stimulation and those from vaginal stimulation. It is now widely thought that all female orgasms are the result of direct or indirect clitoral stimulation. The clitoris can be directly stimulated by hand, mouth, or vibrator, or indirectly during certain positions of intercourse. However the clitoris is stimulated, the center of the orgasmic response is around the vagina or around the uterus. In other words, all female orgasms "are triggered by stimulation of the clitoris and expressed by vaginal contractions" (Kaplan, 1974, p. 31). As you learned in Chapter 2, the clitoris is not necessary for reproduction and is thus the only human organ with the sole purpose of providing pleasure.

Josephine and Irving Singer (1972) postulated that in addition to noting observable physiological changes, emotional satisfaction is an important factor in the female orgasmic response. The Singers describe three types of female orgasm: vulval, uterine, and blended. According to their theory, a vulval orgasm may result from either manual stimulation or coitus. The vulval orgasm is accompanied by contraction of the orgasmic platform and is not followed by a refractory period. A uterine orgasm occurs only as a result of intercourse and is typically characterized by a woman holding her breath and then explosively exhaling at orgasm. This type of orgasm is said to produce a great deal of relaxation and satisfaction and is followed by a refractory period. The blended orgasm is a combination of vulval and uterine orgasms.

"[Some women] never bought Freud's idea of penis envy; who would want a shotgun when you can have a semiautomatic?"

(ANGIER, 1999, P. 63)

Are men as capable of having multiple orgasms as women?

It is not uncommon for a woman to have several sequential orgasms, separated in time by only a brief interval, while the spacing of male orgasms typically is more protracted. There is evidence that some men are capable of teaching themselves to be multiply orgasmic (Comfort, 1972; Robbins & Jensen, 1978). Researchers found one man who experienced six orgasms in the laboratory, with an interval of 36 minutes between the first and the last orgasm, and who maintained an erection during the entire period (Whipple & Myers, 1998). Other researchers (e.g., Dunn & Trost, 1989) report that some men are able to have multiple orgasms, delaying ejaculation until their final climax.

∎

Multiple Orgasms: experiencing one or more additional orgasms within a short time following the first

Simultaneous Orgasm: partners experience orgasm at the same time

www EXPLORING SEXUALITY ONLINE

Virtual Orgasm

Technology is a wonderful thing. A new form of sexual experience is being developed as an offshoot of virtual reality. Virtual reality is envisioned as a way to enhance the pleasure of viewing an erotic scene or activity. Instead of watching others perform, the person participates, providing a much more satisfying experience. The viewer puts on a helmet or enters a virtual reality room and participates in a realistic sexual experience of his or her choice without fear of disease, rejection, or embarrassment. Visual imagery can be enhanced with electronically simulated sensations such as odors, tastes, touch, and pressure. Virtual sex has the potential not only to enhance normal sensations but also to create sensations never before experienced. Visionaries predict that virtual sex programs will not only be available for solo use, but for experiences in which the participant can select one or more partners from a wide range of choices. Couples would be able to use virtual sex to enhance their sensations and explore alternate styles and preferences (Maxwell, 1997).

For most women, penile thrusting is less efficient in causing female orgasm than direct clitoral stimulation. In a famous study by Sheri Hite (1976), for example, only about 30 percent of the women could reach orgasm regularly from intercourse without more direct manual clitoral stimulation. However, approximately 44 percent of those tested experienced regular orgasm from manual stimulation of the clitoris (as "foreplay"), either by a partner or through self-stimulation, and 42 percent experienced regular orgasm during oral stimulation of the clitoris. By comparison, 99.5 percent of women were able to experience orgasm during masturbation.

Multiple and Simultaneous Orgasms

The much-sought-after phenomenon of **multiple orgasms** occurs when one orgasm quickly (although no one has ever defined just how "quickly") follows another. Women are biologically far more likely to have multiple orgasms than men, because of the refractory period that men experience. Some women are able to have several orgasms only seconds apart; men usually need much more time. Although only a small portion of the female population experiences them, Masters and Johnson (1966) and Fisher (1992) suggest that nearly all women are physically capable of multiple orgasm. Many factors could account for the discrepancy between experience and capability, but the most likely is that, once orgasm is reached, stimulation usually stops.

Some couples think that having **simultaneous orgasms** is the ultimate sexual experience. Others believe that while climaxing together might be nice, if and when it occurs, having simultaneous orgasms is no more satisfying than sequential orgasms. The Janus Report (1993) found that the vast majority of men and women surveyed did not feel that simultaneous orgasm is necessary for gratifying sex. It's difficult for two people to "choreograph" the coordination of their orgasms. To do so, you and your partner must time your response cycles so that you know approximately how long it takes for each of you to reach orgasm during a typical sexual experience. As we have discussed, the sexual response cycle varies widely from experience to experience, and the stress of "timing it just right" may very well defeat the purpose. It is more important that partners enjoy one another. Another disadvantage of simultaneous orgasm is that the partners are so wrapped up in their own responses they cannot enjoy each other's orgasms.

Rx: More Orgasms

A statistical study in the *British Medical Journal* found that men who have more orgasms live longer. According to the analysis, having regular sex reduces the risk of death by about half. Men who said they had sex twice a week had a risk of dying half that of those reporting they had sex only once a month. The authors of the study said they had tried to adjust the study's design to account for other factors that might explain their findings, for example, that healthier, fitter men generally engaged in sex more often. Even with this adjustment, the differences in risk could not be explained. Hormonal effects on the body resulting from more frequent sexual activity could be one possible explanation of this phenomenon (Davey-Smith et al., 1997). Until a more complete explanation is found, go ahead and improve your health!

SEXUALITY AND DISABILITIES

In a society where "sexy" is often equated with "healthy," we tend to desexualize the disabled, preferring not to think about their sexual needs and potentials. Those who are physically dependent to any extent are seen as being childlike; because of this, involvement in sexual relationships is considered inappropriate. Many individuals make the assumption that the chronically ill or disabled are unable to have erections, reach orgasm, or enjoy sexual pleasures. These are myths that we hope to dispel in this section.

Arthritis

Rheumatoid arthritis is a chronic multisystem disease characterized by a persistent inflammation of peripheral joints. Inflammation of the joints can interfere with sexual activity. Several small clinical studies have shown that approximately half of arthritic men and women experience sexual problems including fatigue, weakness, pain, and limited movement in joints. Pain and stiffness of the hip joints are the main causes of sexual difficulty for arthritis sufferers, though some report a loss of libido or sex drive. Moreover, some arthritis drugs, especially corticosteroids, have been shown to reduce sex drive (Reinisch, 1991).

Sexual dysfunction in arthritic patients may be difficult to manage for several reasons. The nature of the problem may be difficult to diagnose because it often is complicated by the underlying medical condition. In addition, chronic illness places a great deal of stress on patients and their relationships (Nadler, 1997). Those suffering from arthritis, need to experiment to find one or more positions that avoid or reduce pain and pressure on the affected joints.

Cardiovascular Disease

In the United States 68 million individuals have some form of *cardiovascular disease*, heart-related disorders including coronary artery disease and *arteriosclerosis* or hardening of the arteries. Sexual problems following a heart attack are common. Although researchers have generally agreed that sexual activity initially tends to decline after an acute cardiac event, there usually is an eventual return to the previous level of sexual activity (Stitik & Benevento, 1997). Sexual problems following cardiovascular disease often are due to anxiety or lack of information. While blood pressure does increase during sexual activity, sex is not hazardous to people with high blood pressure if the condition is under control. Most physicians prohibit sexual activity only in severe cases. However, anyone suffering a heart attack should consult a physician before resuming sexual activity.

Arteriosclerosis is among the more common causes of erection problems in older men. This disease can result in a reduction of blood supply to the penis. Erectile problems may be an early symptom of arteriosclerosis. Although common, this problem often responds to treatment.

FAQ:

Can a paralyzed person still have sex?

Christopher Reeve's book *Still Me* (1998) and films, such as *Coming Home, Born on the Fourth of July,* and *The Waterdance,* have dispelled the myth that men with SCI have no sexual feelings. All too often personal discomfort or fear prevents normal sexual interactions. The effect of SCI on sexual functioning depends on the location and severity of the injury. Erection and ejaculation may be affected in men and lubrication and orgasm in women (Sipski, 1997). (See CONSIDERATIONS box.) While intercourse may be impossible or different than before the injury, sexual play may be emotionally and psychologically satisfying. There are many methods of sexual interaction besides intercourse (touching, massage, using a vibrator, oral-genital sex etc.). For erectile difficulties, the woman-on-top position may be beneficial, or a penile implant may be used. Vaginal lubricants also may prove useful. If genital sensations are decreased or absent, interactions may focus on other erogenous zones of the body.

Cerebral Palsy

A mild to severe loss of muscle control, which may disrupt speech, facial expression, balance, and body movements, characterizes *cerebral palsy,* a chronic condition most often caused by damage to the brain during or before birth. Genital sensation is not disturbed by cerebral palsy; sexual interest, the capacity to have orgasm, and fertility are similarly unimpaired. There may be limitations to some sexual activities; for example, certain positions for intercourse may be difficult or impossible, depending on the nature and degree of muscle spasticity. Partners can adjust positions and find alternative ways of pleasuring one another.

Cerebrovascular Accidents

Although *cerebrovascular accidents (CVA),* more commonly known as *strokes,* are the third leading cause of death in North America, little is known regarding sexual problems and sexual expression and adjustment following CVA. Overall, stroke may affect both physical and psychosocial aspects of sexuality. Common physical problems include erectile dysfunction in men and poor vaginal lubrication in women (Monga, 1993; Monga & Osterman, 1995). In addition, *aphasia* (the absence or impairment of the ability to communicate, which can be caused by stroke) and other impairments of language skills can affect sexual relationships (Kinsella & Duffy, 1979). Alternate positioning and means of sexual expression can be helpful for many stroke victims.

Diabetes

Approximately 16 million Americans have *diabetes,* a complex disorder that affects the ability of the body to produce or properly respond to insulin. Sexual problems may result from nerve damage, a routine complication of diabetes (Masters et al., 1992). In a small number of cases, sexual dysfunction may be due to circulatory problems related to the disease. Both the nerve damage and the circulatory problems tend to be permanent and untreatable. Diabetes is the leading organic cause of erectile problems in men. Half of all men with adult-onset diabetes report difficulty or inability to attain or maintain an erection. The use of medications such as Viagra or penile implants are common treatments. Women with adult-onset diabetes are more susceptible to vaginal infections, which can result in decreased vaginal lubrication.

Multiple Sclerosis

Multiple sclerosis (MS), a neurological disease of the brain and spinal cord characterized by degeneration of the protective covering of the nerves, is the most common disabling neurological disease of young adults, affecting approximately 350,000 people in the United States each year (Anderson et al., 1992). Complications of the disease include cognitive, sensory, and motor dysfunction. Effects on sexual functioning depend on which areas of the brain or spinal cord are involved. The level of disease activity, the duration of the disease, and the degree of fatigue, depression, spasticity, and bowel and bladder problems also affect sexual functioning. Many men with MS have difficulty achieving and maintaining erections. In women, numbness and tingling in the vaginal area and difficulty in lubrication are common. In one study, 63 percent of people with MS reported their sexual activity had declined since their diagnosis; other surveys suggest that as many as 91 percent of men and 72 percent of women with MS may be affected by sexual problems (Hendley, 1996). Medications for spasms and pain may be helpful. For problems with fatigue, positions that require less exertion can be used. Other options include medication, penile implants, and lubricants.

Psychiatric Illness

Decreased libido is one of the symptoms of depression, the most frequently diagnosed psychiatric disorder in the United States. *Depression,* the most common form of mood disorder, is characterized by problems with appetite, sleeping, loss of energy, lack of interest and pleasure in usual activities (including sex), depressed or sad mood, and negative self-concept. Unfortunately, many antidepressants prescribed to treat depression have the side effect of decreased sexual desire. Other psychiatric illnesses, such as *bipolar disorder* (formerly called manic-depressive illness, which includes periods of depression that may suddenly lift and are followed immediately by periods of mania in which the person exhibits exaggerated energy and elation) or *schizophrenia* (a serious mental illness characterized by a loss of contact with reality, problems with incoherent thought patterns, and attention, motor, and perceptual problems), also may affect sexual desire and behavior.

There are many misconceptions about sexuality and the mentally disabled. Although many believe otherwise, the "mentally handicapped are more likely to be victims than perpetrators of sexual exploitation" (Reinisch, 1991, p. 283). While research has shown that the sexual development and behavior of the mentally and intellectually disabled is similar to the nondisabled, the physical and emotional changes of puberty may be difficult for them to handle. "Without special education programs to help them learn about physical changes and our society's rules for handling sexual feelings, some inadvertently behave in socially unacceptable ways" (Reinisch, 1991, pp. 283–284). Treatment of any mental illness should include counseling regarding appropriate sexual expression.

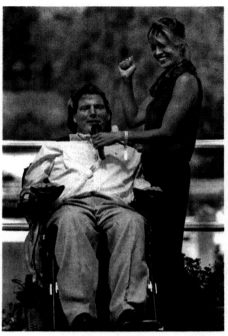

Despite his spinal cord injury, Christopher Reeve and his wife Dana maintain a sexual relationship.

Sensory Impairment

Impairment of one of the senses, such as vision, hearing, or speech, does not directly affect genital responsiveness. For example, the 1991 Kinsey Report notes, "Some research on the sexual behavior of visually impaired people has established that their feelings, attitudes, and behavior are similar to those of sighted people" (Reinisch, 1991, p. 284). Sexual difficulties may be related to a lack of sex education or decreased self-confidence resulting from the impairment. Psychological problems associated with the impairment are far more likely to interfere with a sexual relationship than the impairment itself. Deafness or blindness, particularly if it occurs in adolescence or adulthood, may cause depression, social withdrawal, distorted body image, and/or fear of rejection. These emotions can have an adverse affect on anyone's sexuality. Counseling may be appropriate for anyone with sensory impairment.

Spinal Cord Injuries

Spinal cord injuries (SCI), injuries to the spinal cord from events such as automobile accidents, serious falls, or diving accidents, affect approximately 200,000 Americans. *Spinal cord disease* may affect an additional 300,000 (Sipski, 1997). Such events may cause *paraplegia* (paralysis of the legs) or *quadriplegia* (paralysis of all four limbs) and loss of all sensations below the level of the injury or disease. Normal bladder and bowel function usually is lost, and the individual is apt to have significant loss of sexual function.

You can have sex in a wheelchair, while suffering from arthritis, or after heart surgery. Although there may be difficulties due to physical limitations, the individual's adjustment to the disability, or the availability of partners, individuals with disabilities have the same sexual needs and feelings as anyone else. In any person, able or disabled, a healthy attitude is the most important factor in achieving a healthy sex life.

If a disability occurs early in life it may affect socialization; a smaller social circle limits the opportunity for sexual learning and the availability of sexual partners. A condition can cause direct or indirect effects on sexual functioning. A direct effect is any difference in function of your genitals or another body system that specifically affects sexual response. For example, erectile dysfunction can be a direct effect of prostate cancer. An indirect effect can be symptoms such as pain or fatigue caused by the condi-

The Orgasm Pill

Researchers Barry Komisaruk and Beverly Whipple (1997) believe that they have isolated a chemical that produces orgasms in women, even those who have suffered spinal cord injuries. Through experiments with rats, researchers isolated the neurotransmitter that is believed to cause the sensation of orgasm in the brain. These findings might one day lead to a pill that would give the same sensation as an orgasm.

? *Aside from its obvious use, can you think of any potential abuse for such a pill?*

—*If a pill were available that would provide you with the sensations of orgasm, would you be interested?*

—*Do you think such a pill might replace your desire and need for coitus?*

—*What might be the long-term social implications of such a pill?*

tion that diminishes your ability for and/or interest in sexual activities. For example, those suffering from severe arthritis may have such extreme discomfort that sexual activity becomes undesirable.

Medical treatments can interfere with sexual responses, as can the psychological effects of being sick, injured, or disabled. A belief that you are less attractive or less sexually desirable because of your condition can reduce your willingness to pursue sexual relationships. Your partners' reactions also have an impact. For example, a sexual partner may be afraid that sexual activity will hurt you or worsen your condition. As indicated above, a positive attitude on the part of the disabled person and his or her partner can make all of the difference in the expression of their sexuality.

CHAPTER 3 REVIEW

Most female primates undergo an **1**_____ cycle that includes a period of sexual receptivity followed by ovulation. However, human females are capable of being continuously receptive to and available for sexual activity independent of ovulation. While the physical responses to sexual arousal vary with the individual, the most obvious physical signs of sexual arousal are vaginal **2**_____ for females and penile **3**_____ for males.

The brain may be the most important human sexual organ since it processes emotions, thoughts, fantasies,

and desires. Some typical correlates of sexual excitement are increases in heartbeat, blood to the genitals, **4**_____ (or breathing), and skin sensitivity. In addition, the body may experience **5**_____ (or muscle tension) and engorgement of blood in the genitals.

All five human senses may contribute to sexual arousal. For example, touch or tactile stimulation and smell or olfactory stimulation can increase sexual arousal. **6**_____ are naturally produced chemicals that affect behavior through the sense of smell.

7_____ are chemical substances secreted by the endocrine system. There are three primary categories of sex hormones: **8**_____, _____, and _____. All three are present in varying amounts in males and females. The most important androgen is **9**_____, which is produced by the testes, ovaries, and adrenal glands.

The endocrine system plays an important role in sexual behavior. The hypothalamus regulates the production of sex hormones and sends signals to the pituitary gland that in turn directs the production of androgens in males and estrogens in females. The feedback loop is completed when the testes or ovaries send hormonal signals to the hypothalamus and the pituitary to help self-regulate the system. The chemicals 10_____ and _____, produced by the pituitary, also can be triggered by sex and desire.

Masters and Johnson have proposed the EPOR model of sexual response for males and females. The four phases of this model are: 11_____, _____, _____, and _____. Helen Kaplan has proposed a model of sexual response consisting of three independent components: 12_____, _____, and _____. David Reed's ESP model has four phases: 13_____, _____, _____, and _____.

Studies indicate that the orgasms of males and females feel similar, and that there is more variation among individuals than between males and females. However, females are much more likely than males to experience more than one orgasm, or 14_____. Since the female orgasm is not necessary for human reproduction, much debate continues regarding its evolutionary significance.

A healthy body is not a prerequisite for a healthy sex life. A healthy attitude about your sexuality and yourself is the most important factor. The specific impact of illness or disability on sexual function depends on: (1) the severity of the impairment; (2) personal factors, such as age; (3) partner factors, including sexual history and the nature of past relationships. While it is common to desexualize the disabled, individuals with disabilities can have the same sexual needs and feelings as anyone else.

Cerebral palsy affects muscle control but it does not affect genital sensation, sexual interest, the capacity to have orgasm, or fertility. Multiple sclerosis is the most common neurological disease of young adults in the United States. 15_____, or hardening of the arteries, and diabetes are common causes of erectile problems. Decreased libido may result from depression; moreover, medications prescribed to treat depression also may decrease sexual desire.

Injuries of the 16_____ may cause paraplegia, paralysis of 17_____, or quadriplegia, paralysis of all four limbs. When all sensations are lost below the level of the injury, normal bladder and bowel functions and significant sexual function may be affected, although sexuality can be expressed in alternative ways.

SUGGESTED READINGS

Blum, D. (1998). *Sex on the Brain: The Biological Differences Between Men and Women.* New York: Penguin USA.
Blum examines the structure and function of the male and female brains.

Crenshaw, T. (1997). *The Alchemy of Love and Lust: How Our Sex Hormones Influence Our Relationships.* New York: Pocket Books.
Crenshaw, a sex therapist, discusses the role of hormones in the different sexual stages and how hormones determine the course of human relationships.

Love, S. (1997). *Dr. Susan Love's Hormone Book.* New York: Random House.
This book offers information about hormones and hormone replacement therapy. The emphasis is that menopause is not a disease that needs to be cured but a natural stage of life.

Masters, W., & Johnson, V. (1966). *Human Sexual Response.* Boston: Little Brown & Company.
This is the classic text on the biological patterns of human sexual response.

Sipski, M. L., & Alexander, C. (Eds.). (1997). *Sexual Function in People with Disability and Chronic Illness.* Gaithersburg, MD: Aspen Publications.
This collection offers a comprehensive overview of how various illnesses and disabilities affect sexual function, along with treatment options.

ANSWERS TO CHAPTER REVIEW

1. estrous; **2.** lubrication; **3.** erection; **4.** respiration; **5.** myotonia; **6.** Pheromones; **7.** Hormones; **8.** androgens, estrogens, progesterones; **9.** testosterone; **10.** oxytocin, vasopressin; **11.** excitement, plateau, orgasmic, resolution; **12.** desire, excitement, orgasm; **13.** seduction, sensation, surrender, reflection; **14.** multiple orgasms; **15.** Arteriosclerosis; **16.** spinal cord; **17.** the legs

Appendix A

What's Love Got to Do With It?

Sex Among Our Closest Relatives Is a Rather Open Affair

Meredith F. Small

Maiko and Lana are having sex. Maiko is on top, and Lana's arms and legs are wrapped tightly around his waist. Lina, a friend of Lana's, approaches from the right and taps Maiko on the back, nudging him to finish. As he moves away, Lina enfolds Lana in her arms, and they roll over so that Lana is now on top. The two females rub their genitals together, grinning and screaming in pleasure.

This is no orgy staged for an X-rated movie. It doesn't even involve people— or rather, it involves them only as observers. Lana, Maiko, and Lina are bonobos, a rare species of chimplike ape in which frequent couplings and casual sex play characterize every social relationship—between males and females, members of the same sex, closely related animals, and total strangers. Primatologists are beginning to study the bonobos' unrestrained sexual behavior for tantalizing clues to the origins of our own sexuality.

In reconstructing how early man and woman behaved, researchers have generally looked not to bonobos but to common chimpanzees. Only about 5 million years ago human beings and chimps shared a common ancestor, and we still have much behavior in common: namely, a long period of infant dependency, a reliance on learning what to eat and how to obtain food, social bonds that persist over generations, and the need to deal as a group with many everyday conflicts. The assumption has been that chimp behavior today may be similar to the behavior of human ancestors.

Bonobo behavior, however, offers another window on the past because they, too, shared our 5-million-year-old ancestor, diverging from chimps just 2 million years ago. Bonobos have been less studied than chimps for the simple reason that they are difficult to find. They live only on a small patch of land in Zaire, in central Africa. They were first identified, on the basis of skeletal material, in the 1920s, but it wasn't until the 1970s that their behavior in the wild was studied, and then only sporadically.

Bonobos, also known as pygmy chimpanzees, are not really pygmies but welterweights. The largest males are as big as chimps, and the females of the two species are the same size. But bonobos are more delicate in build, and their arms and legs are long and slender.

On the ground, moving from fruit tree to fruit tree, bonobos often stand and walk on two legs—behavior that makes them seem more like humans than chimps. In some ways their sexual behavior seems more human as well, suggesting that in the sexual arena, at least, bonobos are the more appropriate ancestral model. Males and females frequently copulate face-to-face, which is an uncommon position in animals other than humans. Males usually mount females from behind, but females seem to prefer sex face-to-face. "Sometimes the female will let a male start to mount from behind," says Amy Parish, a graduate student at the University of California at Davis who's been watching female bonobo sexual behavior in several zoo colonies around the world. "And then she'll stop, and of course he's really excited, and then she continues face-to-face." Primatologists assume the female preference is dictated by her anatomy: her enlarged clitoris and sexual swellings are oriented far forward. Females presumably prefer face-to-face contact because it feels better.

"Sex is fun. Sex makes them feel good and keeps the group together."

Like humans but unlike chimps and most other animals, bonobos separate sex from reproduction. They seem to treat sex as a pleasurable activity, and they rely on it as a sort of social glue, to

"What's Love Got to Do with It?: Sex Among Our Closest Relatives Is a Rather Open Affair," by Meredith F. Small, reprinted from *Discover*, June 1992, pp. 46-51.

make or break all sorts of relationships. "Ancestral humans behaved like this," proposes Frans de Waal, an ethologist at the Yerkes Regional Primate Research Center at Emory University. "Later, when we developed the family system, the use of sex for this sort of purpose became more limited, mainly occurring within families. A lot of the things we see, like pedophilia and homosexuality, may be leftovers that some now consider unacceptable in our particular society."

Depending on your morals, watching bonobo sex play may be like watching humans at their most extreme and perverse. Bonobos seem to have sex more often and in more combinations than the average person in any culture, and most of the time bonobo sex has nothing to do with making babies. Males mount females and females sometimes mount them back; females rub against other females just for fun; males stand rump to rump and press their scrotal areas together. Even juveniles participate by rubbing their genital areas against adults, although ethologists don't think that males actually insert their penises into juvenile females. Very young animals also have sex with each other: little males suck on each other's penises or French-kiss. When two animals initiate sex, others freely join in by poking their fingers and toes into the moving parts.

One thing sex does for bonobos is decrease tensions caused by potential competition, often competition for food. Japanese primatologists observing bonobos in Zaire were the first to notice that when bonobos come across a large fruiting tree or encounter piles of provisioned sugarcane, the sight of food triggers a binge of sex. The atmosphere of this sexual free-for-all is decidedly friendly, and it eventually calms the group down. "What's striking is how rapidly the sex drops off," says Nancy Thompson-Handler of the State University of New York at Stony Brook, who has observed bonobos at a site in Zaire called Lomako. "After ten minutes, sexual behavior decreases by fifty percent." Soon the group turns from sex to feeding.

But it's tension rather than food that causes the sexual excitement. "I'm sure the more food you give them, the more sex you'll get," says De Waal. "But it's not really the food, it's competition that triggers this. You can throw in a cardboard box and you'll get sexual behavior." Sex is just the way bonobos deal with competition over limited resources and with the normal tensions caused by living in a group. Anthropologist Frances White of Duke University, a bonobo observer at Lomako since 1983, puts it simply: "Sex is fun. Sex makes them feel good and therefore keeps the group together."

"Females rule the business. It's a good species for feminists, I think."

Sexual behavior also occurs after aggressive encounters, especially among males. After two males fight, one may reconcile with his opponent by presenting his rump and backing up against the other's testicles. He might grab the penis of the other male and stroke it. It's the male bonobo's way of shaking hands and letting everyone know that the conflict has ended amicably.

Researchers also note that female bonobo sexuality, like the sexuality of female humans, isn't locked into a monthly cycle. In most other animals, including chimps, the female's interest in sex is tied to her ovulation cycle. Chimp females sport pink swellings on their hind ends for about two weeks, signaling their fertility, and they're only approachable for sex during that time. That's not the case with humans, who show no outward signs that they are ovulating, and can mate at all phases of the cycle. Female bonobos take the reverse tack, but with similar results. Their large swellings are visible for weeks before and after their fertile periods, and there is never any discernibly wrong time to mate. Like humans, they have sex whether or not they are ovulating.

What's fascinating is that female bonobos use this boundless sexuality in all their relationships. "Females rule the business—sex and food," says De Waal. "It's a good species for feminists, I think." For instance, females regularly use sex to cement relationships with other females. A genital-genital rub, better known as GG-rubbing by observers, is the most frequent behavior used by bonobo females to reinforce social ties or relieve tension. GG-rubbing takes a variety of forms. Often one female rolls on her back and extends her arms and legs. The other female mounts her and they rub their swellings right and left for several seconds, massaging their clitorises against each other. GG-rubbing occurs in the presence of food because food causes tension and excitement, but the intimate contact has the effect of making close friends.

Sometimes females would rather GG-rub with each other than copulate with a male. Parish filmed a 15-minute scene at a bonobo colony at the San Diego Wild Animal Park in which a male, Vernon, repeatedly solicited two females, Lisa and Loretta. Again and again he arched his back and displayed his erect penis— the bonobo request for sex. The females moved away from him, tactfully turning him down until they crept behind a tree and GG-rubbed with each other.

Unlike most primate species, in which males usually take on the dangerous task of leaving home, among bonobos females are the ones who leave the group when they reach sexual maturity, around the age of eight, and work their way into unfamiliar groups. To aid in their assimilation into a new community, the female bonobos make good use of their endless sexual favors. While watching a bonobo group at a feeding tree, White saw a young female systematically have sex with each member before feeding. "An adolescent female, presumably a recent transfer female, came up to the tree, mated with all five males, went into the tree, and solicited GG-rubbing from all the females present," says White.

Once inside the new group, a female bonobo must build a sisterhood from scratch. In groups of humans or chimps, unrelated females construct friendships through the rituals of shopping together or grooming. Bonobos do it sexually. Although pleasure may be the motivation

HIDDEN HEAT

Standing upright is not a position usually—or easily—associated with sex. Among people, at least, anatomy and gravity prove to be forbidding obstacles. Yet our two-legged stance may be the key to a distinctive aspect of human sexuality: the independence of women's sexual desires from a monthly calendar.

Males in the two species most closely related to us, chimpanzees and bonobos, don't spend a lot of time worrying, "Is she interested or not?" The answer is obvious. When ovulatory hormones reach a monthly peak in female chimps and bonobos, and their eggs are primed for fertilization, their genital area swells up, and both sexes appear to have just one thing on their mind. "These animals really turn on when this happens. Everything else is dropped," says primatologist Frederick Szalay of Hunter College in New York.

Women, however, don't go into heat. And this departure from our relatives' sexual behavior has long puzzled researchers. Clear signals of fertility and the willingness to do something about it bring major evolutionary advantages: ripe eggs lead to healthier pregnancies, which leads to more of your genes in succeeding generations, which is what evolution is all about. In addition, male chimps give females that are waving these red flags of fertility first chance at high-protein food such as meat.

So why would our ancestors give this up? Szalay and graduate student Robert Costello have a simple explanation. Women gave heat up, they say, because our ancestors stood up. Fossil footprints indicate that somewhere around 3.5 million years ago hominids—non-ape primates—began walking on two legs. "In hominids, something dictated getting up. We don't know what it was," Szalay says. "But once it did, there was a problem with the signaling system." The problem was that it didn't work. Swollen genital areas that were visible when their owners were down on all fours became hidden between the legs. The mating signal was lost.

"Uprightness meant very tough times for females working with the old ovarian cycle," Szalay says. Males wouldn't notice them, and the swellings themselves, which get quite large, must have made it hard for two-legged creatures to walk around.

Those who found a way out of this quandary, Szalay suggests, were females with small swellings but with a little less hair on their rears and a little extra fat. It would have looked a bit like the time-honored mating signal. They got more attention, and produced more offspring. "You don't start a completely new trend in signaling," Szalay says. "You have a little extra fat, a little nakedness to mimic the ancestors. If there was an ever-so-little advantage because, quite simply, you look good, it would be selected for."

And if a little nakedness and a little fat worked well, Szalay speculates, then a lot of both would work even better. "Once you start a trend in sexual signaling, crazy things happen," he notes. "It's almost like: let's escalate, let's add more. That's what happens in horns with sheep. It's a particular part of the body that brings an advantage.' In a few million years human ancestors were more naked than ever, with fleshy rears not found in any other primate. Since these features were permanent, unlike the monthly ups and downs of swellings, sex was free to become a part of daily life.

It's a provocative notion, say Szalay's colleagues, but like any attempt to conjure up the past from the present there's no real proof of cause and effect. Anthropologist Helen Fisher of the American Museum of Natural History notes that Szalay is merely assuming that fleshy buttocks evolved because they were sex signals. Yet their mass really comes from muscles which chimps don't have, that are associated with walking. And anthropologist Sarah Blaffer Hrdy of the University of California at Davis points to a more fundamental problem: our ancestors may not have had chimplike swellings that they needed to dispense with. Chimps and bonobos are only two of about 200 primate species, and the vast majority of those species don't have big swellings. Though they are our closest relatives, chimps and bonobos have been evolving during the last 5 million years just as we have, and swollen genitals may be a recent development. The current unswollen human pattern may be the ancestral one.

"Nobody really knows what happened," says Fisher. "Everybody has an idea. You pays your money and you takes your choice."

—Joshua Fischman

---

behind a female-female assignation, the function is to form an alliance.

These alliances are serious business, because they determine the pecking order at food sites. Females with powerful friends eat first, and subordinate females may not get any food at all if the resource is small. When times are rough, then, it pays to have close female friends. White describes a scene at Lomako in which an adolescent female, Blanche, benefited from her established friendship with Freda. "I was following Freda and her boyfriend, and they found a tree that they didn't expect to be there. It was a small tree, heavily in fruit with one of their favorites. Freda went straight up the tree and made a food call to Blanche. Blanche came tearing over—she was quite away—and went tearing up the tree to Freda, and they GG-rubbed like crazy.

Alliances also give females lever over larger, stronger males who otherwise would push them around. Females have discovered there is strength in numbers. Unlike other species of primates such as chimpanzees or baboons (or too often, humans), where tensions run high between males and females, bonobo females are not afraid of males, and the sexes mingle peacefully. "What is consistently different from chimps," says Thompson-Handler, "is the composition of parties. The vast majority are mixed, so there are males and females of all different ages."

Female bonobos cannot be coerced into anything, including sex. Parish recounts an interaction between Lana and a male called Akili at the San Diego Wild Animal Park. "Lana had just been introduced into the group. For a long time she lay on the grass with a huge swelling. Akili would approach her with a big erection and hover over her. It would have been easy for him to do a mount. But he wouldn't. He just kept trying to catch her eye, hovering around her, and she would scoot around the ground, avoiding him. And then he'd try again. She went around full circle." Akili was big enough to force himself on her. Yet he refrained.

In another encounter, a male bonobo was carrying a large clump of branches. He moved up to a female and presented his erect penis by spreading his legs and arching his back. She rolled onto her back and they copulated. In the midst of their joint ecstasy, she reached out and grabbed a branch from the male. When he pulled back, finished and satisfied, she moved away, clutching the branch to her chest. There was no tension between them, and she essentially traded copulation for food. But the key here is that the male allowed her to move away with the branch—it didn't occur to him to threaten her, because their status was virtually equal.

Although the results of sexual liberation are clear among bonobos, no one is sure why sex has been elevated to such a high position in this species and why it is restricted merely to reproduction among chimpanzees. "The puzzle for me," says De Waal, "is that chimps do all this bonding with kissing and embracing, with body contact. Why do bonobos do it in a sexual manner?" He speculates that the use of sex as a standard way to underscore relationships began between adult males and adult females as an extension of the mating process and later spread to all members of the group. But no one is sure exactly how this happened.

It is also unclear whether bonobo sexually became exaggerated only after their split from the human lineage or whether the behavior they exhibit today is the modern version of our common ancestor's sex play. Anthropologist Adrienne Zihlman of the University of California at Santa Cruz, who has used the evidence of fossil bones to argue that our earliest known non-ape ancestors, the australopithecines, had body proportions similar to those of bonobos, says, "The path of evolution is not a straight line from either species, but what I think is important is that the bonobo information gives us more possibilities for looking at human origins."

Some anthropologists, however, are reluctant to include the details of bonobo life, such as wide-ranging sexuality and a strong sisterhood, into scenarios of human evolution. "The researchers have all these commitments to male dominance [as in chimpanzees], and yet bonobos have egalitarian relationships," says De Waal. "They also want to see humans as unique, yet bonobos fit very nicely into many of the scenarios, making humans appear less unique."

Our divergent, non-ape path has led us away from sex and toward a culture that denies the connection between sex and social cohesion. But bonobos, with their versatile sexuality, are here to remind us that our heritage may very well include a primordial urge to make love, not war.

Appendix B

CHAPTER 1

1. Carl Sagan, "A Cosmic Calendar," *Natural History*, December 1975, 70–73.
2. Arthur O. Lovejoy, *The Great Chain of Being: A Study of the History of an Idea* (Cambridge, MA: Harvard University Press, 1964), pp. 58–63.
3. Quoted in ibid., p. 63.
4. Ibid., p. 183.
5. See Loren C. Eiseley, *Darwin's Century: Evolution and the Men Who Discovered It* (Garden City, NY: Doubleday, 1958), pp. 17–26; and Ernst Mayr, *The Growth of Biological Thought: Diversity, Evolution, and Inheritance* (Cambridge, MA: Belknap Press of Harvard University Press, 1982), pp. 171–75, 340–41.
6. Mayr, *The Growth of Biological Thought*, pp. 339–60.
7. Ernst Mayr, "The Nature of the Darwinian Revolution," *Science*, June 2, 1972, 981–89.
8. Alfred Russel Wallace, "On the Tendency of Varieties to Depart Indefinitely from the Original Type," *Journal of the Proceedings of the Linnaean Society*, August 1858, reprinted in Louise B. Young, ed., *Evolution of Man* (New York: Oxford University Press, 1970), p. 75.
9. Mayr, *The Growth of Biological Thought*, p. 423.
10. Darwin had a still longer title. It continued, *Or the Preservation of the Favoured Races in the Struggle for Life.* Darwin's notion of "struggle for life" is often misinterpreted to refer to a war of all against all. Although animals may fight with each other at times over access to resources, Darwin was referring mainly to their metaphorical "struggle" with the environment, particularly to obtain food.
11. Charles Darwin, *The Origin of Species*, excerpted in Young, ed., *Evolution of Man*, p. 78.
12. See Douglas Futuyma's *Science on Trial* (New York: Pantheon, 1982) for an overview of this long controversy.
13. Quoted in Ashley Montagu's introduction to Thomas H. Huxley, "Man's Place in Nature," in Young, ed., *Evolution of Man*, pp. 183–84.
14. Robert N. Brandon, *Adaptation and Environment* (Princeton, NJ: Princeton University Press, 1990), pp. 6–7.
15. George C. Williams, *Natural Selection: Domains, Levels, and Challenges* (New York: Oxford University Press, 1992), p. 7.
16. John Maynard Smith, *Evolutionary Genetics* (New York: Oxford University Press, 1989), pp. 42–45.
17. Charles Devillers and Jean Chaline, *Evolution: An Evolving Theory* (New York: Springer-Verlag, 1993), pp. 22–23.
18. G. A. Harrison, James M. Tanner, David R. Pilbeam, and P. T. Baker, *Human Biology: An Introduction to Human Evolution, Variation, Growth, and Adaptability*, 3rd ed. (Oxford: Oxford University Press, 1988), pp. 209–12.
19. William H. Durham, *Coevolution: Genes, Culture, and Human Diversity* (Stanford, CA: Stanford University Press, 1991), pp. 122–23.
20. Bruce Alberts, Dennis Bray, Julian Lewis, Martin Raff, Keith Roberts, and James D. Watson, *Molecular Biology of the Cell* (New York: Garland, 1983), p. 185.
21. Ibid., pp. 99–103.
22. George Beadle and Muriel Beadle, *The Language of Life* (Garden City, NY: Doubleday, 1966), p. 216.
23. Frederic Golden, Michael Lemonick, and Dick Thompson, "The Race Is Over," *Time*, July 3, 2000, 18–23; Thomas Hayden, "A Genome Milestone," *Newsweek*, July 3, 2000, 51–52; John Travis, "Human Genome Work Reaches Milestone," *Science News*, July 1, 2000, 4–5; Eliot Marshall, "Rival Genome Sequencers Celebrate a Milestone Together," *Science*, June 30, 2000, 2294–295; Elizabeth Pennisi, "Finally, the Book of Life and Instructions for Navigating It," *Science*, June 30, 2000, 2304–307.
24. Alberts et al., *Molecular Biology of the Cell*, pp. 107–11.
25. Paul Berg and Maxine Singer, *Dealing with Genes: The Language of Heredity* (Mill Valley, CA: University Science Books, 1992), p. 53.
26. Alberts et al., *Molecular Biology of the Cell*, pp. 107–11.
27. Ibid., p. 842.
28. Beadle and Beadle, *The Language of Life*, p. 123.
29. Alberts et al., *Molecular Biology of the Cell*.
30. Theodosius Dobzhansky, *Mankind Evolving: The Evolution of the Human Species* (New Haven, CT: Yale University Press, 1962), pp. 138–40.
31. Ibid., p. 139.
32. Harrison et al., *Human Biology*, pp. 205–206.
33. Ibid., pp. 205–208.
34. John Relethford, *The Human Species: An Introduction to Biological Anthropology* (Mountain View, CA: Mayfield, 1990), p. 94.
35. Harrison et al., *Human Biology*, pp. 198–200.
36. C. Loring Brace, "A Four-Letter Word Called Race," in Larry T. Reynolds and Leonard Leiberman, eds, *Race and Other Misadventures: Essays in Honor of Ashley Montagu in His Ninetieth Year* (New York: General Hall, 1996).
37. David P. Barash, *Sociobiology and Behavior* (New York: Elsevier, 1977).
38. J. R. Krebs and N. B. Davies, eds., *Behavioural Ecology: An Evolutionary Approach*, 2nd ed. (Sunderland, MA: Sinauer, 1984); J. R. Krebs and N. B. Davies, *An Introduction to Behavioural Ecology*, 2nd ed. (Sunderland, MA: Sinauer, 1987).
39. George B. Schaller, *The Serengeti Lion: A Study of Predator-Prey Relations* (Chicago: University of Chicago Press, 1972), cited in Edward O. Wilson, *Sociobiology: The New Synthesis* (Cambridge, MA: Belknap Press of Harvard University Press, 1975), p. 504.
40. Wilson, *Sociobiology*, quoted in Bobbi Low, "Behavioral Ecology, 'Sociobiology' and Human Behavior," in Carol R. Ember, Melvin Ember, and Peter N. Peregrine, eds., *Research Frontiers in Anthropology* (Upper Saddle River, NJ: Prentice Hall, 1998). Prentice Hall/Simon & Schuster Custom Publishing.
41. Low, "Behavioral Ecology, 'Sociobiology' and Human Behavior."
42. Donald T. Campbell, "Variation and Selective Retention in Socio-Cultural Evolution," in Herbert Barringer, George Blankstein, and Raymond Mack, eds., *Social Change in Developing Areas: A Re-Interpretation of Evolutionary Theory* (Cambridge, MA: Schenkman, 1965), pp. 19–49.
43. Henry W. Nissen, "Axes of Behavioral Comparison," in Anne Roe and George Gaylord Simpson, eds., *Behavior and Evolution* (New Haven, CT: Yale University Press, 1958), pp. 183–205.
44. Robert Boyd and Peter J. Richerson, *Culture and the Evolutionary Process* (Chicago: University of Chicago Press, 1985).
45. William H. Durham, *Coevolution: Genes, Culture, and Human Diversity* (Stanford, CA: Stanford University Press, 1991).

Taken from: *Physical Anthropology and Archaeology*
by Carol R. Ember, Melvin Ember, and Peter N. Peregrine

1. The classic description of common primate traits is J. R. Napier and P. H. Napier, *A Handbook of Living Primates* (New York: Academic Press, 1967). See also Barbara B. Smuts, Dorothy L. Cheney, Robert M. Seyfarth, Richard W. Wrangham, and Thomas T. Struhsaker, eds., *Primate Societies* (Chicago: University of Chicago Press, 1987).

2. Simon K. Bearder, "Lorises, Bushbabies, and Tarsiers: Diverse Societies in Solitary Foragers," in Smuts et al., eds., *Primate Societies*, p. 14.

3. Alison F. Richard, *Primates in Nature* (New York: Freeman, 1985), p. 22ff.

4. Robert D. Martin, "Strategies of Reproduction," *Natural History*, November 1975, 50. The opossum, which is not a primate but lives in trees and has many babies at one time, is a marsupial and has a pouch in which to keep the babies when they are very young.

5. H. F. Harlow et al., "Maternal Behavior of Rhesus Monkeys Deprived of Mothering and Peer Association in Infancy," *Proceedings of the American Philosophical Society*, 110 (1966): 58–66.

6. Nancy A. Nicolson, "Infants, Mothers, and Other Females," in Smuts et al., eds., *Primate Societies*, p. 339.

7. See J. Patrick Gray, *Primate Sociobiology* (New Haven, CT: HRAF Press, 1985), pp. 144–63, for a discussion of research that attempts to explain the variation among primates in the degree of male parental care.

8. Anne E. Russon, "The Development of Peer Social Interaction in Infant Chimpanzees: Comparative Social, Piagetian, and Brain Perspectives," in Sue Taylor Parker and Kathleen Rita Gibson, eds., *"Language" and Intelligence in Monkeys and Apes: Comparative Developmental Perspectives* (New York: Cambridge University Press, 1990), p. 379.

9. Phyllis Jay Dohlinow and Naomi Bishop, "The Development of Motor Skills and Social Relationships among Primates through Play," in Phyllis Jay Dohlinow, ed., *Primate Patterns* (New York: Holt, Rinehart & Winston, 1972), pp. 321–25.

10. D. S. Sade, "Some Aspects of Parent-Offspring and Sibling Relationships in a Group of Rhesus Monkeys, with a Discussion of Grooming," *American Journal of Physical Anthropology*, 23 (1965): 1–17; and Glenn Hausfater, Jeanne Altmann, and Stuart Altmann, "Long-Term Consistency of Dominance Relations among Female Baboons," *Science*, August 20, 1982, 752–54.

11. Elisabetta Visaberghi and Dorothy Munkenbeck Fragaszy, "Do Monkeys Ape?" in Parker and Gibson, eds., *"Language" and Intelligence in Monkeys and Apes*, p. 265; Michael Tomasello, "Cultural Transmission in the Tool Use and Communicatory Signaling of Chimpanzees," in Parker and Gibson, eds., *"Language" and Intelligence in Monkeys and Apes*, pp. 304–305.

12. Jane van Lawick-Goodall, *In the Shadow of Man* (Boston: Houghton Mifflin, 1971), p. 242.

13. Visaberghi and Fragaszy, "Do Monkeys Ape?" pp. 264–65.

14. Robert Martin, "Classification and Evolutionary Relationships," in Steve Jones, Robert Martin, and David Pilbeam, eds., *The Cambridge Encyclopedia of Human Evolution* (Cambridge: Cambridge University Press, 1992), pp. 17–19; Glenn C. Conroy, *Primate Evolution* (New York: Norton, 1990), pp. 8–15.

15. This simplified chart of primate classification adapts information provided in Martin, "Classification and Evolutionary Relationships," p. 21.

16. G. A. Doyle and R. D. Martin, eds., *The Study of Prosimian Behavior* (New York: Academic Press, 1979); and Ian Tattersall, *The Primates of Madagascar* (New York: Columbia University Press, 1982).

17. Alison F. Richard, "Malagasy Prosimians: Female Dominance," in Smuts et al., eds., *Primate Societies*, p. 32.

18. Bearder, "Lorises, Bushbabies, and Tarsiers," p. 13.

19. Pierre Charles-Dominique, *Ecology and Behaviour of Nocturnal Primates*, trans. Robert D. Martin (New York: Columbia University Press, 1977), p. 258. See also Robert D. Martin and Simon K. Bearder, "Radio Bush Baby," *Natural History*, October 1979, 77–81; and Bearder, "Lorises, Bushbabies, and Tarsiers," pp. 18–22.

20. John MacKinnon and Kathy MacKinnon, "The Behavior of Wild Spectral Tarsiers," *International Journal of Primatology*, 1 (1980): 361–79.

21. Matt Cartmill, "Non-Human Primates," in Jones, Martin, and Pilbeam, eds., *The Cambridge Encyclopedia of Human Evolution*, p. 28; John G. Fleagle, *Primate Adaptation and Evolution*, 2nd ed. (San Diego: Academic Press, 1999), pp. 118–22.

22. Napier and Napier, *A Handbook of Living Primates*, pp. 32–33.

23. Richard, *Primates in Nature*, pp. 164–65.

24. Cartmill, "Non-Human Primates," p. 29; Anne Wilson Goldizen, "Tamarins and Marmosets: Communal Care of Offspring," in Smuts et al., eds., *Primate Societies*, p. 34. See also John F. Eisenberg, "Comparative Ecology and Reproduction of New World Monkeys," in Devra Kleinman, ed., *The Biology and Conservation of the Callitrichidae* (Washington, DC: Smithsonian Institution, 1977), pp. 13–22; and Robert W. Sussman and Warren G. Kinzey, "The Ecological Role of the Callitrichidae: A Review," *American Journal of Physical Anthropology*, 64 (1984): 419–49; Fleagle, *Primate Adaptation and Evolution*, pp. 168–74.

25. Eisenberg, "Comparative Ecology and Reproduction of New World Monkeys," pp. 15–17.

26. John G. Robinson, Patricia C. Wright, and Warren G. Kinzey, "Monogamous Cebids and Their Relatives: Intergroup Calls and Spacing," in Smuts et al., eds., *Primate Societies*, pp. 44–53; Carolyn Crockett and John F. Eisenberg, "Howlers: Variations in Group Size and Demography," in Smuts et al., eds., *Primate Societies*, pp. 54–68; John G. Robinson and Charles H. Janson, "Capuchins, Squirrel Monkeys, and Atelines: Socioecological Convergence with Old World Primates," in Smuts et al., eds., *Primate Societies*, pp. 69–82.

27. Sarah Blaffer Hrdy, *The Langurs of Abu: Female and Male Strategies of Reproduction* (Cambridge, MA: Harvard University Press, 1977), p. 18.

28. Ibid., pp. 18–19.

29. J. R. Napier, "Paleoecology and Catarrhine Evolution," in J. R. Napier and P. H. Napier, eds., *Old World Monkeys: Evolution, Systematics, and Behavior* (New York: Academic Press, 1970), pp. 80–82.

30. Linda Marie Fedigan, *Primate Paradigms: Sex Roles and Social Bonds* (Montreal: Eden Press, 1982), p. 11.

31. Ibid., pp. 123–24.

32. Phyllis C. Lee, "Home Range, Territory and Intergroup Encounters," in Robert A. Hinde, ed., *Primate Social Relationships: An Integrated Approach* (Sunderland, MA: Sinauer, 1983), p. 231.

33. Fleagle, *Primate Adaptation and Evolution*, p. 302.

34. W. E. LeGros Clark, *The Fossil Evidence for Human Evolution* (Chicago: University of Chicago Press, 1964), p. 184.

35. Holger Preuschoft, David J. Chivers, Warren Y. Brockelman, and Norman Creel, eds., *The Lesser Apes: Evolutionary and*

Behavioural Biology (Edinburgh: Edinburgh University Press, 1984).

36. C. R. Carpenter, "A Field Study in Siam of the Behavior and Social Relations of the Gibbon (*Hylobates lar*)," *Comparative Psychology Monographs*, 16, no. 5 (1940): 1–212; David John Chivers, *The Siamang in Malaya* (Basel: Karger, 1974); and David J. Chivers, ed., *Malayan Forest Primates: Ten Years' Study in Tropical Rain Forest* (New York: Plenum, 1980).

37. H. D. Rijksen, *A Fieldstudy on Sumatran Orang Utans* (Pongo Pygmaeus Abelii Lesson 1827): Ecology, Behaviour and Conservation (Wageningen, Netherlands: H. Veenman and Zonen B.V., 1978), p. 22.

38. Dennis Normile, "Habitat Seen Playing Larger Role in Shaping Behavior," *Science*, March 6, 1998, 1454–455.

39. Biruté M. F. Galdikas, "Orangutan Adaptation at Tanjung Puting Reserve: Mating and Ecology," in David A. Hamburg and Elizabeth R. McCown, eds., *The Great Apes* (Menlo Park, CA: Benjamin/Cummings, 1979), pp. 220–23.

40. Dorothy L. Cheney and Richard W. Wrangham, "Predation," in Smuts et al., eds., *Primate Societies*, p. 236.

41. Rijksen, *A Fieldstudy on Sumatran Orang Utans*, p. 321.

42. Dian Fossey, *Gorillas in the Mist* (Boston: Houghton Mifflin, 1983), p. xvi.

43. Russell H. Tuttle, *Apes of the World: Their Social Behavior, Communication, Mentality, and Ecology* (Park Ridge, NJ: Noyes, 1986), pp. 99–114.

44. George Schaller, *The Mountain Gorilla: Ecology and Behavior* (Chicago: University of Chicago Press, 1963). See also Schaller's *The Year of the Gorilla* (Chicago: University of Chicago Press, 1964).

45. Fossey, *Gorillas in the Mist*, p. 47.

46. A. H. Harcourt, "The Social Relations and Group Structure of Wild Mountain Gorillas," in Hamburg and McCown, eds., *The Great Apes*, pp. 187–92.

47. R. L. Sussman, *The Pygmy Chimpanzee: Evolutionary Biology and Behavior* (New York: Plenum, 1984); F. J. White, "*Pan paniscus* 1973 to 1996: Twenty-three Years of Field Research," *Evolutionary Anthropology*, 5 (1996): 11–17.

48. Frans de Waal and Frans Lanting, *Bonobo: The Forgotten Ape* (Berkeley: University of California Press, 1997).

49. Craig B. Stanford, "The Social Behavior of Chimpanzees and Bonobos: Empirical Evidence and Shifting Assumptions," *Current Anthropology*, 39 (1998): 399–420.

50. Jane Goodall, "My Life among Wild Chimpanzees," *National Geographic*, August 1963, 272–308; and van Lawick-Goodall, *In the Shadow of Man*.

51. Geza Teleki, "The Omnivorous Chimpanzee," *Scientific American*, January 1973, 32–42.

52. Craig Stanford, "Chimpanzee Hunting Behavior and Human Evolution," in Peter N. Peregrine, Carol R. Ember, and Melvin Ember, eds, *Physical Anthropology: Original Readings in Method and Practice* (Upper Saddle River, NJ: Prentice Hall, 2002).

53. Ibid., pp. 35–41.

54. Normile, "Habitat Seen Playing Larger Role."

55. Tuttle, *Apes of the World*, pp. 266–69.

56. Morris Goodman, "Reconstructing Human Evolution from Proteins," in Jones, Martin, and Pilbeam, eds., *The Cambridge Encyclopedia of Human Evolution*, pp. 307–12.

57. T. H. Clutton-Brock and Paul H. Harvey, "Primate Ecology and Social Organization," *Journal of Zoology*, London, 183 (1977): 8–9.

58. L. C. Aiello, "Body Size and Energy Requirements," in Jones, Martin, and Pilbeam, eds., *The Cambridge Encyclopedia of Human Evolution*, pp. 41–44; Alison Jolly, *The Evolution of Primate Behavior*, 2nd ed. (New York: Macmillan, 1985), pp. 53–54.

59. Aiello, "Body Size and Energy Requirements."

60. Jolly, The *Evolution of Primate Behavior*, pp. 53–54.

61. Sue Taylor Parker, "Why Big Brains Are So Rare," in Parker and Gibson, eds., *"Language" and Intelligence in Monkeys and Apes*, p. 130.

62. Katharine Milton, "Distribution Patterns of Tropical Plant Foods as an Evolutionary Stimulus to Primate Mental Development," *American Anthropologist*, 83 (1981): 534–48; T. H. Clutton-Brock and Paul H. Harvey, "Primates, Brains and Ecology," *Journal of Zoology*, London, 190 (1980): 309–23.

63. Katharine Milton, "Foraging Behaviour and the Evolution of Primate Intelligence," in Richard W. Bryne and Andrew Whiten, eds., *Machiavellian Intelligence: Social Expertise and the Evolution of Intellect in Monkeys, Apes, and Humans* (Oxford: Clarendon Press, 1988), pp. 285–305.

64. Jolly, The *Evolution of Primate Behavior*, p. 119.

65. Clutton-Brock and Harvey, "Primate Ecology and Social Organization," p. 9.

66. John Terborgh, *Five New World Primates: A Study in Comparative Ecology* (Princeton, NJ: Princeton University Press, 1983), pp. 224–25.

67. Jolly, *The Evolution of Primate Behavior*, p. 120.

68. Ibid., p. 122.

69. Richard W. Wrangham, "An Ecological Model of Female-Bonded Primate Groups," *Behaviour*, 75 (1980): 262–300.

70. Dean Falk, "Hominid Paleoneurology," *Annual Review of Anthropology*, 16 (1987): 13–30.

71. Female bonobo, or pygmy chimpanzees, engage in sexual intercourse nearly as often as human females. See Nancy Thompson-Handler, Richard K. Malenky, and Noel Badrian, "Sexual Behavior of *Pan paniscus* under Natural Conditions in the Lomako Forest, Equateur, Zaire," in Randall L. Susman, ed., *The Pygmy Chimpanzee: Evolutionary Biology and Behavior* (New York: Plenum, 1984), pp. 347–66. For a review of field research on pygmy chimpanzees, see White, "*Pan paniscus* 1973 to 1996."

72. By male-female bonding, we mean that at least one of the sexes is "faithful," that is, typically has intercourse with just one opposite-sex partner throughout at least one estrus or menstrual cycle or breeding season. Note that the bonding may not be monogamous; an individual may be bonded to more than one individual of the opposite sex. See Melvin Ember and Carol R. Ember, "Male-Female Bonding: A Cross-Species Study of Mammals and Birds," *Behavior Science Research*, 14 (1979): 37–41.

73. Ember and Ember, "Male-Female Bonding," p. 43; see also Carol R. Ember and Melvin Ember, "The Evolution of Human Female Sexuality: A Cross-Species Perspective," *Journal of Anthropological Research*, 40 (1984): 203–204.

74. Ember and Ember, "The Evolution of Human Female Sexuality," p. 207.

75. Ibid., pp. 208–209.

76. de Waal and Lanting, *Bonobo*.

77. Duane M. Rumbaugh, "Learning Skills of Anthropoids," in L. A. Rosenblum, ed., *Primate Behavior*, vol. 1 (New York: Academic Press, 1970), pp. 52–58.

78. Observation by others cited by Jolly, *The Evolution of Primate Behavior*, p. 53.

79. Alison C. Hannah and W. C. McGrew, "Chimpanzees Using Stones to Crack Open Oil Palm Nuts in Liberia," *Primates*, 28 (1987): 31–46.

80. "The First Dentist," *Newsweek*, March 5, 1973, 73.

81. Robert M. Seyfarth, Dorothy L. Cheney, and Peter Marler,

"Monkey Response to Three Different Alarm Calls: Evidence of Predator Classification and Semantic Communication," *Science,* November 14, 1980, 801–803.

82. R. Allen Gardner and Beatrice T. Gardner, "Teaching Sign Language to a Chimpanzee," *Science,* August 15, 1969, 664–72.

83. Beatrice T. Gardner and R. Allen Gardner, "Two Comparative Psychologists Look at Language Acquisition," in K. E. Nelson, ed., *Children's Language,* vol. 2 (New York: Halsted Press, 1980), pp. 331–69.

84. Patricia Marks Greenfield and E. Sue Savage-Rumbaugh, "Grammatical Combination in *Pan paniscus:* Processes of Learning and Invention in the Evolution and Development of Language," in Parker and Gibson, eds., *"Language" and Intelligence in Monkeys and Apes,* pp. 540–78.

Appendix C

BIBLIOGRAPHY

ADAMS, ROBERT McC. *Heartland of Cities: Surveys of Ancient Settlement and Land Use on the Central Floodplain of the Euphrates.* Chicago: University of Chicago Press, 1981.

ADAMS, ROBERT M. "The Origin of Cities." *Scientific American,* September 1960, 153–68.

AHERN, EMILY M. "Sacred and Secular Medicine in a Taiwan Village: A Study of Cosmological Disorders." In Arthur Kleinman et al., eds., *Medicine in Chinese Cultures: Comparative Studies of Health Care in Chinese and Other Societies.* Washington, DC: U.S. Department of Health, Education, and Welfare, National Institutes of Health, 1975, as seen in the eHRAF Collection of Ethnography on the Web, 2000.

AIELLO, L. C. "Body Size and Energy Requirements." In Jones, Martin, and Pilbeam, eds., *The Cambridge Encyclopedia of Human Evolution.*

AIELLO, LESLIE. "The Origin of the New World Monkeys." In W. George and R. Lavocat, eds., *The Africa-South America Connection.* Oxford: Clarendon Press, 1993, pp. 100–18.

AIELLO, LESLIE, AND CHRISTOPHER DEAN. *An Introduction to Human Evolutionary Anatomy.* London: Academic Press, 1990, pp. 268–74.

AITKEN, M. J. *Thermoluminescence Dating.* London: Academic Press, 1985.

ALBERTS, BRUCE, DENNIS BRAY, JULIAN LEWIS, MARTIN RAFF, KEITH ROBERTS, AND JAMES D. WATSON. *Molecular Biology of the Cell.* New York: Garland, 1983.

ALEXANDER, JOHN P. "Alas, Poor Notharctus." *Natural History,* August 1992, 55–59.

ALGAZE, GUILLERMO. *The Uruk World System: The Dynamics of Expansion of Early Mesopotamian Civilization.* Chicago: University of Chicago Press, 1993.

ALLEN, JOHN S., AND SUSAN M. CHEER. "The Non-Thrifty Genotype." *Current Anthropology,* 37 (1996): 831–42.

ALLEN, JOHN S., A. J. LAMBERT, F. Y. ATTAH JOHNSON, K. SCHMIDT, AND K. L. NERO. "Antisaccadic Eye Movements and Attentional Asymmetry in Schizophrenia in Three Pacific Populations." *Acta Psychiatrica Scandinavia,* 94 (1996): 258–65.

ANDREWS, PETER. "*Proconsul.*" In Tattersall, Delson, and van Couvering, eds., *Encyclopedia of Human Evolution and Prehistory.*

ANDREWS, PETER. "Propliopithecidae." In Tattersall, Delson, and van Couvering, eds., *Encyclopedia of Human Evolution and Prehistory.*

ANDREWS, PETER, AND CHRISTOPHER STRINGER. *Human Evolution: An Illustrated Guide.* London: British Museum, 1989.

ANYON, ROGER, AND T. J. FERGUSON. "Cultural Resources Management at the Pueblo of Zuni, New Mexico, USA." *Antiquity,* 69 (1995): 913–30.

"Appendix A: Report of the Committee on Ethics, Society for Applied Anthropology." In Fluehr-Lobban, ed., *Ethics and the Profession of Anthropology.*

"Appendix C: Statements on Ethics: Principles of Professional Responsibility, Adopted by the Council of the American Anthropological Association, May 1971." In Fluehr-Lobban, ed., *Ethics and the Profession of Anthropology.*

"Appendix F: Professional and Ethical Responsibilities, SfAA." In Fluehr-Lobban, ed., *Ethics and the Profession of Anthropology.*

"Appendix H: National Association of Practicing Anthropologists' Ethical Guidelines for Practitioners, 1988." In Fluehr-Lobban, ed., *Ethics and the Profession of Anthropology.*

"Appendix I: Revised Principles of Professional Responsibility, 1990." In Fluehr-Lobban, ed., *Ethics and the Profession of Anthropology.*

ASCH, NANCY B., AND DAVID L. ASCH. "The Economic Potential of *Iva annua* and Its Prehistoric Importance in the Lower Illinois Valley." In Ford, ed., *The Nature and Status of Ethnobotany.*

ASCHER, ROBERT. "Analogy in Archaeological Interpretation." *Southwestern Journal of Anthropology,* 17 (1961): 317–25.

ASFAW, BERHANE, TIM WHITE, OWEN LOVEJOY, BRUCE LATIMER, SCOTT SIMPSON, AND GLEN SUWA. "*Australopithecus garhi:* A New Species of Early Hominid from Ethiopia." *Science,* 284 (1999): 629–36.

"Association Business: Clyde Snow, Forensic Anthropologist, Works for Justice." *Anthropology News,* October 2000, 12.

AUSTIN, LEWIS. "Visual Symbols, Political Ideology, and Culture." *Ethos,* 5 (1977): 306–25.

AYALA, FRANCISCO J. Communication in *Science,* November 29, 1996, 1354.

AYALA, FRANCISCO J. "The Myth of Eve: Molecular Biology and Human Origins." *Science,* December 22, 1995, 1930–936.

BAER, HANS A., MERRILL SINGER, AND IDA SUSSER. *Medical Anthropology and the World System: A Critical Perspective.* Westport, CT: Bergin & Garvey, 1997.

BAHN, P. *Archaeology: A Very Short Introduction.* New York: Oxford University Press, 1996.

BAHN, PAUL. "Neanderthals Emancipated." *Nature,* 394 (1998): 719–20.

BAHN, P., AND J. VERTUT. *Images of the Ice Age.* New York: Facts on File, 1988.

BAILEY, ROBERT C., GENEVIEVE HEAD, MARK JENIKE, BRUCE OWEN, ROBERT RECTMAN, AND ELZBIETA ZECHENTER. "Hunting and Gathering in Tropical Rain Forest: Is It Possible?" *American Anthropologist,* 91 (1989): 59–82.

BALTER, MICHAEL, AND ANN GIBBONS. "A Glimpse of Humans' First Journey Out of Africa." *Science,* 288 (2000): 948–50.

BARASH, DAVID P. *Sociobiology and Behavior.* New York: Elsevier, 1977.

BARRINGER, HERBERT, GEORGE BLANKSTEIN, AND RAYMOND MACK, EDS. *Social Change in Developing Areas: A Re-Interpretation of Evolutionary Theory.* Cambridge, MA: Schenkman, 1965.

BEADLE, GEORGE, AND MURIEL BEADLE. *The Language of Life.* Garden City, NY: Doubleday, 1966.

BEARDER, SIMON K. "Lorises, Bushbabies, and Tarsiers: Diverse Societies in Solitary Foragers." In Smuts et al., eds., *Primate Societies.*

BEGUN, DAVID. "Miocene Apes." In Peregrine, Ember, and Ember, eds., *Physical Anthropology.*

BERG, PAUL, AND MAXINE SINGER. *Dealing with Genes: The Language of Heredity.* Mill Valley, CA: University Science Books, 1992.

BERGGREN, WILLIAM A., DENNIS V. KENT, JOHN D. OBRADOVICH, AND CARL C. SWISHER III. "Toward a Revised Paleogene Geochronology." In Prothero and Berggren, eds., *Eocene-Oliocene Climatic and Biotic Evolution.*

Taken from: *Physical Anthropology and Archaeology*
by Carol R. Ember, Melvin Ember, and Peter N. Peregrine

BERLIN, BRENT. *Ethnobiological Classification: Principles of Categorization of Plants and Animals in Traditional Societies.* Princeton, NJ: Princeton University Press, 1992.

BERLIN, E. A. "General Overview of Maya Ethnomedicine." In Berlin and Berlin, *Medical Ethnobiology of the Highland Maya of Chiapas, Mexico,* pp. 52–53.

BERLIN, ELOIS ANN, AND BRENT BERLIN. *Medical Ethnobiology of the Highland Maya of Chiapas, Mexico: The Gastrointestinal Diseases.* Princeton, NJ: Princeton University Press, 1996.

BERRY, JOHN W., YPE H. POORTINGA, MARSHALL H. SEGALL, AND PIERRE R. DASEN. *Cross-Cultural Psychology: Research and Applications.* New York: Cambridge University Press, 1992.

BICKERTON, DEREK. "Creole Languages." *Scientific American,* July 1983, 116–22.

BILSBOROUGH, ALAN. *Human Evolution.* New York: Blackie Academic & Professional, 1992.

BINDON, JAMES R., AND DOUGLAS E. CREWS. "Changes in Some Health Status Characteristics of American Samoan Men: Preliminary Observations from a 12-Year Follow-up Study." *American Journal of Human Biology,* 5 (1993): 31–37.

BINDON, JAMES R., AMY KNIGHT, WILLIAM W. DRESSLER, AND DOUGLAS E. CREWS. "Social Context and Psychosocial Influences on Blood Pressure among American Samoans." *American Journal of Physical Anthropology,* 103 (1997): 7–18.

BINFORD, LEWIS R. *Faunal Remains from Klasies River Mouth.* Orlando, FL: Academic Press, 1984.

BINFORD, LEWIS R. *In Pursuit of the Past: Decoding the Archaeological Record,* New York: Thames and Hudson, 1983.

BINFORD, LEWIS R. "Interassemblage Variability: The Mousterian and the 'Functional' Argument." In Renfrew, ed., *The Explanation of Culture Change.*

BINFORD, LEWIS R. "Post-Pleistocene Adaptations." In Struever, ed., *Prehistoric Agriculture.*

BINFORD, LEWIS R. "Were There Elephant Hunters at Torralba?" In Nitecki and Nitecki, eds., *The Evolution of Human Hunting.*

BINFORD, LEWIS R., AND CHUAN KUN HO. "Taphonomy at a Distance: Zhoukoudian, 'The Cave Home of Beijing Man'?" *Current Anthropology,* 26 (1985): 413–42.

BINFORD, SALLY R., AND LEWIS R. BINFORD. "Stone Tools and Human Behavior." *Scientific American,* April 1969, 70–84.

BISHOP, W. A., AND J. A. MILLER, EDS. *Calibration of Hominid Evolution.* Toronto: University of Toronto Press, 1972.

BLACK, FRANCIS L. "Why Did They Die?" *Science,* December 11, 1992, 1739–40.

BLANTON, RICHARD. *Monte Albán: Settlement Patterns at the Ancient Zapotec Capital.* New York: Academic Press, 1978.

BLANTON, RICHARD. "The Origins of Monte Albán." In Cleland, ed., *Cultural Continuity and Change.*

BLANTON, RICHARD E. "The Rise of Cities." In Sabloff, ed., *Supplement to the Handbook of Middle American Indians,* Vol. 1.

BLANTON, RICHARD E., STEPHEN A. KOWALEWSKI, GARY FEINMAN, AND JILL APPEL. *Ancient Mesoamerica: A Comparison of Change in Three Regions.* New York: Cambridge University Press, 1981.

BLANTON, RICHARD E., STEPHEN A. KOWALEWSKI, GARY M. FEINMAN, AND LAURA M. FINSTEN. *Ancient Mesoamerica: A Comparison of Change in Three Regions.* 2nd ed. Cambridge: Cambridge University Press, 1993.

BLOUNT, BEN G. "The Development of Language in Children." In Munroe, Munroe, and Whiting, eds., *Handbook of Cross-Cultural Human Development.*

BLUMLER, MARK A., AND ROGER BYRNE. "The Ecological Genetics of Domestication and the Origins of Agriculture." *Current Anthropology,* 32 (1991): 23–35.

BOAS, FRANZ. "On Grammatical Categories." In Hymes, ed., *Language in Culture and Society.* (Originally published 1911.)

BOAS, FRANZ. *The Religion of the Kwakiutl.* Columbia University Contributions to Anthropology, Vol. 10, pt. 2. New York: Columbia University, 1930.

BOAZ, N. T., AND A. J. ALMQUIST, *Biological Anthropology: A Synthetic Approach to Human Evolution.* Upper Saddle River, NJ: Prentice Hall, 1997.

BOAZ, NOEL T., AND ALAN J. ALMQUIST. *Essentials of Biological Anthropology.* Upper Saddle River, NJ: Prentice Hall, 1999.

BOGIN, BARRY. *Patterns of Human Growth.* Cambridge: Cambridge University Press, 1988.

BOLTON, RALPH. "AIDS and Promiscuity: Muddled in the Models of HIV Prevention." *Medical Anthropology,* 14 (1992): 145–223.

BOLTON, RALPH. "Introduction: The AIDS Pandemic, a Global Emergency." *Medical Anthropology,* 10 (1989): 93–104.

BORCHERT, CATHERINE, AND ADRIENNE ZIHLMAN. "The Ontogeny and Phylogeny of Symbolizing." In M. LeC. Foster and L. J. Botsharow. *The Life of Symbols.* Boulder, CO: Westview, 1990, pp. 15–44.

BORDAZ, JACQUES. *Tools of the Old and New Stone Age.* Garden City, NY: Natural History Press, 1970.

BORDES, FRANÇOIS. "Mousterian Cultures in France." *Science,* September 22, 1961, 803–10.

BORDES, FRANÇOIS. *The Old Stone Age.* New York: McGraw-Hill, 1968, pp. 51–97.

BOYD, ROBERT, AND PETER J. RICHERSON. *Culture and the Evolutionary Process.* Chicago: University of Chicago Press, 1985.

BOYD, ROBERT, AND JOAN SILK. *How Humans Evolved.* 2nd ed. New York: Norton, 2000, pp. 249–50.

BRACE, C. LORING. "A Four-Letter Word Called Race." In Larry T. Reynolds and Leonard Leiberman, eds., *Race and Other Misadventures: Essays in Honor of Ashley Montague in His Ninetieth Year.* New York: General Hall, 1996.

BRACE, C. LORING, DAVID P. TRACER, LUCIA ALLEN YAROCH, JOHN ROBB, KARI BRANDT, AND A. RUSSELL NELSON. "Clines and Clusters versus 'Race': A Test in Ancient Egypt and the Case of a Death on the Nile." *Yearbook of Physical Anthropology,* 36 (1993): 1–31.

BRAIDWOOD, ROBERT J. "The Agricultural Revolution." *Scientific American,* September 1960, 130–48.

BRAIDWOOD, ROBERT J., AND GORDON R. WILLEY. "Conclusions and Afterthoughts." In Braidwood and Willey, eds., *Courses toward Urban Life.*

BRAIDWOOD, ROBERT J., AND GORDON R. WILLEY, EDS. *Courses toward Urban Life: Archaeological Considerations of Some Cultural Alternatives.* Viking Fund Publications in Anthropology No. 32. Chicago: Aldine, 1962.

BRAIN, C. K., AND A. SILLEN. "Evidence from the Swartkrans Cave for the Earliest Use of Fire." *Nature,* December 1, 1988, 464–66.

BRANDA, RICHARD F., AND JOHN W. EATON. "Skin Color and Nutrient Photolysis: An Evolutionary Hypothesis." *Science,* August 18, 1978, 625–26.

BRANDON, ROBERT N. *Adaptation and Environment.* Princeton, NJ: Princeton University Press, 1990.

BRÄUER, GÜNTER. "A Craniological Approach to the Origin of Anatomically Modern *Homo sapiens* in Africa and Implica-

142

tions for the Appearance of Modern Europeans." In F. Smith and Spencer, eds., *The Origins of Modern Humans.*

BRODEY, JANE E. "Effects of Milk on Blacks Noted." *New York Times,* October 15, 1971, p. 15.

BROMAGE, TIMOTHY G. "Paleoanthropology and Life History, and Life History of a Paleoanthropologist." In C. R. Ember, Ember, and Peregrine, eds., *Research Frontiers in Anthropology,* Vol. 1; reprinted in *Physical Anthropology.*

BROMAGE, TIMOTHY G., AND M. CHRISTOPHER DEAN. "Re-evaluation of the Age at Death of Immature Fossil Hominids." *Nature,* October 10, 1985, 525–27.

BROOKS, ALISON S., FATIMAH LINDA COLLIER JACKSON, AND R. RICHARD GRINKER. "Race and Ethnicity in America." *Anthro Notes* (National Museum of Natural History Bulletin for Teachers), 15, no. 3 (Fall 1993): 1–3, 11–15.

BROOM, ROBERT. *Finding the Missing Link.* London: Watts, 1950.

BROTHWELL, DON, AND ERIC HIGGS, EDS. *Science in Archaeology.* New York: Basic Books, 1963.

BROWN, FRANK H. "Geochronometry." In Tattersall, Delson, and van Couvering, eds., *Encyclopedia of Human Evolution and Prehistory.*

BROWN, FRANK H. "Methods of Dating." In Jones, Martin, and Pilbeam, eds., *The Cambridge Encyclopedia of Human Evolution.*

BROWN, JAMES A. "Long-Term Trends to Sedentism and the Emergence of Complexity in the American Midwest." In Price and Brown, eds., pp. 201–31.

BROWN, JAMES A. "Summary." In J. L. Phillips and J. A. Brown, eds., *Archaic Hunters and Gatherers in the American Midwest.* New York: Academic Press, 1983, pp. 5–10.

BROWN, JAMES A., AND T. DOUGLAS PRICE. "Complex Hunter-Gatherers: Retrospect and Prospect." In Price and Brown, *Prehistoric Hunter-Gatherers.*

BROWN, PETER J. "Culture and the Evolution of Obesity." In Podolefsky and Brown, eds., *Applying Cultural Anthropology.*

BROWN, ROGER. "The First Sentence of Child and Chimpanzee." In Sebeok and Umiker-Sebeok, eds., *Speaking of Apes.*

BROWNER, C. H. "Criteria for Selecting Herbal Remedies." *Ethnology,* 24 (1985): 13–32.

BRUMFIEL, ELIZABETH. "Aztec State Making: Ecology, Structure, and the Origin of the State." *American Anthropologist,* 85 (1983): 261–84.

BRUMFIEL, ELIZABETH M. "Distinguished Lecture in Archeology: Breaking and Entering the Ecosystem—Gender, Class, and Faction Steal the Show." *American Anthropologist,* 94 (1992): 551–67.

BRUMFIEL, ELIZABETH M., ED. *The Economic Anthropology of the State.* Lanham, MD: University Press of America, 1994.

BRUMFIEL, ELIZABETH M. "Origins of Social Inequality." In C. R. Ember, Ember, and Peregrine, *Research Frontiers in Anthropology,* vol. 1, reprinted in Peregrine, Ember, and Ember, eds., *Archaeology.*

BRUMFIEL, ELIZABETH M. "Regional Growth in the Eastern Valley of Mexico: A Test of the 'Population Pressure' Hypothesis." In Flannery, ed., *The Early Mesoamerican Village.*

BRYANT, CAROL A., AND DORAINE F. C. BAILEY. "The Use of Focus Group Research in Program Development." In van Willigen and Finan, eds., *Soundings.*

BRYNE, RICHARD, AND ANDREW WHITEN, EDS. *Machiavellian Intelligence: Social Expertise and the Evolution of Intellect in Monkeys, Apes, and Humans.* Oxford: Clarendon Press, 1988.

BUDIANSKY, STEPHEN. *The Covenant of the Wild: Why Animals Chose Domestication.* New York: Morrow, 1992.

BUETTNER-JANUSCH, JOHN. *Physical Anthropology: A Perspective.* New York: Wiley, 1973.

BURENHULT, G., ED. *Old World Civilizations: The Rise of Cities and States.* St. Lucia, Queensland, Australia: University of Queensland Press, 1994.

BUTZER, KARL W. "Geomorphology and Sediment Stratigraphy." In Singer and Wymer, *The Middle Stone Age at Klasies River Mouth in South Africa.*

BYRNE, ROGER. "Climatic Change and the Origins of Agriculture." In Manzanilla, ed., *Studies in the Neolithic and Urban Revolutions.*

CALVIN, WILLIAM H. *The Throwing Madonna: Essays on the Brain.* New York: McGraw-Hill, 1983.

CAMPBELL, ALLAN M. "Microbes: The Laboratory and the Field." In Davis, ed., *The Genetic Revolution.*

CAMPBELL, BERNARD G. *Humankind Emerging.* 4th ed. Boston: Little, Brown, 1985.

CAMPBELL, DONALD T. "Variation and Selective Retention in Socio-Cultural Evolution." In Barringer, Blankstein, and Mack, eds., *Social Change in Developing Areas.*

CAMPBELL, JOSEPH. *The Hero with a Thousand Faces.* New York: Pantheon, 1949.

CANN, REBECCA. "DNA and Human Origins." *Annual Review of Anthropology,* 17 (1988): 127–43.

CANN, REBECCA, M. STONEKING, AND A. C. WILSON. "Mitochondrial DNA and Human Evolution." *Nature,* 325 (1987): 31–36.

CARNEIRO, ROBERT L. "The Circumscription Theory: Challenge and Response." *American Behavioral Scientist,* 31 (1988): 497–511.

CARNEIRO, ROBERT L. "A Theory of the Origin of the State." *Science,* August 21, 1970, 733–38.

CARPENTER, C. R. "A Field Study in Siam of the Behavior and Social Relations of the Gibbon (*Hylobates lar*)." *Comparative Psychology Monographs,* 16, no. 5 (1940): 1–212.

CARTMILL, MATT. "Explaining Primate Origins." In Peregrine, Ember, and Ember, eds., *Physical Anthropology.*

CARTMILL, MATT. "New Views on Primate Origins." *Evolutionary Anthropology,* 1 (1992): 105–11.

CARTMILL, MATT. "Non-Human Primates." In Jones, Martin, and Pilbeam, eds., *The Cambridge Encyclopedia of Human Evolution.*

CHAMBERS, ERVE. *Applied Anthropology: A Practical Guide.* Rev. ed. Prospect Heights, IL: Waveland, 1989.

CHANG, KWANG-CHIH. *The Archaeology of Ancient China.* New Haven, CT: Yale University Press, 1968.

CHANG, KWANG-CHIH. *Archaeology of Ancient China.* 4th ed. New Haven, CT: Yale University Press, 1986 pp. 234–94.

CHANG, KWANG-CHIH. "The Beginnings of Agriculture in the Far East." *Antiquity,* 44, no. 175 (September 1970): 175–85.

CHANG, K. C. "In Search of China's Beginnings: New Light on an Old Civilization." *American Scientist,* 69 (1981): 148–60.

CHAPMAN, JEFFERSON. *Tellico Archaeology.* Knoxville: Tennessee Valley Authority, 1985.

CHARD, CHESTER S. *Man in Prehistory.* New York: McGraw-Hill, 1969.

CHARLES-DOMINIQUE, PIERRE. *Ecology and Behaviour of Nocturnal Primates.* Trans. R. D. Martin. New York: Columbia University Press, 1977.

CHARNAIS, PETER. "Economic Factors in the Decline of the Roman Empire." *Journal of Economic History,* 13 (1953): 412–24.

CHENEY, DOROTHY, AND ROBERT SEYFARTH. *How Monkeys See the World.* Chicago: University of Chicago Press, 1990.

CHENEY, DOROTHY L., AND RICHARD W. WRANGHAM. "Predation." In Smuts et al., eds., *Primate Societies.*

CHIA, L., *The Story of Peking Man: From Archaeology to Mystery.* Oxford: Oxford University Press, 1990.

CHILDE, V. GORDON. "The Urban Revolution." *Town Planning Review,* 21 (1950): 3–17.

CHIVERS, DAVID JOHN. *The Siamang in Malaya.* Basel, Switzerland: Karger, 1974.

CHIVERS, DAVID J., ED. *Malayan Forest Primates: Ten Years' Study in Tropical Rain Forest.* New York: Plenum, 1980.

CHIVERS, DAVID J., BERNARD A. WOOD, AND ALAN BILSBOROUGH, EDS. *Food Acquisition and Processing in Primates.* New York: Plenum, 1984.

CHOMSKY, NOAM. *Reflections on Language.* New York: Pantheon, 1975.

CIOCHON, RUSSELL L., AND ROBERT S. CORRUCCINI, EDS. *New Interpretations of Ape and Human Ancestry.* New York: Plenum, 1983.

CIOCHON, RUSSELL L., AND DENNIS A. ETLER. "Reinterpreting Past Primate Diversity." In Corruccini and Ciochon, eds., *Integrative Paths to the Past.*

CIOCHON, RUSSELL L., AND JOHN G. FLEAGLE, EDS. *The Human Evolution Source Book.* Englewood Cliffs, NJ: Prentice Hall, 1993.

CIOCHON, RUSSELL, JOHN OLSEN, AND JAMIE JAMES. *Other Origins: The Search for the Giant Ape in Human Prehistory.* New York: Bantam, 1990.

CLAASSEN, CHERYL. "Gender and Archaeology." In Peregrine, Ember, and Ember, eds., *Archaeology.*

CLAASEN, CHERYL. "Gender, Shellfishing, and the Shell Mound Archaic." In Gero and Conkey, eds., *Engendering Archaeology.*

CLARK, GEOFFREY A., ED. *Perspectives on the Past: Theoretical Biases in Mediterranean Hunter-Gatherer Research.* Philadelphia: University of Pennsylvania Press, 1991.

CLARK, GRAHAME. *The Earlier Stone Age Settlement of Scandinavia.* Cambridge: Cambridge University Press, 1975.

CLARK, GRAHAME, AND STUART PIGGOTT. *Prehistoric Societies.* New York: Knopf, 1965.

CLARK, J. DESMOND. "Interpretations of Prehistoric Technology from Ancient Egyptian and Other Sources. Pt. II: Prehistoric Arrow Forms in Africa as Shown by Surviving Examples of the Traditional Arrows of the San Bushmen." *Paleorient,* 3 (1977): 127–50.

CLARK, J. DESMOND. *The Prehistory of Africa.* New York: Praeger, 1970.

CLARK, W. E. LEGROS. *The Fossil Evidence for Human Evolution.* Chicago: University of Chicago Press, 1964, p. 184.

CLARKE, RONALD J., AND P. V. TOBIAS. "Sterkfontein Member 2 Foot Bones of the Oldest South African Hominid." *Science,* 269 (1995): 521–24.

CLAYMAN, CHARLES B., ED. *American Medical Association Encyclopedia of Medicine.* New York: Random House, 1989, pp. 857–58.

CLELAND, C., ED. *Cultural Continuity and Change.* New York: Academic Press, 1976.

CLUTTON-BROCK, JULIET. "Dog." In Mason, *Evolution of Domesticated Animals.*

CLUTTON-BROCK, JULIET. "Domestication of Animals." In Jones, Martin, and Pilbeam, eds., *The Cambridge Encyclopedia of Human Evolution.*

CLUTTON-BROCK, JULIET. "Origins of the Dog: Domestication and Early History." In James Serpell, ed., *The Domestic Dog: Its Evolution, Behaviour, and Interactions with People.* Cambridge: Cambridge University Press, 1995, pp. 8–20.

CLUTTON-BROCK, T. H., AND PAUL H. HARVEY. "Primate Ecology and Social Organization." *Journal of Zoology, London,* 183 (1977): 1–39.

CLUTTON-BROCK, T. H., AND PAUL H. HARVEY. "Primates, Brains and Ecology." *Journal of Zoology, London,* 190 (1980): 309–23.

COALE, ANSLEY J. "The History of the Human Population." *Scientific American,* 1974.

COE, MICHAEL D. *The Maya.* New York: Praeger, 1966.

COHEN, ALEX. *The Mental Health of Indigenous Peoples: An International Overview.* Geneva: Department of Mental Health, World Health Organization, 1999.

COHEN, MARK N. *The Food Crisis in Prehistory: Overpopulation and the Origins of Agriculture.* New Haven, CT: Yale University Press, 1977.

COHEN, MARK NATHAN. *Health and the Rise of Civilization.* New Haven, CT: Yale University Press, 1989.

COHEN, MARK N. "Population Pressure and the Origins of Agriculture." In Reed, ed., *Origins of Agriculture.*

COHEN, MARK N. "The Significance of Long-Term Changes in Human Diet and Food Economy." In Harris and Ross, eds., *Food and Evolution.*

COHEN, MARK N. "Were Early Agriculturalists Less Healthy Than Food Collectors?" In Peregrine, Ember, and Ember, eds., *Archaeology.*

COHEN, MARK NATHAN, AND GEORGE J. ARMELAGOS. "Paleopathology at the Origins of Agriculture: Editors' Summation." In M. N. Cohen and Armelagos, eds., *Paleopathology at the Origins of Agriculture.*

COHEN, MARK NATHAN, AND GEORGE J. ARMELAGOS, EDS. *Paleopathology at the Origins of Agriculture.* Orlando, FL: Academic Press, 1984.

COHEN, RONALD, AND ELMAN R. SERVICE, EDS. *Origins of the State: The Anthropology of Political Evolution.* Philadelphia: Institute for the Study of Human Issues, 1978.

COHMAP PERSONNEL. "Climatic Changes of the Last 18,000 Years." *Science,* 241 (1988): 1043–52.

COLLIER, STEPHEN, AND J. PETER WHITE. "Get Them Young? Age and Sex Inferences on Animal Domestication in Archaeology." *American Antiquity,* 41 (1976): 96–102.

COLLINS, DESMOND. "Later Hunters in Europe." In Collins, ed., *The Origins of Europe.*

CONNAH, GRAHAM. *African Civilizations: Precolonial Cities and States in Tropical Africa, an Archaeological Perspective.* Cambridge: Cambridge University Press, 1987.

CONROY, GLENN C. *Primate Evolution.* New York: Norton, 1990.

COREIL, JEANNINE. "Lessons from a Community Study of Oral Rehydration Therapy in Haiti." In van Willigen, Rylko-Bauer, and McElroy, eds., *Making Our Research Useful.*

CORRUCCINI, ROBERT S., AND RUSSELL L. CIOCHON, EDS. *Integrative Paths to the Past: Paleoanthropological Advances in Honor of F. Clark Howell.* Englewood Cliffs, NJ: Prentice Hall, 1994.

COSTIN, CATHY LYNNE. "Cloth Production and Gender Relations in the Inka Empire." In Peregrine, Ember, and Ember, eds., *Archaeology.*

COWAN, C. WESLEY, AND PATTY JO WATSON, EDS. *The Origins of Agriculture.* Washington, DC: Smithsonian Institution Press, 1992.

CRAWFORD, GARY W. "Prehistoric Plant Domestication in East Asia." In Cowan and Watson, eds., *The Origins of Agriculture.*

CRAWFORD, R. D. "Turkey." In Mason, ed., *Evolution of Domesticated Animals.*

CROCKETT, CAROLYN, AND JOHN F. EISENBERG. "Howlers: Variations in Group Size and Demography." In Smuts et al., eds., *Primate Societies.*

CULOTTA, ELIZABETH. "New Hominid Crowds the Field." *Science,* August 18, 1995.

CURTIN, PHILIP D. *Cross-Cultural Trade in World History.* Cambridge: Cambridge University Press, 1984.

DAMON, ALBERT, ED. *Physiological Anthropology.* New York: Oxford University Press, 1975.

DANIEL, I. RANDOLPH. "Early Eastern Archaic." In P. N. Peregrine and M. Ember, eds., *Encyclopedia of Prehistory.* Vol. 6: North America (Kluwer Academic/Plenum, 2001).

DART, RAYMOND. "*Australopithecus africanus:* The Man-Ape of South Africa." *Nature,* 115 (1925): 195.

DARWIN, CHARLES. "The Origin of Species." (Originally published 1859.) In Young, ed., *Evolution of Man.*

DAVIS, BERNARD D. "The Issues: Prospects versus Perceptions." In Davis, ed., *The Genetic Revolution.*

DAVIS, BERNARD D. "Summary and Comments: The Scientific Chapters." In Davis, ed., *The Genetic Revolution.*

DAVIS, BERNARD D., ED. *The Genetic Revolution: Scientific Prospects and Public Perceptions.* Baltimore: Johns Hopkins University Press, 1991.

DAWSON, ALISTAR. *Ice Age Earth.* London: Routledge, 1992, pp. 24–71.

DAY, MICHAEL. *Guide to Fossil Man.* 4th ed. Chicago: University of Chicago Press, 1986.

DEACON, TERRENCE. "Primate Brains and Senses." In Jones, Martin, and Pilbeam, eds., *The Cambridge Encyclopedia of Human Evolution.*

DEACON, TERRENCE. *The Symbolic Species: The Co-Evolution of Language and the Brain.* New York: Norton, 1997.

DELSON, ERIC, ED. *Ancestors: The Hard Evidence.* New York: Alan R. Liss, 1985.

DE LUMLEY, HENRY. "A Paleolithic Camp at Nice." *Scientific American,* May 1969, 42–50.

DEVILLERS, CHARLES, AND JEAN CHALINE. *Evolution: An Evolving Theory.* New York: Springer Verlag, 1993.

DE VILLIERS, PETER A., AND JILL G. DE VILLIERS. *Early Language.* Cambridge, MA: Harvard University Press, 1979.

DE WAAL, FRANS, AND FRANS LANTING. *Bonobo: The Forgotten Ape.* Berkeley: University of California Press, 1997.

DIAMOND, JARED. "The Accidental Conqueror." *Discover,* December 1989, 71–76.

DIAMOND, JARED. *Guns, Germs, and Steel.* New York: Norton, 1997, pp. 205–207.

DIAMOND, JARED. "Location, Location, Location: The First Farmers." *Science,* November 14, 1997, 1243–244.

DIAMOND, JARED. "Who Are the Jews?" *Natural History,* November 1993, 12–19.

DIAMOND, STANLEY. *In Search of the Primitive: A Critique of Civilization.* New Brunswick, NJ: Transaction Books, 1974.

DIBBLE, HAROLD, P. CHASE, S. MCPHERRON, AND A. TUFREAU. "Testing the Reality of a 'Living Floor' with Archaeological Data." *American Antiquity,* 62 (1997): 629–51.

DIBBLE, H. L., AND P. MELLARS, EDS. *The Middle Paleolithic: Adaptation, Behavior, and Variability.* Philadelphia: University Museum, 1992.

DICKSON, D. BRUCE. *The Dawn of Belief.* Tucson: University of Arizona Press, 1990, pp. 42–44.

DILLEHAY, THOMAS. *The Settlement of the Americas.* New York: Basic Books, 2000.

DIRKS, ROBERT. "Starvation and Famine." *Cross-Cultural Research,* 27 (1993): 28–69.

DIVALE, WILLIAM, AND CLIFFORD ZIPIN. "Hunting and the Development of Sign Language: A Cross-Cultural Test." *Journal of Anthropological Research,* 33 (1977): 185–201.

DOBRES, MARCIA-ANNE. "Venus Figurines." In B. Fagan, ed., *Oxford Companion to Archaeology.* Oxford: Oxford University Press, 1998, pp. 740–41.

DOBZHANSKY, THEODOSIUS. *Mankind Evolving: The Evolution of the Human Species.* New Haven, CT: Yale University Press, 1962.

DOHLINOW, PHYLLIS JAY, AND NAOMI BISHOP. "The Development of Motor Skills and Social Relationships among Primates through Play." In Phyllis Jay Dohlinow, ed., *Primate Patterns.* New York: Holt, Rinehart & Winston, 1972.

DOW, JAMES. *The Shaman's Touch: Otomi Indian Symbolic Healing.* Salt Lake City: University of Utah Press, 1986.

DOYLE, G. A., AND R. D. MARTIN, EDS. *The Study of Prosimian Behavior.* New York: Academic Press, 1979.

DRESSLER, WILLIAM W. *Stress and Adaptation in the Context of Culture.* Albany: State University of New York Press, 1991.

DUARTE, CIDALIA, J. MAURICIO, P. B. PETTITT, P. SOUTO, E. TRINKAUS, H. VAN DER PLICHT, AND J. ZILHAO, "The Early Upper Paleolithic Human Skeleton from the Abrigo do Lagar Velho (Portugal) and Modern Human Emergence in Iberia." *Proceedings of the National Academy of Sciences of the United States,* 96 (1999): 7604–609.

DUHARD, JEAN-PIERRE. "Upper Paleolithic Figures as a Reflection of Human Morphology and Social Organization." *Antiquity,* 67 (1993): 83–91.

DUNBAR, ROBIN. *Primate Social Systems.* Ithaca, NY: Comstock, 1988, pp. 107–10.

DURHAM, WILLIAM H. *Coevolution: Genes, Culture and Human Diversity.* Stanford, CA: Stanford University Press, 1991.

EDDY, ELIZABETH M., AND WILLIAM L. PARTRIDGE, EDS. *Applied Anthropology in America.* New York: Columbia University Press, 1978.

EDDY, ELIZABETH M., AND WILLIAM L. PARTRIDGE, EDS. *Applied Anthropology in America.* 2nd ed. New York: Columbia University Press, 1987.

EDGERTON, ROBERT B. "Conceptions of Psychosis in Four East African Societies." *American Anthropologist,* 68 (1966): 408–25.

EDGERTON, ROBERT B. *Sick Societies: Challenging the Myth of Primitive Harmony.* New York: Free Press, 1992.

EISELEY, LOREN C. "The Dawn of Evolutionary Theory." In Loren C. Eiseley, *Darwin's Century: Evolution and the Men Who Discovered It.* Garden City, NY: Doubleday, 1958.

EISENBERG, JOHN F. "Comparative Ecology and Reproduction of New World Monkeys." In Devra Kleinman, ed., *The Biology and Conservation of the Callitrichidae.* Washington, DC: Smithsonian Institution, 1977.

ELDREDGE, NILES, AND IAN TATTERSALL. *The Myths of Human Evolution.* New York: Columbia University Press, 1982.

ELIOT, T. S. "The Love Song of J. Alfred Prufrock." In *Collected Poems, 1909–1962.* New York: Harcourt, Brace & World, 1963.

ELLISON, PETER T. "Natural Variation in Human Fecundity." In Peregrine, Ember, and Ember, eds., *Physical Anthropology.*

EMBER, CAROL R. "The Relative Decline in Women's Contribution to Agriculture with Intensification." *American Anthropologist,* 85 (1983): 285–304.

EMBER, CAROL R., AND MELVIN EMBER. "Resource Unpredictability, Mistrust, and War: A Cross-Cultural Study." *Journal of Conflict Resolution,* 36 (1992): 242–62.

EMBER, CAROL R., MELVIN EMBER, AND PETER N. PEREGRINE, EDS. *Research Frontiers in Anthropology.* Upper Saddle River, NJ: Prentice Hall, 1998. Prentice Hall/Simon & Schuster Custom Publishing. Three volumes.

EMBER, MELVIN, AND CAROL R. EMBER. "Male-Female Bonding: A Cross-Species Study of Mammals and Birds." *Behavior Science Research,* 14 (1979): 37–56.

EMBER, MELVIN, CAROL R. EMBER, AND DAVID LEVINSON, EDS. *Portraits of Culture: Ethnographic Originals.* Upper Saddle River, NJ: Prentice Hall, 1998. Prentice Hall/Simon & Schuster Custom Publishing.

EMENER, WILLIAM G., AND MARGARET DARROW, EDS. *Career Explorations in Human Services.* Springfield, IL: Charles C. Thomas, 1991.

ETIENNE, ROBERT. *Pompeii: The Day a City Died.* New York: Abrams, 1992.

ETKIN, NINA L., AND PAUL J. ROSS. "Malaria, Medicine, and Meals: A Biobehavioral Perspective." In Romanucci-Ross, Moerman, and Tancredi, eds., *The Anthropology of Medicine,* pp. 169–209.

EVELETH, PHYLLIS B., AND JAMES M. TANNER. *Worldwide Variation in Human Growth.* 2nd ed. Cambridge: Cambridge University Press, 1990.

FAGAN, BRIAN M. *Ancient North America: The Archaeology of a Continent.* London: Thames and Hudson, 1991.

FAGAN, BRIAN M. *In the Beginning.* Boston: Little, Brown, 1972.

FAGAN, BRIAN M. *People of the Earth: An Introduction to World Prehistory.* 6th ed. Glenview, IL: Scott, Foresman, 1989.

FAGAN, B. M. *People of the Earth: An Introduction to World Prehistory.* 9th ed. New York: HarperCollins, 1997.

FALK, DEAN. *Brain Dance.* New York: Henry Holt, 1992.

FALK, DEAN. "Cerebral Cortices of East African Early Hominids." *Science,* 221 (1983): 1072–74.

FALK, D. "Enlarged Occipital/Marginal Sinuses and Emissary Foramina: Their Significance in Hominid Evolution." In Grine, ed., *Evolutionary History of the "Robust" Australopithecines.*

FALK, DEAN. "A Good Brain Is Hard to Cool." *Natural History,* 102 (August 1993): 65–66.

FALK, DEAN. "Hominid Paleoneurology." *Annual Review of Anthropology,* 16 (1987): 13–30.

FARMER, PAUL. "Ethnography, Social Analysis, and the Prevention of Sexually Transmitted HIV Infection among Poor Women in Haiti." In Inhorn and Brown, *The Anthropology of Infectious Disease,* pp. 413–38.

FEDER, K. *Past in Perspective.* Mountain View, CA: Mayfield, 1996.

FEDIGAN, LINDA MARIE. *Primate Paradigms: Sex Roles and Social Bonds.* Montreal: Eden Press, 1982.

FEIBEL, CRAIG S., AND FRANCIS H. BROWN. "Microstratigraphy and Paleoenvironments." In Walker and Leakey, eds., *The Nariokotome* Homo erectus *Skeleton.*

FEINMAN, GARY M., STEPHEN A. KOWALEWSKI, LAURA FINSTEN, RICHARD E. BLANTON, AND LINDA NICHOLAS. "Long-Term Demographic Change: A Perspective from the Valley of Oaxaca, Mexico." *Journal of Field Archaeology,* 12 (1985): 333–62.

FEINMAN, GARY M., AND J. MARCUS, EDS. *Archaic States.* Santa Fe, NM: School of American Research Press, 1998.

FELDMAN, DOUGLAS A., AND THOMAS M. JOHNSON. "Introduction." In Feldman and Johnson, eds., *The Social Dimensions of AIDS.*

FELDMAN, DOUGLAS A., AND THOMAS M. JOHNSON, EDS. *The Social Dimensions of AIDS: Method and Theory.* New York: Praeger, 1986.

FELDMAN, DOUGLAS A., AND J. W. MILLER. *The AIDS Crisis: A Documentary History.* Westport, CT: Greenwood Press, 1998.

FERGUSON, R. BRIAN, AND NEIL L. WHITEHEAD. "The Violent Edge of Empire." In R. B. Ferguson and N. Whitehead, eds., *War in the Tribal Zone.* Santa Fe: School of American Research Press, 1992, pp. 1–30.

FERRARO, GARY P. *The Cultural Dimension of International Business.* 4th ed. Englewood Cliffs, NJ: Prentice Hall, 2002.

"The First Dentist." *Newsweek,* March 5, 1973, 73.

"The First Tool Kit." *Science,* January 31, 1997, 623.

FISCHMAN, JOSHUA. "Putting Our Oldest Ancestors in Their Proper Place." *Science,* September 30, 1994, 2011–12.

FISH, PAUL R. "Beyond Tools: Middle Paleolithic Debitage Analysis and Cultural Inference." *Journal of Anthropological Research,* 37 (1981): 374–86.

FISHER, JULIE. "Grassroots Organizations and Grassroots Support Organizations: Patterns of Interaction." In Moran, *Transforming Societies.*

FISHER, WILLIAM H. "Megadevelopment, Environmentalism, and Resistance: The Institutional Context of Kayapo Indigenous Politics in Central Brazil." *Human Organization,* 53 (1994): 220–32.

FLANNERY, KENT V. "Adaptation, Evolution, and Archaeological Phases: Some Implications of Reynolds' Simulation." In Flannery, ed., *Guila Naquitz,* p. 502.

FLANNERY, KENT V. "The Cultural Evolution of Civilizations." *Annual Review of Ecology and Systematics,* 3 (1972): 399–426.

FLANNERY, KENT V. "The Ecology of Early Food Production in Mesopotamia." *Science,* March 12, 1965, 1247–56.

FLANNERY, KENT V. "Guila Naquitz in Spatial, Temporal, and Cultural Context." In Flannery, ed., *Guila Naquitz,* pp. 31–42.

FLANNERY, KENT V. "The Origins of Agriculture." *Annual Review of Anthropology,* 2 (1973): 271–310.

FLANNERY, KENT V. "The Origins and Ecological Effects of Early Domestication in Iran and the Near East." In Struever, ed., *Prehistoric Agriculture.*

FLANNERY, KENT V. "The Origins of the Village as a Settlement Type in Mesoamerica and the Near East: A Comparative Study." In Tringham, ed., *Territoriality and Proxemics.*

FLANNERY, KENT V. "The Research Problem." In Flannery, ed., *Guila Naquitz.*

FLANNERY, KENT V., ED. *The Early Mesoamerican Village.* New York: Academic Press, 1976.

FLANNERY, KENT V., ED. *Guila Naquitz: Archaic Foraging and Early Agriculture in Oaxaca, Mexico.* Orlando, FL: Academic Press, 1986.

FLEAGLE, JOHN G. "Anthropoid Origins." In Corruccini and Ciochon, eds., *Integrative Paths to the Past.*

FLEAGLE, JOHN G. *Primate Adaptation and Evolution.* San Diego: Academic Press, 1988.

FLEAGLE, JOHN G. *Primate Adaptation and Evolution.* 2nd ed. San Diego: Academic Press, 1999, pp. 404–409.

FLEAGLE, JOHN G., CHARLES H. JANSON, AND KAYE E. REED, EDS. *Primate Communities.* Cambridge: Cambridge University Press, 1999.

FLEAGLE, JOHN G., AND R. F. KAY, EDS. *Anthropoid Origins.* New York: Plenum, 1994.

FLEAGLE, JOHN G., AND RICHARD F. KAY. "New Interpretations of the Phyletic Position of Oligocene Hominoids." In Ciochon and Corruccini, eds., *New Interpretations of Ape and Human Ancestry.*

FLEAGLE, JOHN G., AND RICHARD F. KAY. "The Paleobiology of Catarrhines." In Delson, ed., *Ancestors.*

FLEAGLE, JOHN G., AND R. F. KAY. "The Phyletic Position of the Parapithecidae." *Journal of Human Evolution,* 16 (1987): 483–531.

FLEISCHER, ROBERT L., AND HOWARD R. HART, JR. "Fission-Track Dating: Techniques and Problems." In Bishop and Miller, eds., *Calibration of Hominid Evolution.*

FLEISCHER, ROBERT L., P. B. PRICE, R. M. WALKER, AND L. S. B. LEAKEY. "Fission-Track Dating of Bed I, Olduvai Gorge." *Science,* April 2, 1965, 72–74.

FLUEHR-LOBBAN, CAROLYN, ED. *Ethics and the Profession of Anthropology: Dialogue for a New Era.* Philadelphia: University of Pennsylvania Press, 1991.

FOLEY, W. A. *Anthropological Linguistics: An Introduction.* Malden, MA: Blackwell, 1997.

FORD, RICHARD I., ED. *The Nature and Status of Ethnobotany.* Anthropological Papers No. 67, Museum of Anthropology. Ann Arbor: University of Michigan, 1978.

FOSSEY, DIAN. *Gorillas in the Mist.* Boston: Houghton Mifflin, 1983.

FOSTER, GEORGE M. *Applied Anthropology.* Boston: Little, Brown, 1969.

FOSTER, GEORGE M. *Hippocrates' Latin American Legacy: Humoral Medicine in the New World.* Amsterdam: Gordon and Breach, 1994.

FOWLER, BRENDA. *Iceman: Uncovering the Life and Times of a Prehistoric Man Found in an Alpine Glacier.* New York: Random House, 2000.

FOWLER, MELVIN L. "A Pre-Columbian Urban Center on the Mississippi." *Scientific American,* August 1975, 92–101.

FRANCISCUS, ROBERT G., AND ERIK TRINKAUS. "Nasal Morphology and the Emergence of *Homo erectus.*" *American Journal of Physical Anthropology,* 75 (1988): 517–27.

FRANKEL, BARBARA, AND M. G. TREND. "Principles, Pressures and Paychecks: The Anthropologist as Employee." In Fluehr-Lobban, ed., *Ethics and the Profession of Anthropology.*

FRAYER, DAVID W. "Body Size, Weapon Use, and Natural Selection in the European Upper Paleolithic and Mesolithic." *American Anthropologist,* 83 (1981): 57–73.

FRAYER, DAVID W. "Testing Theories and Hypotheses about Human Origins." In Peregrine, Ember, and Ember, eds., *Physical Anthropology.*

FRAYER, DAVID, M. WOLPOFF, A. THORNE, F. SMITH, AND G. POPE. "Theories of Modern Human Origins: The Paleontological Test." *American Anthropologist,* 95 (1993): 24–27.

FREEMAN, LESLIE G. "Torralba and Ambrona: A Review of Discoveries." In Corruccini and Ciochon, eds., *Integrative Paths to the Past.*

FRIED, MORTON H., ED. *Readings in Anthropology.* 2nd ed., Vol. 1. New York: Thomas Y. Crowell, 1968.

FRIEDMAN, J., AND M. J. ROWLANDS, EDS. *The Evolution of Social Systems.* London: Duckworth, 1977.

FRIEDMAN, SAUL S. "Holocaust." In *Academic American* [now Grolier] *Encyclopedia.* Vol. 10. Princeton, NJ: Arete, 1980.

FRISANCHO, A. ROBERTO, AND LAWRENCE P. GREKSA. "Development Responses in the Acquisition of Functional Adaptation to High Altitude." In Little and Haas, eds., *Human Population Biology.*

FRISCH, JOHN. "Individual Behavior and Intergroup Variability in Japanese Macaques." In P. C. Jay, ed., *Primates: Studies in Adaptation and Variability.* New York: Holt, Rinehart & Winston, 1968, pp. 243–52.

FRISCH, ROSE E. "Fatness, Puberty, and Fertility." *Natural History,* October 1980, 16–27.

FRUNET, MICHEL, ALAIN BEAUVILAIN, YVES COPPENS, ELILE HEINTZ, ALADJI H. E. MOUTAYE, AND DAVID PILBEAM. "The First Australopithecine 2500 Kilometers West of the Rift Valley (Chad)." *Nature,* 378 (1995): 273–75.

FUTUYMA, DOUGLAS. *Science on Trial.* New York: Pantheon, 1982.

GABUNIA, LEO, A. VEKUA, D. LORDKIPANIDZE, ET AL. "Earliest Pleistocene Hominid Cranial Remains from Dmanisi, Republic of Georgia: Taxonomy, Geological Setting, and Age." *Science,* 288 (2000): 1019–25.

GALDIKAS, BIRUTÉ M. F. "Orangutan Adaptation at Tanjung Puting Reserve: Mating and Ecology." In Hamburg and McCown, eds., *The Great Apes.*

GARDNER, BEATRICE T., AND R. ALLEN GARDNER. "Two Comparative Psychologists Look at Language Acquisition." In Nelson, ed., *Children's Language,* Vol. 2.

GARDNER, R. ALLEN, AND BEATRICE T. GARDNER. "Teaching Sign Language to a Chimpanzee." *Science,* August 15, 1969, 664–72.

GARN, STANLEY M. *Human Races.* 3rd ed. Springfield, IL: Charles C. Thomas, 1971.

GENTNER, W., AND H. J. LIPPOLT. "The Potassium-Argon Dating of Upper Tertiary and Pleistocene Deposits." In Brothwell and Higgs, eds., *Science in Archaeology.*

GERO, JOAN M., AND MARGARET W. CONKEY, EDS. *Engendering Archaeology: An Introduction to Women and Prehistory.* Oxford: Blackwell, 1991.

GESLER, W. *The Cultural Geography of Health Care.* Pittsburgh: University of Pittsburgh Press, 1991.

GIBBON, G. *Anthropological Archaeology.* New York: Columbia University Press, 1984.

GIBBONS, ANN. "First Americans: Not Mammoth Hunters, but Forest Dwellers?" *Science,* April 19, 1995, 346–47.

GINGERICH, P. D. "*Pleisiadipis* and the Delineation of the Order Primates." In B. Wood, L. Martin, and P. Andrews, eds., *Major Topics in Primate Evolution.* Cambridge: Cambridge University Press, 1986, pp. 32–46.

GLADWIN, THOMAS, AND SEYMOUR B. SARASON. *Truk: Man in Paradise.* New York: Wenner-Gren Foundation for Anthropological Research, 1953, as seen in eHRAF Collection of Ethnography on the Web, 2000.

GLEITMAN, LILA R., AND ERIC WANNER. "Language Acquisition: The State of the State of the Art." In Wanner and Gleitman, eds., *Language Acquisition.*

GOLDEN, FREDERIC, MICHAEL LEMONICK, AND DICK THOMPSON. "The Race Is Over." *Time,* July 3, 2000, 18–23.

GOLDIZEN, ANNE WILSON. "Tamarins and Marmosets: Communal Care of Offspring." In Smuts et al., eds., *Primate Societies.*

GOODALL, JANE. "My Life among Wild Chimpanzees." *National Geographic,* August 1963, 272–308.

GOODALL, JANE. *Through a Window*. Boston: Houghton Mifflin, 1990.

GOODENOUGH, WARD H. *Cooperation in Change*. New York: Russell Sage Foundation, 1963.

GOODMAN, ALAN H., AND GEORGE J. ARMELAGOS. "Disease and Death at Dr. Dickson's Mounds." *Natural History*, September 1985, 12–19.

GOODMAN, ALAN H., JOHN LALLO, GEORGE J. ARMELAGOS, AND JEROME C. ROSE. "Health Changes at Dickson Mounds, Illinois (A.D. 950–1300)." In M. N. Cohen and Armelagos, eds., *Paleopathology at the Origins of Agriculture*.

GOODMAN, ALAN H., AND THOMAS L. LEATHERMAN, EDS. *Building a New Biocultural Synthesis: Political-Economic Perspectives on Human Biology*. Ann Arbor: University of Michigan Press, 1998.

GOODMAN, MORRIS. "Reconstructing Human Evolution from Proteins." In Jones, Martin, and Pilbeam, eds., *The Cambridge Encyclopedia of Human Evolution*.

GOODRICH, L. CARRINGTON. *A Short History of the Chinese People*. 3rd ed. New York: Harper & Row, 1959.

GORMAN, CHESTER. "The Hoabinhian and After: Subsistence Patterns in Southeast Asia during the Late Pleistocene and Early Recent Periods." *World Archaeology*, 2 (1970): 315–19.

GRANT, PETER R. "Natural Selection and Darwin's Finches." *Scientific American*, October 1991, 82–87.

GRAY, J. PATRICK. *Primate Sociobiology*. New Haven, CT: HRAF Press, 1985.

GRAY, J. PATRICK, AND LINDA D. WOLFE. "Height and Sexual Dimorphism of Stature among Human Societies." *American Journal of Physical Anthropology*, 53 (1980): 446–52.

GRAY, J. PATRICK, AND LINDA WOLFE. "What Accounts for Population Variation in Height?" In Peregrine, Ember, and Ember, eds., *Physical Anthropology*.

GRAYSON, DONALD K. "Explaining Pleistocene Extinctions: Thoughts on the Structure of a Debate." In P. S. Martin and Klein, eds., *Quaternary Extinctions*.

GRAYSON, DONALD K. "Pleistocene Avifaunas and the Overkill Hypothesis." *Science*, February 18, 1977, pp. 691–92.

GREENBERG, JOSEPH H., AND MERRITT RUHLEN. "Linguistic Origins of Native Americans." *Scientific American*, November 1992, 94–99.

GREENE, L., AND F. E. JOHNSTON, EDS. *Social and Biological Predictors of Nutritional Status, Physical Growth, and Neurological Development*. New York: Academic Press, 1980.

GREENFIELD, PATRICIA MARKS, AND E. SUE SAVAGE-RUMBAUGH. "Grammatical Combination in *Pan paniscus*: Processes of Learning and Invention in the Evolution and Development of Language." In Parker and Gibson, eds., *"Language" and Intelligence in Monkeys and Apes*.

GREKSA, LAWRENCE P., AND CYNTHIA M. BEALL. "Development of Chest Size and Lung Function at High Altitude." In Little and Haas, eds., *Human Population Biology*.

GRINE, FREDERICK E. "Australopithecine Taxonomy and Phylogeny: Historical Background and Recent Interpretation." In Ciochon and Fleagle, eds., *The Human Evolution Source Book*.

GRINE, FREDERICK E. "Dental Evidence for Dietary Differences in *Australopithecus* and *Paranthropus*: A Quantitative Analysis of Permanent Molar Microwear." *Journal of Human Evolution*, 15 (1986): 783–822.

GRINE, FREDERICK E. "Evolutionary History of the 'Robust' Australopithecines: A Summary and Historical Perspective." In Grine, ed., *Evolutionary History of the "Robust" Australopithecines*.

GRINE, FREDERICK E., ED. *Evolutionary History of the "Robust" Australopithecines*. New York: Aldine, 1988.

GROSS, DANIEL R., AND BARBARA A. UNDERWOOD. "Technological Change and Caloric Costs: Sisal Agriculture in Northeastern Brazil." *American Anthropologist*, 73 (1971): 725–40.

GRUBB, HENRY J. "Intelligence at the Low End of the Curve: Where Are the Racial Differences?" *Journal of Black Psychology*, 14 (1987): 25–34.

GRUBB, HENRY J., AND ANDREA G. BARTHWELL. "Superior Intelligence and Racial Equivalence: A Look at Mensa." Paper presented at the 1996 annual meeting of the Society for Cross-Cultural Research.

GUNDERS, S., AND J. W. M. WHITING. "Mother-Infant Separation and Physical Growth." *Ethnology*, 7 (1968): 196–206.

GUTHRIE, DALE R. "Mosaics, Allelochemics, and Nutrients: An Ecological Theory of Late Pleistocene Megafaunal Extinctions." In P. S. Martin and Klein, eds., *Quaternary Extinctions*.

HABICHT, J.K.A., *Paleoclimate, Paleomagnetism, and Continental Drift*. Tulsa, OK: American Association of Petroleum Geologists, 1979.

HACKENBERG, ROBERT A. "Scientists or Survivors? The Future of Applied Anthropology under Maximum Uncertainty." In Trotter, ed., *Anthropology for Tomorrow*.

HAHN, EMILY. "Chimpanzees and Language." *New Yorker*, April 24, 1971, 54ff.

HAHN, ROBERT A. *Sickness and Healing: An Anthropological Perspective*. New Haven, CT: Yale University Press, 1995.

HALDANE, J. B. S. "Human Evolution: Past and Future." In Jepsen, Mayr, and Simpson, eds., *Genetics, Paleontology, and Evolution*.

HALL, EDWARD T. *The Hidden Dimension*. Garden City, NY: Doubleday, 1966.

HALL, K. L. R. "Social Learning in Monkeys." In P. C. Jay, ed., *Primates: Studies in Adaptation and Variability*. New York: Holt, Rinehart & Winston, 1968, pp. 383–97.

HALLOWELL, A. IRVING. "Ojibwa World View and Disease." In *Contributions to Anthropology: Selected Papers of A. Irving Hallowell*. Chicago: University of Chicago Press, 1976, pp. 410–13.

HAMBURG, DAVID A., AND ELIZABETH R. MCCOWN, EDS. *The Great Apes*. Menlo Park, CA: Benjamin/Cummings, 1979.

HANNA, JOEL M., MICHAEL A. LITTLE, AND DONALD M. AUSTIN. "Climatic Physiology." In Little and Haas, eds., *Human Population Biology*.

HANNAH, ALISON C., AND W. C. MCGREW. "Chimpanzees Using Stones to Crack Open Oil Palm Nuts in Liberia." *Primates*, 28 (1987): 31–46.

HARCOURT, A. H. "The Social Relations and Group Structure of Wild Mountain Gorillas." In Hamburg and McCown, eds., *The Great Apes*.

HARLAN, JACK R. "A Wild Wheat Harvest in Turkey." *Archaeology*, 20, no. 3 (June 1967): 197–201.

HARLOW, HARRY F., ET AL. "Maternal Behavior of Rhesus Monkeys Deprived of Mothering and Peer Association in Infancy." *Proceedings of the American Philosophical Society*, 110 (1966): 58–66.

HARRIS, DAVID R. "Settling Down: An Evolutionary Model for the Transformation of Mobile Bands into Sedentary Communities." In Friedman and Rowlands, eds., *The Evolution of Social Systems*. London: Duckworth, 1977.

HARRIS, MARVIN. *Cultural Materialism: The Struggle for a Science of Culture*. New York: Random House, 1979.

HARRIS, MARVIN, AND ERIC B. ROSS. *Food and Evolution: Toward a Theory of Human Food Habits.* Philadelphia: Temple University Press, 1987.

HARRISON, G. A., JAMES M. TANNER, DAVID R. PILBEAM, AND P. T. BAKER. *Human Biology: An Introduction to Human Evolution, Variation, Growth, and Adaptability.* 3rd ed. Oxford: Oxford University Press, 1988.

HARRISON, GAIL G. "Primary Adult Lactase Deficiency: A Problem in Anthropological Genetics." *American Anthropologist,* 77 (1975): 812–35.

HARRISON, PETER D., AND B. L. TURNER II, EDS. *Pre-Hispanic Maya Agriculture.* Albuquerque: University of New Mexico Press, 1978.

HARRISON, T. "A Reassessment of the Phylogenetic Relationships of *Oreopithecus bamboli.*" *Journal of Human Evolution,* 15 (1986): 541–84.

HARRISON, T., AND L. ROOK. "Enigmatic Anthropoid or Misunderstood Ape? The Phylogenetic Status of *Oreopithecus bamboli* Reconsidered." In D. R. Begun, C. V. Ward, and M. D. Rose, eds., *Function, Phylogeny and Fossils: Miocene Hominoid Evolution and Adaptation.* New York: Plenum, 1997, pp. 327–62.

HARTWIG, W. C. "Pattern, Puzzles and Perspectives on Platyrrhine Origins." In Corruccini and Ciochon, eds., *Integrative Paths to the Past,* pp. 69–93.

HARVEY, PHILIP W., AND PETER F. HEYWOOD. "Twenty-five Years of Dietary Change in Simbu Province, Papua New Guinea." *Ecology of Food and Nutrition,* 13 (1983): 27–35.

HASSAN, FEKRI A. *Demographic Archaeology.* New York: Academic Press, 1981.

HASTORF, CHRISTINE. "Gender, Space, and Food Prehistory." In Gero and Conkey, eds., *Engendering Archaeology.*

HAUSFATER, GLENN, JEANNE ALTMANN, AND STUART ALTMANN. "Long-Term Consistency of Dominance Relations among Female Baboons." *Science,* August 20, 1982, 752–54.

HAWKINS, ALICIA, AND M. KLEINDIENST. "Aterian." In P. N. Peregrine and M. Ember, eds., *Encyclopedia of Prehistory.* Vol. 1: Africa. New York: Kluwer Academic/Plenum, 2001, pp. 23–45.

HAYDEN, THOMAS. "A Genome Milestone." *Newsweek,* July 3, 2000, 51–52.

HAYNES, VANCE. "The Calico Site: Artifacts or Geofacts?" *Science,* 181 (1973): 305–10.

HAYS, TERENCE E. "From Ethnographer to Comparativist and Back Again." In C. R. Ember, Ember, and Peregrine, eds., *Research Frontiers in Anthropology.* Vol. 3.

HAYS, TERENCE E. "Sound Symbolism, Onomatopoeia, and New Guinea Frog Names. *Journal of Linguistic Anthropology,* 4 (1994): 153–74.

HELMS, MARY W. *Middle America.* Englewood Cliffs, NJ: Prentice Hall, 1975.

HENNIG, WILLI. *Phylogenetic Systematics.* Urbana: University of Illinois Press, 1966.

HENRY, DONALD O. *From Foraging to Agriculture: The Levant at the End of the Ice Age.* Philadelphia: University of Pennsylvania Press, 1989.

HENRY, DONALD O. "Foraging, Sedentism, and Adaptive Vigor in the Natufian: Rethinking the Linkages." In G. A. Clark, ed., *Perspectives on the Past.*

HERRNSTEIN, RICHARD J., AND CHARLES MURRAY. *The Bell Curve: Intelligence and Class Structure in American Life.* New York: Free Press, 1994.

HEWES, GORDON W. "Food Transport and the Origin of Hominid Bipedalism." *American Anthropologist,* 63 (1961): 687–710.

HIGGINS, PATRICIA J., AND J. ANTHONY PAREDES, EDS. *Classics of Practicing Anthropology: 1978–1998.* Oklahoma City, OK: Society for Applied Anthropology.

HILL, JANE H. "Apes and Language." *Annual Review of Anthropology,* 7 (1978): 89–112.

HILL, JANE H. "Do Apes Have Language?" In C. R. Ember, Ember, and Peregrine, eds., *Research Frontiers in Anthropology.* Vol. 3.

HOCKETT, C. F., AND R. ASCHER. "The Human Revolution." *Current Anthropology,* 5 (1964): 135–68.

HODDER, I. *The Domestication of Europe: Structure and Contingency in Neolithic Societies.* Oxford: Blackwell, 1990.

HOFFECKER, JOHN F., W. ROGER POWERS, AND TED GOEBEL. "The Colonization of Beringia and the Peopling of the New World." *Science,* January 1, 1993, 46–53.

HOLDAWAY, R. N., AND C. JACOMB. "Rapid Extinction of the Moas (Aves: Dinornithiformes): Model, Test, and Implications." *Science,* 287 (2000): 2250–57.

HOLDEN, CONSTANCE. "Selective Power of UV." *Science,* 289 (2000): 1461.

HOLE, FRANK. "Environmental Shock and Urban Origins." In Stein and Rothman, eds., *Chiefdoms and Early States in the Near East.*

HOLE, FRANK. "Origins of Agriculture." In Jones, Martin, and Pilbeam, eds., *The Cambridge Encyclopedia of Human Evolution.*

HOLE, FRANK, ED. *Archaeology of Western Iran.* Washington, DC: Smithsonian Institution Press, 1987.

HOLE, FRANK, KENT V. FLANNERY, AND JAMES A. NEELY. *Prehistory and Human Ecology of the Deh Luran Plain.* Memoirs of the Museum of Anthropology No. 1. Ann Arbor: University of Michigan, 1969.

HOLE, FRANK, AND ROBERT F. HEIZER. *An Introduction to Prehistoric Archeology.* 3rd ed. New York: Holt, Rinehart & Winston, 1973.

HOLLOWAY, RALPH L. "The Casts of Fossil Hominid Brains." *Scientific American,* July 1974, 106–15.

HONIGMANN, JOHN J. *Personality in Culture.* New York: Harper & Row, 1967.

HOUSTON, STEPHEN D. "The Phonetic Decipherment of Mayan Glyphs." *Antiquity,* 62 (1988): 126–35.

HOWELL, F. CLARK. "Observations on the Earlier Phases of the European Lower Paleolithic." In *Recent Studies in Paleoanthropology. American Anthropologist,* special publication, April 1966, pp. 88–200.

HOWELL, NANCY. *Demography of the Dobe !Kung.* New York: Academic Press, 1979.

HOWELLS, W. *Getting Here: The Story of Human Evolution.* 2nd ed. Washington, DC: Compass Press, 1997.

HRDY, SARAH BLAFFER. *The Langurs of Abu: Female and Male Strategies of Reproduction.* Cambridge, MA: Harvard University Press, 1977.

HSU, FRANCIS L. K., ED. *Psychological Anthropology.* 2nd ed. Cambridge, MA: Schenkman, 1972.

HUSS-ASHMORE, REBECCA, AND FRANCIS E. JOHNSTON. "Bioanthropological Research in Developing Countries." *Annual Review of Anthropology,* 14 (1985): 475–527.

HUXLEY, THOMAS H. "Man's Place in Nature." In Young, ed., *Evolution of Man.*

HYMES, DELL, ED. *Language in Culture and Society: A Reader in Linguistics and Anthropology.* New York: Harper & Row, 1964.

INHORN, MARCIA C., AND PETER J. BROWN. *The Anthropology of Infectious Disease: International Health Perspectives.* Amsterdam: Gordon and Breach, 1997.

ISAAC, GLYNN. "The Archaeology of Human Origins: Studies of the Lower Pleistocene in East Africa, 1971–1981." In Wendorf and Close, eds., *Advances in World Archaeology.*

ISAAC, GLYNN. "The Diet of Early Man: Aspects of Archaeological Evidence from Lower and Middle Pleistocene Sites in Africa." *World Archaeology,* 2 (1971): 277–99.

ISAAC, GLYNN, ED., assisted by Barbara Isaac. *Plio-Pleistocene Archaeology.* Oxford: Clarendon Press, 1997.

ITOIGAWA, NAOSUKE, YUKIMARU SUGIYAMA, GENE P. SACKETT, AND ROGER K. R. THOMPSON, EDS. *Topics in Primatology.* Vol. 2. Tokyo: University of Tokyo Press, 1992.

JABLONSKI, NINA, AND GEORGE CHAPLIN. "The Evolution of Human Skin Color." *Journal of Human Evolution,* 39 (2000): 57–106.

JAEGER, J., T. THEIN, M. BENAMMI, Y. CHAIMANEE, A. N. SOE, T. LWIN, T. TUN, S. WAI, AND S. DUCROCQ. "A New Primate from the Middle Eocene of Myanmar and the Asian Early Origins of Anthropoids." *Science,* 286 (1999): 528–30.

JAYASWAL, VIDULA. "South Asian Upper Paleolithic." In P. N. Peregrine and M. Ember, eds., *Encyclopedia of Prehistory.* Vol. 8: *South and Southwest Asia.* New York: Kluwer Academic/Plenum, 2002.

JELLIFFE, DERRICK B., AND E. F. PATRICE JELLIFFE. "Human Milk, Nutrition, and the World Resource Crisis." *Science,* May 9, 1975, 557–61.

JENNINGS, J. D. *Prehistory of North America.* New York: McGraw-Hill, 1968.

JENSEN, ARTHUR. "How Much Can We Boost IQ and Scholastic Achievement?" *Harvard Educational Review,* 29 (1969): 1–123.

JEPSEN, GLENN L., ERNST MAYR, AND GEORGE GAYLORD SIMPSON, EDS. *Genetics, Paleontology, and Evolution.* New York: Atheneum, 1963.

JOHANSON, DONALD C., AND MAITLAND EDEY. *Lucy: The Beginnings of Humankind.* New York: Simon & Schuster, 1981.

JOHANSON, DONALD C., AND TIM D. WHITE. "A Systematic Assessment of Early African Hominids." *Science,* January 26, 1979, 321–30.

JOHNSON, ALLEN, AND TIMOTHY EARLE. *The Evolution of Human Societies: From Foraging Group to Agrarian State.* Stanford, CA: Stanford University Press, 1987.

JOHNSON, GREGORY A. "Aspects of Regional Analysis in Archaeology." *Annual Review of Anthropology,* 6 (1977): 479–508.

JOHNSON, GREGORY. "The Changing Organization of Uruk Administration on the Susiana Plain." In Hole, ed., *Archaeology of Western Iran.*

JOHNSON, THOMAS M., AND CAROLYN F. SARGENT, EDS. *Medical Anthropology: Contemporary Theory and Method.* Westport, CT: Praeger, 1990.

JOLLY, ALISON. *The Evolution of Primate Behavior.* 2nd ed. New York: Macmillan, 1985.

JOLLY, CLIFFORD. "The Seed-Eaters: A New Model of Hominid Differentiation Based on a Baboon Analogy." *Man,* 5 (1970): 5–28.

JONES, STEVE, ROBERT MARTIN, AND DAVID PILBEAM, EDS. *The Cambridge Encyclopedia of Human Evolution.* New York: Cambridge University Press, 1992.

JORDAN, ANN T., ED. *Practicing Anthropology in Corporate America: Consulting on Organizational Culture.* NAPA Bulletin No. 14. Arlington, VA: American Anthropological Association, 1994.

JUDGE, W. JAMES, AND JERRY DAWSON. "Paleo-Indian Settlement Technology in New Mexico." *Science,* June 16, 1972, 1210–16.

JUNGERS, WILLIAM L. "New Estimates of Body Size in Australopithecines." In Grine, ed., *Evolutionary History of the "Robust" Australopithecines.*

JUNGERS, WILLIAM L. "Relative Joint Size and Hominoid Locomotor Adaptations with Implications for the Evolution of Hominid Bipedalism." *Journal of Human Evolution,* 17 (1988): 247–65.

KAMIN, LEON J. "Behind the Curve." *Scientific American,* February 1995, 99–103.

KAPPELMAN, JOHN. "The Attraction of Paleomagnetism." *Evolutionary Anthropology,* 2, no. 3 (1993): 89–99.

KASARDA, JOHN D. "Economic Structure and Fertility: A Comparative Analysis." *Demography,* 8, no. 3 (August 1971): 307–18.

KAY, RICHARD F. "Parapithecidae." In Tattersall, Delson, and van Couvering, eds., *Encyclopedia of Human Evolution and Prehistory.*

KAY, RICHARD F. "Teeth." In Tattersall, Delson, and van Couvering, eds., *Encyclopedia of Human Evolution and Prehistory.*

KAY, RICHARD F., C. ROSS, AND B. A. WILLIAMS. "Anthropoid Origins." *Science,* 275 (1997): 797–804.

KEELEY, LAWRENCE H. *Experimental Determination of Stone Tool Uses: A Microwear Analysis.* Chicago: University of Chicago Press, 1980.

KEELEY, LAWRENCE. "The Functions of Paleolithic Flint Tools." *Scientific American,* 237 (1977): 108–26.

KELLEY, JAY. "The Evolution of Apes." In Jones, Martin, and Pilbeam, eds., *The Cambridge Encyclopedia of Human Evolution.*

KERR, RICHARD A. "Sea-Floor Dust Shows Drought Felled Akkadian Empire." *Science,* January 16, 1998, 325–26.

KIMBEL, WILLIAM H., T. D. WHITE, AND D. C. JOHANSEN. "Cranial Morphology of *Australopithecus afarensis*: A Comparative Study Based on Composite Reconstruction of the Adult Skull." *American Journal of Physical Anthropology,* 64 (1984): 337–88.

KINGSTON, JOHN D., BRUNO D. MARINO, AND ANDREW HILL. "Isotopic Evidence for Neogene Hominid Paleoenvironments in the Kenya Rift Valley." *Science,* May 13, 1994, 955–59.

KLEIN, RICHARD G. "The Ecology of Early Man in Southern Africa." *Science,* July 8, 1977, 115–26.

KLEIN, RICHARD G. *The Human Career: Human Biological and Cultural Origins.* Chicago: University of Chicago Press, 1989.

KLEIN, RICHARD G. "Ice-Age Hunters of the Ukraine." *Scientific American,* June 1974, 96–105.

KLEIN, RICHARD G. "Reconstructing How Early People Exploited Animals: Problems and Prospects." In Nitecki and Nitecki, eds., *The Evolution of Human Hunting.*

KLEIN, RICHARD G. "Southern Africa before the Ice Age." In Corruccini and Ciochon, eds., *Integrative Paths to the Past.*

KLEIN, RICHARD G. "The Stone Age Prehistory of Southern Africa." *Annual Review of Anthropology,* 12 (1983): 25–48.

KLEINBERG, JILL. "Practical Implications of Organizational Culture Where Americans and Japanese Work Together." In Jordan, ed., *Practicing Anthropology in Corporate America.*

KLEINMAN, ARTHUR. *Rethinking Psychiatry: From Cultural Category to Personal Experience.* New York: Macmillan, 1988.

KLEINMAN, ARTHUR, AND BYRON GOOD, EDS. *Culture and Depression: Studies in the Anthropology and Cross-Cultural Psychia-*

try of Affect and Disorder. Berkeley: University of California Press, 1985.

KLEINMAN, ARTHUR, VEENA DAS, AND MARGARET LOCK, EDS. *Social Suffering.* Berkeley: University of California Press, 1997.

KLIMA, BOHUSLAV. "The First Ground-Plan of an Upper Paleolithic Loess Settlement in Middle Europe and Its Meaning." In Braidwood and Willey, eds., *Courses toward Urban Life.*

KLINEBERG, OTTO. *Negro Intelligence and Selective Migration.* New York: Columbia University Press, 1935.

KLINEBERG, OTTO, ED. *Characteristics of the American Negro.* New York: Harper & Brothers, 1944.

KONNER, MELVIN, AND CAROL WORTHMAN. "Nursing Frequency, Gonadal Function, and Birth Spacing among !Kung Hunter-Gatherers." *Science,* February 15, 1980, 788–91.

KOZLOWSKI, S. K., ED. *The Mesolithic in Europe.* Warsaw: Warsaw University Press, 1973.

KRAMER, ANDREW. "The Natural History and Evolutionary Fate of *Homo erectus.*" In Peregrine, Ember, and Ember, eds., *Physical Anthropology.*

KRAMER, SAMUEL NOEL. *The Sumerians: Their History, Culture, and Character.* Chicago: University of Chicago Press, 1963.

KREBS, J. R., AND N. B. DAVIES. *An Introduction to Behavioural Ecology.* 2nd ed. Sunderland, MA: Sinauer, 1987.

KREBS, J. R., AND N. B. DAVIES, EDS. *Behavioural Ecology: An Evolutionary Approach.* 2nd ed. Sunderland, MA: Sinauer, 1984.

KRINGS, MATTHIAS, A. STONE, R. W. SCHMITZ, H. KRAINITZKI, M. STONEKING, AND S. PAABO. "Neandertal DNA Sequences and the Origin of Modern Humans." *Cell,* 90 (1997): 19–30.

KUEHN, STEVEN. "New Evidence for Late Paleoindian-Early Archaic Subsistence Behavior in the Western Great Lakes." *American Antiquity,* 63 (1998): 457–76.

KUSHNER, GILBERT. "Applied Anthropology." In Emener and Darrow, eds., *Career Explorations in Human Services.*

LANDAUER, THOMAS K. "Infantile Vaccination and the Secular Trend in Stature." *Ethos,* 1 (1973): 499–503.

LANDAUER, THOMAS K., AND JOHN W. M. WHITING. "Correlates and Consequences of Stress in Infancy." In Munroe, Munroe, and Whiting, eds., *Handbook of Cross-Cultural Human Development.*

LANDAUER, THOMAS K., AND JOHN W. M. WHITING. "Infantile Stimulation and Adult Stature of Human Males." *American Anthropologist,* 66 (1964): 1007–28.

LARSEN, CLARK SPENSER. "Bare Bones Anthropology: The Bioarchaeology of Human Remains." In Peregrine, Ember, and Ember, eds., *Archaeology.*

"The Last of the Cahokians." *Science,* April 19, 1996, 351.

LEAKEY, L. S. B. "Finding the World's Earliest Man." *National Geographic,* September 1960, 420–35.

LEAKEY, MARY. *Olduvai Gorge: Excavations in Beds I and II.* Cambridge: Cambridge University Press, 1971.

LEAKEY, MARY. *Olduvai Gorge: My Search for Early Man.* London: Collins, 1979; Leakey, Louis, *Olduvai Gorge.* Vol. 1: *A Preliminary Report on the Geology and Fauna.* Cambridge: Cambridge University Press, 1961.

LEAKEY, MEAVE, C. S. FEIBEL, I. McDOUGALL, AND A. WALKER. "New Four-Million-Year-Old Hominid Species from Kanapoi and Allia Bay, Kenya." *Nature,* 376 (1995): 565–71.

LEE, PHYLLIS C. "Home Range, Territory and Intergroup Encounters." In Robert A. Hinde, ed., *Primate Social Relationship: An Integrated Approach.* Sunderland, MA: Sinauer, 1983.

LEE, RICHARD B. *The !Kung San: Men, Women, and Work in a Foraging Society.* Cambridge: Cambridge University Press, 1979.

LEE, RICHARD B. "Population Growth and the Beginnings of Sedentary Life among the !Kung Bushmen." In Spooner, ed., *Population Growth.*

LESLIE, C. "Introduction." In C. Leslie, ed., *Asian Medical Systems: A Comparative Study.* Los Angeles: University of California Press, 1976.

LÉVI-STRAUSS, CLAUDE. "The Sorcerer and His Magic." In Lévi-Strauss, *Structural Anthropology.*

LÉVI-STRAUSS, CLAUDE. *Structural Anthropology.* Trans. Claire Jacobson and Brooke Grundfest Schoepf. New York: Basic Books, 1963.

LEVY, JERROLD E. "Hopi Shamanism: A Reappraisal." In Raymond J. DeMallie and Alfonzo Ortiz, eds., *North American Indian Anthropology: Essays on Society and Culture.* Norman: University of Oklahoma Press, 1994, pp. 307–27, as seen in eHRAF Collection of Ethnography on the Web, 2000.

LEWIN, ROGER. "Fossil Lucy Grows Younger, Again." *Science,* January 7, 1983, 43–44.

LEWIN, ROGER. "Is the Orangutan a Living Fossil?" *Science,* December 16, 1983, 1222–23.

LIEBERMAN, DANIEL E. "Testing Hypotheses about Recent Human Evolution from Skulls: Integrating Morphology, Function, Development, and Phylogeny." *Current Anthropology,* 36 (1995): 159–97.

LIEBERMAN, LEONARD. "Scientific Insignificance." *Anthropology Newsletter,* 40, no. 8 (1999): 11–12.

LIEBERMAN, PHILIP. *Uniquely Human: The Evolution of Speech, Thought, and Selfless Behavior.* Cambridge, MA: Harvard University Press, 1991.

LITTLE, M. A. "Growth and Development of Turkana Pastoralists." In Peregrine, Ember, and Ember, *Physical Anthropology.*

LITTLE, MICHAEL A., AND JERE D. HAAS, EDS. *Human Population Biology: A Transdisciplinary Science.* New York: Oxford University Press, 1989.

LOOMIS, W. FARNSWORTH. "Skin-Pigment Regulation of Vitamin-D Biosynthesis in Man." *Science,* August 4, 1967, 501–506.

LOUSTAUNAU, MARTHA O., AND ELISA J. SOBO. *The Cultural Context of Health, Illness, and Medicine.* Westport, CT: Bergin & Garvey, 1997.

LOVEJOY, ARTHUR O. *The Great Chain of Being: A Study of the History of an Idea.* Cambridge, MA: Harvard University Press, 1964.

LOVEJOY, C. OWEN. "Evolution of Human Walking." *Scientific American,* November 1988, 118–25.

LOVEJOY, C. OWEN. "The Origin of Man." *Science,* January 23, 1981, 341–50.

LOVEJOY, OWEN, KINGSBURY HEIPLE, AND ALBERT BERNSTEIN. "The Gait of *Australopithecus.*" *American Journal of Physical Anthropology,* 38 (1973): 757–79.

LUMBRERAS, LUIS. *The Peoples and Cultures of Ancient Peru.* Washington, DC: Smithsonian Institution Press, 1974.

LUTZ, CATHERINE. "Depression and the Translations of Emotional Worlds." In Kleinman and Good, eds., *Culture and Depression.*

MACARTHUR, R. H., AND E. O. WILSON. *Theory of Island Biogeography.* Princeton, NJ: Princeton University Press, 1967.

McCORRISTON, JOY, AND FRANK HOLE. "The Ecology of Seasonal Stress and the Origins of Agriculture in the Near East." *American Anthropologist,* 93 (1991): 46–69.

McCRACKEN, ROBERT D. "Lactase Deficiency: An Example of Dietary Evolution." *Current Anthropology,* 12 (1971): 479–500.

McDermott, LeRoy. "Self-representation in Female Figurines." *Cultural Anthropology*, 37 (1996): 227–75.

McDonald, Kim A. "New Evidence Challenges Traditional Model of How the New World Was Settled." *Chronicle of Higher Education*, March 13, 1998, A22.

McElroy, Ann, and Patricia Townsend. *Medical Anthropology in Ecological Perspective*. 3rd ed. Boulder, CO: Westview, 1996.

McGarvey, Stephen T. "The Thrifty Gene Concept and Adiposity Studies in Biological Anthropology." *Journal of the Polynesian Society*, 103 (1994): 29–42.

McGrew, W. *Chimpanzee Material Culture: Implications for Human Evolution*. Cambridge: Cambridge University Press, 1992.

McHenry, Henry M. "New Estimates of Body Weight in Early Hominids and Their Significance to Encephalization and Megadontia in 'Robust' Australopithecines." In Grine, ed., *Evolutionary History of the "Robust" Australopithecines*.

McHenry, Henry M. "The Pattern of Human Evolution: Studies on Bipedalism, Mastication, and Encephalization." *Annual Review of Anthropology*, 11 (1982): 151–73.

McHenry, Henry M. "'Robust' Australopithecines, Our Family Tree, and Homoplasy." In Peregrine, Ember, and Ember, eds., *Physical Anthropology*.

McKee, Lauris. "Sex Differentials in Survivorship and the Customary Treatment of Infants and Children." *Medical Anthropology*, 8 (1984): 91–108.

MacKinnon, John, and Kathy MacKinnon. "The Behavior of Wild Spectral Tarsiers." *International Journal of Primatology*, 1 (1980): 361–79.

MacKintosh, N. J. *IQ and Human Intelligence*. Oxford: Oxford University Press, 1998.

McNeill, William H. *Plagues and Peoples*. Garden City, NY: Doubleday/Anchor, 1976.

MacNeish, Richard S. "The Evaluation of Community Patterns in the Tehuacán Valley of Mexico and Speculations about the Cultural Processes." In Tringham, ed., *Ecology and Agricultural Settlements*.

MacNeish, Richard S. *The Origins of Agriculture and Settled Life*. Norman: University of Oklahoma Press, 1991.

Madigral, Lorena. "Hemoglobin Genotype, Fertility, and the Malaria Hypothesis." *Human Biology*, 61 (1989): 311–25.

Magner, L. *A History of Medicine*. New York: Marcel Dekker, 1992.

Mahony, Frank Joseph. *A Trukese Theory of Medicine*. Ann Arbor, MI: University Microfilms, 1070 [1971]), as seen in the eHRAF Collection of Ethnography on the Web, 2000.

Manhein, Mary H. *The Bone Lady: Life as a Forensic Anthropologist*. Baton Rouge: Louisiana State University Press, 1999.

Manzanilla, Linda, ed. *Studies in the Neolithic and Urban Revolutions*. British Archaeological Reports International Series 349. Oxford, 1987.

Marcus, Joyce. "Maya Hieroglyphs: History or Propaganda?" In Peregrine, Ember, and Ember, eds., *Archaeology*.

Marcus, Joyce. "On the Nature of the Mesoamerican City." In Vogt and Leventhal, eds., *Prehistoric Settlement Patterns*.

Marcus, Joyce, and Kent V. Flannery. *Zapotec Civilization*. London: Thames and Hudson, 1996, pp. 49–50.

Marks, Jonathan. "Black, White, Other: Racial Categories Are Cultural Constructs Masquerading as Biology." *Natural History*, December 1994, 32–35.

Marshack, Alexander. *The Roots of Civilization*. New York: McGraw-Hill, 1972.

Marshall, Eliot. "Rival Genome Sequencers Celebrate a Milestone Together." *Science*, June 30, 2000, 2294–295.

Marshall, Larry G. "Who Killed Cock Robin? An Investigation of the Extinction Controversy." In Martin and Klein, eds., *Quaternary Extinctions*.

Martin, Paul S. "The Discovery of America." *Science*, March 9, 1973, 969–74.

Martin, Paul S., and Richard Klein, eds. *Quaternary Extinctions: A Prehistoric Revolution*. Tucson: University of Arizona Press, 1984.

Martin, Paul S., and H. E. Wright, eds. *Pleistocene Extinctions: The Search for a Cause*. New Haven, CT: Yale University Press, 1967.

Martin, Robert. "Classification and Evolutionary Relationships." In Jones, Martin, and Pilbeam, eds., *The Cambridge Encyclopedia of Human Evolution*.

Martin, Robert D. *Primate Origins and Evolution: A Phylogenetic Reconstruction*. Princeton, NJ: Princeton University Press, 1990.

Martin, Robert D. "Strategies of Reproduction." *Natural History*, November 1975, 48–57.

Martin, Robert D., and Simon K. Bearder. "Radio Bush Baby." *Natural History*, October 1979, 77–81.

Martorell, Reynaldo. "Interrelationships between Diet, Infectious Disease and Nutritional Status." In Greene and Johnston, eds., *Social and Biological Predictors of Nutritional Status, Physical Growth and Neurological Development*.

Martorell, Reynaldo, Juan Rivera, Haley Kaplowitz, and Ernesto Pollitt. "Long-Term Consequences of Growth Retardation during Early Childhood." Paper presented at the Sixth International Congress of Auxology, September 15–19, 1991, Madrid.

Mascie-Taylor, C. G. Nicholas. "The Biology of Social Class." In C. G. Nicholas Mascie-Taylor, ed., *Biosocial Aspects of Social Class*. Oxford: Oxford University Press, 1990, pp. 117–42.

Mascie-Taylor, C. G. N., and G. W. Lasker. *Applications of Biological Anthropology to Human Affairs*. New York: Cambridge University Press, 1991.

Mason, Ian L. *Evolution of Domesticated Animals*. New York: Longman, 1984.

Mayr, Ernst. *The Growth of Biological Thought: Diversity, Evolution, and Inheritance*. Cambridge, MA: Belknap Press of Harvard University Press, 1982.

Mayr, Ernst. *One Long Argument: Charles Darwin and the Genesis of Modern Evolutionary Thought*. Cambridge, MA: Harvard University Press, 1993.

Mayr, Ernst. "The Nature of the Darwinian Revolution." *Science*, June 2, 1972, 981–89.

Mazess, Richard B. "Human Adaptation to High Altitude." In Damon, ed., *Physiological Anthropology*.

Mead, Margaret. "Applied Anthropology: The State of the Art." In Wallace et al., eds., *Perspectives on Anthropology 1976*.

Mead, Margaret. "The Evolving Ethics of Applied Anthropology." In Eddy and Partridge, eds., *Applied Anthropology in America*.

Meggers, Betty J., ed. *Anthropological Archaeology in the Americas*. Washington, DC: Anthropological Society of Washington, 1968.

Mellaart, James. "A Neolithic City in Turkey." *Scientific American*, April 1964, 94–104.

Mellaart, James. "Roots in the Soil." In Piggott, ed., *The Dawn of Civilization*.

MELLARS, PAUL. "The Fate of the Neanderthals." *Nature*, 395 (1998): 539–40.

MELLARS, PAUL. *The Neanderthal Legacy*. Princeton, NJ: Princeton University Press, 1996, pp. 405–19.

MELLARS, PAUL. "The Upper Paleolithic Revolution." In B. Cunliffe, ed., *The Oxford Illustrated Prehistory of Europe*. Oxford: Oxford University Press, 1994, pp. 42–78.

MELTZER, DAVID J. "Pleistocene Peopling of the Americas." *Evolutionary Anthropology*. Vol. 1. 1993.

MELTZER, DAVID J. *Search for the First Americans*. Washington, DC: Smithsonian Institution, 1993.

MELTZER, DAVID J., DON D. FOWLER, AND JEREMY A. SABLOFF, EDS. *American Archaeology Past and Future*. Washington, DC: Smithsonian Institution Press, 1986.

MERBS, CHARLES F. "A New World of Infectious Disease." *Yearbook of Physical Anthropology*, 35 (1992): 3–42.

MICHEL, R. H., McGOVERN, P. E., AND BADLER, V. R. "The First Wine and Beer: Chemical Detection of Ancient Fermented Beverages." *Analytical Chemistry*, 65 (1993): 408A–13A.

MILLER, HENRY I. "Regulation." In Davis, ed., *The Genetic Revolution*.

MILLER, NAOMI F. "The Origins of Plant Cultivation in the Near East." In Cowan and Watson, eds., *The Origins of Agriculture*.

MILLON, RENÉ. "Social Relations in Ancient Teotihuacán." In Wolf, ed., *The Valley of Mexico*.

MILLON, RENÉ. "Teotihuacán." *Scientific American*, June 1967, 38–48.

MILTON, KATHARINE. "Distribution Patterns of Tropical Plant Foods as an Evolutionary Stimulus to Primate Mental Development." *American Anthropologist*, 83 (1981): 534–48.

MILTON, KATHARINE. "The Evolution of a Physical Anthropologist." In Peregrine, Ember, and Ember, eds., *Physical Anthropology*.

MILTON, KATHARINE. "Foraging Behaviour and the Evolution of Primate Intelligence." In Byrne and Whiten, eds., *Machiavellian Intelligence*.

MINUGH-PURVIS, NANCY. "Neandertal Growth: Examining Developmental Adaptations in Earlier *Homo sapiens*." In Peregrine, Ember, and Ember, eds., *Physical Anthropology*.

MIRACLE, ANDREW W. "A Shaman to Organizations." In C. R. Ember, Ember, and Peregrine, eds., *Research Frontiers in Anthropology*. Vol. 3.

MITTERMEIER, RUSSELL A., AND ELEANOR J. STERLING. "Conservation of Primates." In Jones, Martin, and Pilbeam, eds., *The Cambridge Encyclopedia of Human Evolution*.

MOERMAN, DANIEL E. "Physiology and Symbols: The Anthropological Implications of the Placebo Effect." In Romanucci-Ross, Moerman, and Tancredi, eds., *The Anthropology of Medicine*, pp. 240–53.

MOLNAR, STEPHEN. *Human Variation: Races, Types, and Ethnic Groups*. 4th ed. Upper Saddle River, NJ: Prentice Hall, 1998.

MONTAGU, A. *A Man's Most Dangerous Myth: The Fallacy of Race*. 6th ed. Walnut Creek, CA: Alta Mira, 1997.

MOORE, CARMELLA CARACCI. "An Optimal Scaling of Murdock's Theories of Illness Data—An Approach to the Problem of Interdependence." *Behavior Science Research*, 22 (1988): 161–179.

MORAN, EMILIO F. *Human Adaptability: An Introduction to Ecological Anthropology*. 2nd ed. Boulder, CO: Westview, 2000.

MORAN, EMILIO F., ED. *Transforming Societies, Transforming Anthropology*. Ann Arbor: University of Michigan Press, 1996.

MORELL, VIRGINIA. "The Earliest Art Becomes Older—And More Common." *Science*, March 31, 1995, 1908–1909.

MORRIS, LAURA NEWELL, ED. *Human Populations, Genetic Variation, and Evolution*. San Francisco: Chandler, 1971.

MOSER, STEPHANIE. *Ancestral Images: The Iconography of Human Origins*. Ithaca, NY: Cornell University Press, 1998.

MOTULSKY, ARNO. "Metabolic Polymorphisms and the Role of Infectious Diseases in Human Evolution." In Morris, ed., *Human Populations, Genetic Variation, and Evolution*.

MUKERJEE, MADHUSREE. "Field Notes: Interview with a Parrot." *Scientific American*, April 1996, 28.

MÜLLER-HAYE, B. "Guinea Pig or Cuy." In Mason, *Evolution of Domesticated Animals*.

MUNROE, RUTH H., ROBERT L. MUNROE, AND BEATRICE B. WHITING, EDS. *Handbook of Cross-Cultural Human Development*. New York: Garland, 1981.

MURDOCK, GEORGE PETER. *Theories of Illness: A World Survey*. Pittsburgh: University of Pittsburgh Press, 1980.

MURPHY, JANE. "Abnormal Behavior in Traditional Societies: Labels, Explanations, and Social Reactions." In Munroe, Munroe, and Whiting, eds., *Handbook of Cross-Cultural Human Development*.

MURRAY, GERALD F. "The Domestication of Wood in Haiti: A Case Study in Applied Anthropology." In Podolefsky and Brown, *Applying Cultural Anthropology*.

NAPIER, J. R. "Paleoecology and Catarrhine Evolution." In J. R. Napier and P. H. Napier, eds., *Old World Monkeys: Evolution, Systematics, and Behavior*. New York: Academic Press, 1970.

NAPIER, J. R., AND P. H. NAPIER. *A Handbook of Living Primates*. New York: Academic Press, 1967.

NEEL, JAMES V., WILLARD R. CENTERWALL, NAPOLEON A. CHAGNON, AND HELEN L. CASEY. "Notes on the Effect of Measles and Measles Vaccine in a Virgin-Soil Population of South American Indians." *American Journal of Epidemiology*, 91 (1970): 418–29.

NELSON, K. E., ED. *Children's Language*. Vol. 2. New York: Halsted Press, 1980.

NICOLSON, NANCY A. "Infants, Mothers, and Other Females." In Smuts et al., eds., *Primate Societies*.

NIEDERBERGER, CHRISTINE. "Early Sedentary Economy in the Basin of Mexico." *Science*, January 12, 1979, 131–42.

NIEHOFF, ARTHUR H. *A Casebook of Social Change*. Chicago: Aldine, 1966.

NISHIDA, TOSHISADA. "Introduction to the Conservation Symposium." In Naosuke Itoigawa, Yukimaru Sugiyama, Gene P. Sackett, and Roger K. R. Thompson, *Topics in Primatology*. Vol. 2. Tokyo: University of Tokyo Press, 1992.

NISHIDA, TOSHISADA, WILLIAM C. McGREW, PETER MARLER, MARTIN PICKFORD, AND FRANS B. M. DE WAAL, EDS. *Topics in Primatology*. Vol. 1: *Human Origins*. Tokyo: University of Tokyo Press, 1992.

NISSEN, HENRY W. "Axes of Behavioral Comparison." In Anne Roe and George Gaylord Simpson, eds., *Behavior and Evolution*. New Haven, CT: Yale University Press, 1958.

NITECKI, MATTHEW H., AND DORIS V. NITECKI, EDS. *The Evolution of Human Hunting*. New York: Plenum, 1987.

NOBLE, WILLIAM, AND IAN DAVIDSON. *Human Evolution, Language, and Mind*. Cambridge: Cambridge University Press, 1996, pp. 162–214.

NORMILE, DENNIS. "Habitat Seen Playing Larger Role in Shaping Behavior." *Science*, March 6, 1998, 1454–455.

OAKLEY, KENNETH P. "Analytical Methods of Dating Bones." In Brothwell and Higgs, eds., *Science in Archaeology.*

OAKLEY, KENNETH. "On Man's Use of Fire, with Comments on Tool-Making and Hunting." In Washburn, ed., *Social Life of Early Man.*

OLSZEWSKI, DEBORAH I. "Social Complexity in the Natufian? Assessing the Relationship of Ideas and Data." In Clark, ed., *Perspectives on the Past.*

ORTIZ DE MONTELLANO, B. R., AND C. H. BROWNER. "Chemical Bases for Medicinal Plant Use in Oaxaca, Mexico." *Journal of Ethnopharmacology,* 13 (1985): 57–88.

OXBY, CLARE. "Farmer Groups in Rural Areas of the Third World." *Community Development Journal,* 18 (1983): 50–59.

PANTER-BRICK, CATHERINE, DEBORAH S. LOTSTEIN, AND PETER T. ELLISON. "Seasonality of Reproductive Function and Weight Loss in Rural Nepali Women." *Human Reproduction,* 8 (1993): 684–90.

PARFIT, MICHAEL. "Who Were the First Americans?" *National Geographic,* December 2000, pp. 41–67.

PARKER, SUE TAYLOR. "Why Big Brains Are So Rare." In Parker and Gibson, eds., *"Language" and Intelligence in Monkeys and Apes.*

PARKER, SUE TAYLOR, AND KATHLEEN RITA GIBSON, EDS. *"Language" and Intelligence in Monkeys and Apes: Comparative Developmental Perspectives.* New York: Cambridge University Press, 1990.

PARRY, WILLIAM J. "When and How Did Humans Populate the New World?" In Peregrine, Ember, and Ember, eds., *Archaeology.*

PARTRIDGE, WILLIAM L., AND ELIZABETH M. EDDY. "The Development of Applied Anthropology in America." In Eddy and Partridge, eds., *Applied Anthropology in America,* 2nd ed.

PATTERSON, LELAND. "Criteria for Determining the Attributes of Man-Made Lithics." *Journal of Field Archaeology,* 10 (1983): 297–307.

PATTERSON, THOMAS C. "Central Peru: Its Population and Economy." *Archaeology,* 24 (1971): 316–21.

PATTERSON, THOMAS C. *The Evolution of Ancient Societies: A World Archaeology.* Englewood Cliffs, NJ: Prentice Hall, 1981.

PEACOCK, NADINE, AND ROBERT BAILEY. "Efe: Investigating Food and Fertility in the Ituri Rain Forest." In M. Ember, Ember, and Levinson, eds., *Portraits of Culture.*

PEARSALL, DEBORAH. "The Origins of Plant Cultivation in South America." In Cowan and Watson, eds., *The Origins of Agriculture.*

PEARSON, J. D., GARY D. JAMES, AND DANIEL E. BROWN. "Stress and Changing Lifestyles in the Pacific: Physiological Stress Responses of Samoans in Rural and Urban Settings." *American Journal of Human Biology,* 5 (1993): 49–60.

PENNISI, ELIZABETH. "Finally, the Book of Life and Instructions for Navigating It." *Science,* June 30, 2000, 2304–307.

PEREGRINE, PETER. *Archaeological Research: A Brief Introduction.* Upper Saddle River, NJ: Prentice Hall, 2001.

PEREGRINE, PETER N. "Cross-Cultural Approaches in Archaeology." *Annual Review of Anthropology,* 30 (2001).

PEREGRINE, PETER N. *Outline of Archaeological Traditions.* New Haven, CT: HRAF, 2001.

PEREGRINE, PETER N. "Social Change in the Woodland-Mississippian Transition: A Study of Household and Community Patterns in the American Bottom." *North American Archaeologist,* 13 (1992): 131–47.

PEREGRINE, PETER N. "Southern and Eastern Africa Later Stone Age." In Peregrine and Ember, *Encyclopedia of Prehistory.* Vol. 1, pp. 272–73.

PEREGRINE, PETER N., AND PETER BELLWOOD. "Southeast Asia Upper Paleolithic." In P. N. Peregrine and M. Ember, eds., *Encyclopedia of Prehistory.* Vol. 3: *East Asia and Oceania.* New York: Kluwer Academic/Plenum, 2001, pp. 307–09.

PEREGRINE, PETER N., C. R. EMBER, AND M. EMBER. "Teaching Critical Evaluation of Rushton." *Anthropology Newsletter,* 41, no. 2 (2000): 29–30.

PEREGRINE, PETER N., CAROL R. EMBER, AND MELVIN EMBER, EDS. *Archaeology: Original Readings in Method and Practice.* Upper Saddle River, NJ: Prentice Hall, 2002.

PEREGRINE, PETER N., CAROL R. EMBER, AND MELVIN EMBER, EDS. *Physical Anthropology: Original Readings in Method and Practice.* Upper Saddle River, NJ: Prentice Hall, 2002.

PEREGRINE, PETER N., AND MELVIN EMBER, EDS. *Encyclopedia of Prehistory.* Vol. 1: *Africa.* New York: Kluwer Academic/Plenum, 2001.

PETERSEN, ERIK B. "A Survey of the Late Paleolithic and the Mesolithic of Denmark." In Kozlowski, ed., *The Mesolithic in Europe.*

PFEIFFER, JOHN E. *The Emergence of Man.* 3rd ed. New York: Harper & Row, 1978.

PHILLIPSON, DAVID W. *African Archaeology.* 2nd ed. New York: Cambridge University Press, 1993.

PICCHI, DEBRA. "Bakairí: The Death of an Indian." In M. Ember, Ember, and Levinson, eds., *Portraits of Culture.*

PICCHI, DEBRA. "The Impact of an Industrial Agricultural Project on the Bakairí Indians of Central Brazil." *Human Organization,* 50 (1991): 26–38.

PIGGOT, STUART, ED. *The Dawn of Civilization.* London: Thames & Hudson, 1961.

PILBEAM, DAVID. *The Ascent of Man.* New York: Macmillan, 1972.

PILBEAM, DAVID, AND STEPHEN JAY GOULD. "Size and Scaling in Human Evolution." *Science,* December 6, 1974, 892–900.

PODOLEFSKY, AARON, AND PETER J. BROWN. *Applying Cultural Anthropology: An Introductory Reader.* Mountain View, CA: Mayfield, 1997.

POGGIE, JOHN J., JR., BILLIE R. DEWALT, AND WILLIAM W. DRESSLER, EDS. *Anthropological Research: Process and Application.* Albany: State University of New York Press, 1992.

POLANYI, KARL, CONRAD M. ARENSBERG, AND HARRY W. PEARSON, EDS. *Trade and Market in the Early Empires.* New York: Free Press, 1957.

POLEDNAK, ANTHONY P. "Connective Tissue Responses in Negroes in Relation to Disease." *American Journal of Physical Anthropology,* 41 (1974): 49–57.

POLGAR, STEVEN, ED. *Population, Ecology, and Social Evolution.* The Hague: Mouton, 1975.

POPE, GEOFFREY G. "Bamboo and Human Evolution." *Natural History,* October 1989, 49–57.

POST, PETER W., FARRINGTON DANIELS, JR., AND ROBERT T. BINFORD, JR. "Cold Injury and the Evolution of 'White' Skin." *Human Biology,* 47 (1975): 65–80.

POTTS, RICHARD. *Early Hominid Activities at Olduvai.* New York: Aldine, 1988.

POTTS, RICHARD. "Home Bases and Early Hominids." *American Scientist,* 72 (1984): 338–47.

PRAG, JOHN, AND RICHARD NEAVE. *Making Faces: Using Forensic and Archaeological Evidence.* College Station: Texas A&M University Press, 1997.

PREUSCHOFT, HOLGER, DAVID J. CHIVERS, WARREN Y. BROCKELMAN, AND NORMAN CREEL, EDS. *The Lesser Apes: Evolutionary and Behavioural Biology.* Edinburgh: Edinburgh University Press, 1984.

PRICE, T. DOUGLAS, AND JAMES A. BROWN. *Prehistoric Hunter-Gatherers: The Emergence of Cultural Complexity.* Orlando, FL: Academic Press, 1985.

PRICE, T. DOUGLAS, AND A. B. GEBAUER, EDS. *Last Hunters, First Farmers: New Perspectives on the Prehistoric Transition to Agriculture.* Santa Fe, NM: School of American Research Press, 1995.

PRINGLE, HEATHER. "The Slow Birth of Agriculture." *Science,* 282 (1998): 1446–50.

PROTHERO, DONALD R., AND WILLIAM A. BERGGREN, EDS. *Eocene-Oliocene Climatic and Biotic Evolution.* Princeton, NJ: Princeton University Press, 1992.

PURDY, B. *How to Do Archaeology the Right Way.* Gainesville: University Press of Florida, 1996.

QUANDT, SARA A. "Nutrition in Anthropology." In Sargent and Johnson, eds., *Handbook of Medical Anthropology,* pp. 272–89.

RADINSKY, LEONARD. "The Oldest Primate Endocast." *American Journal of Physical Anthropology,* 27 (1967): 358–88.

RASMUSSEN, D. TAB. "Primate Origins: Lessons from a Neotropical Marsupial." *American Journal of Primatology,* 22 (1990): 263–77.

RASMUSSEN, T., ED. *The Origin and Evolution of Humans and Humanness.* Boston: Jones and Bartlett, 1993.

RATHJE, WILLIAM L. "The Origin and Development of Lowland Classic Maya Civilization." *American Antiquity,* 36 (1971): 275–85.

REDMAN, CHARLES L. *The Rise of Civilization: From Early Farmers to Urban Society in the Ancient Near East.* San Francisco: W. H. Freeman, 1978.

REED, CHARLES A., ED. *Origins of Agriculture.* The Hague: Mouton, 1977.

RELETHFORD, JOHN. *The Human Species: An Introduction to Biological Anthropology.* Mountain View, CA: Mayfield, 1990.

RENFREW, COLIN. "Trade and Culture Process in European History." *Current Anthropology,* 10 (April–June 1969): 156–69.

RENFREW, COLIN, ED. *The Explanation of Culture Change: Models in Prehistory.* Pittsburgh: University of Pittsburgh Press, 1973.

RENFREW, COLIN, AND P. BAHN. *Archaeology; Theories, Methods, and Practice.* New York: Thames and Hudson, 1996.

RHINE, STANLEY. *Bone Voyage: A Journey in Forensic Anthropology.* Albuquerque: University of New Mexico Press, 1998.

RICE, PATRICIA. "Prehistoric Venuses: Symbols of Motherhood or Womanhood?" *Journal of Anthropological Research,* 37 (1981): 402–14.

RICE, PATRICIA C., AND ANN L. PATERSON. "Cave Art and Bones: Exploring the Interrelationships." *American Anthropologist,* 87 (1985): 94–100.

RICE, PATRICIA C., AND ANN L. PATERSON. "Validating the Cave Art—Archeofaunal Relationship in Cantabrian Spain." *American Anthropologist,* 88 (1986): 658–67.

RICHARD, ALISON F. "Malagasy Prosimians: Female Dominance." In Smuts et al., eds., *Primate Societies.*

RICHARD, ALISON F. *Primates in Nature.* New York: W. H. Freeman, 1985.

RIESENFELD, ALPHONSE. "The Effect of Extreme Temperatures and Starvation on the Body Proportions of the Rat." *American Journal of Physical Anthropology,* 39 (1973): 427–59.

RIGHTMIRE, G. PHILIP. *The Evolution of* Homo erectus: *Comparative Anatomical Studies of an Extinct Human Species.* Cambridge: Cambridge University Press, 1990.

RIGHTMIRE, G. PHILIP. "Homo erectus." In Tattersall, Delson, and van Couvering, eds., *Encyclopedia of Human Evolution and Prehistory.*

RIGHTMIRE, G. PHILIP. "Homo sapiens in Sub-Saharan Africa." In F. H. Smith and Spencer, eds., *The Origins of Modern Humans.*

RIGHTMIRE, PHILIP. "Human Evolution in the Middle Pleistocene: The Role of *Homo heidelbergensis.*" *Evolutionary Anthropology,* 6 (1997): 281–27.

RIGHTMIRE, G. PHILIP. "The Tempo of Change in the Evolution of Mid-Pleistocene *Homo.*" In Delson, ed., *Ancestors.*

RIJKSEN, H. D. *A Fieldstudy on Sumatran Orang Utans (Pongo Pygmaeus Abelii Lesson 1827): Ecology, Behaviour and Conservation.* Wageningen, The Netherlands: H. Veenman and Zonen, 1978.

ROBERTS, D. F. "Body Weight, Race, and Climate." *American Journal of Physical Anthropology,* (1953): 533–58.

ROBERTS, D. F. *Climate and Human Variability.* 2nd ed. Menlo Park, CA: Cummings, 1978.

ROBINSON, JOHN G., AND CHARLES H. JANSON. "Capuchins, Squirrel Monkeys, and Atelines: Socioecological Convergence with Old World Primates." In Smuts et al., eds., *Primate Societies.*

ROBINSON, JOHN G., PATRICIA C. WRIGHT, AND WARREN G. KINZEY. "Monogamous Cebids and Their Relatives: Intergroup Calls and Spacing." In Smuts et al., eds., *Primate Societies.*

ROBINSON, ROY. "Cat." In Mason, *Evolution of Domesticated Animals.*

ROGERS, EVERETT M. *Diffusion of Innovations.* 3rd ed. New York: Free Press, 1983.

ROMANUCCI-ROSS, LOLA, DANIEL E. MOERMAN, AND LAURENCE R. TANCREDI, EDS. *The Anthropology of Medicine: From Culture to Method.* 3rd ed. Westport, CO: Bergin & Garvey, 1997.

ROMNEY, A. KIMBALL, SUSAN C. WELLER, AND WILLIAM H. BATCHELDER. "Culture as Consensus: A Theory of Culture and Informant Accuracy." *American Anthropologist,* 88 (1986): 313–38.

ROOSEVELT, ANNA CURTENIUS. "Population, Health, and the Evolution of Subsistence: Conclusions from the Conference." In Cohen and Armelagos, eds., *Paleopathology at the Origins of Agriculture.*

ROOSEVELT, ANNA CURTENIUS, ET AL. "Paleoindian Cave Dwellers in the Amazon: The Peopling of the Americas." *Science,* April 19, 1996, 373–84.

ROSE, M. D. "Food Acquisition and the Evolution of Positional Behaviour: The Case of Bipedalism." In Chivers, Wood, and Bilsborough, eds., *Food Acquisition and Processing in Primates.*

ROSENBERGER, A. L. "Cranial Anatomy and Implications of *Dolichocebus,* a Late Oligocene Ceboid Primate." *Nature,* 279 (1979): 416–18.

ROSENBLUM, L. A., ED. *Primate Behavior.* Vol. 1. New York: Academic Press, 1970.

ROSS, MARC HOWARD. "Ethnocentrism and Ethnic Conflict." In C. R. Ember, Ember, and Peregrine, eds., *Research Frontiers in Anthropology.* Vol. 3.

ROWE, N. *The Pictorial Guide to the Living Primates.* East Hampton, NY: Pogonias Press, 1996.

RUBEL, ARTHUR J., AND MICHAEL R. HASS. "Ethnomedicine." In Johnson and Sargent, *Medical Anthropology,* pp. 115–31;

reprinted in Sargent and Johnson, *Handbook of Medical Anthropology.*

RUBEL, ARTHUR J., CARL O. NELL, AND ROLANDO COLLADO-ARDÓN (with the assistance of John Krejci and Jean Krejci). *Susto: A Folk Illness.* Berkeley: University of California Press, 1984.

RUFF, CHRISTOPHER B., AND ALAN WALKER. "Body Size and Body Shape." In Walker and Leakey, eds., *The Nariokotome* Homo erectus *Skeleton.* Cambridge, MA: Harvard University Press, 1993.

RUMBAUGH, DUANE M. "Learning Skills of Anthropoids." In Rosenblum, ed., *Primate Behavior,* Vol. 1.

RUSSON, ANNE E. "The Development of Peer Social Interaction in Infant Chimpanzees: Comparative Social, Piagetian, and Brain Perspectives." In Parker and Gibson, eds., *"Language" and Intelligence in Monkeys and Apes.*

SABLOFF, JEREMY A., ED. *Supplement to the Handbook of Middle American Indians.* Vol. 1. Austin: University of Texas Press, 1981.

SADE, D. S. "Some Aspects of Parent-Offspring and Sibling Relationships in a Group of Rhesus Monkeys, with a Discussion of Grooming." *American Journal of Physical Anthropology,* 23 (1965): 1–17.

SAGAN, CARL. "A Cosmic Calendar." *Natural History,* December 1975, 70–73.

SANDERS, WILLIAM T. "Hydraulic Agriculture, Economic Symbiosis, and the Evolution of States in Central Mexico." In Meggers, ed., *Anthropological Archaeology in the Americas.*

SANDERS, WILLIAM T., JEFFREY R. PARSONS, AND ROBERT S. SANTLEY. *The Basin of Mexico: Ecological Processes in the Evolution of a Civilization.* New York: Academic Press, 1979.

SANDERS, WILLIAM T., AND BARBARA J. PRICE. *Mesoamerica.* New York: Random House, 1968.

SARGENT, CAROLYN F., AND THOMAS M. JOHNSON, EDS. *Handbook of Medical Anthropology: Contemporary Theory and Method.* Rev. ed. Westport, CT: Greenwood Press, 1996, pp. 272–89.

SARICH, VINCENT M. "The Origin of Hominids: An Immunological Approach." In Washburn and Jay, eds., *Perspectives on Human Evolution,* Vol. 1.

SARICH, VINCENT M., AND ALLAN C. WILSON. "Quantitative Immunochemistry and the Evolution of Primate Albumins: Micro-Component Fixations." *Science,* December 23, 1966, 1563–66.

SASSAMAN, KENNETH. "Early Archaic Settlement in the South Carolina Coastal Plain." In D. G. Anderson and K. E. Sassaman, eds., *The Paleoindian and Early Archaic Southeast.* Tuscaloosa: University of Alabama Press, 1996, pp. 58–83.

SAVAGE-RUMBAUGH, E. S. "Hominid Evolution: Looking to Modern Apes for Clues." In Duane Quiatt and Junichiro Itani, eds., *Hominid Culture in Primate Perspective.* Niwot: University Press of Colorado, 1994.

SAVAGE-RUMBAUGH, E. S. "Language Training of Apes." In Jones, Martin, and Pilbeam, eds., *The Cambridge Encyclopedia of Human Evolution.*

SCHALLER, GEORGE. *The Mountain Gorilla: Ecology and Behavior.* Chicago: University of Chicago Press, 1963.

SCHALLER, GEORGE B. *The Serengeti Lion: A Study of Predator-Prey Relations.* Chicago: University of Chicago Press, 1972.

SCHALLER, GEORGE. *The Year of the Gorilla.* Chicago: University of Chicago Press, 1964.

SCHICK, KATHY D., AND NICHOLAS TOTH. *Making Silent Stones Speak.* New York: Simon & Schuster, 1993.

SCHIFFER, MICHAEL B. *Formation Processes of the Archaeological Record.* Albuquerque: University of New Mexico Press, 1987.

SCHOEPF, B. "Women, AIDS and Economic Crisis in Central Africa." *Canadian Journal of African Studies,* 22 (1988): 625–44.

SCHWARCZ, HENRY P. *The Origin of Modern Humans and the Impact of Chronometric Dating.* Princeton, NJ: Princeton University Press, 1993.

SCHWARCZ, HENRY P. "Uranium-Series Dating and the Origin of Modern Man." In Schwarz, *The Origin of Modern Humans and the Impact of Chronometric Dating.*

SCUDDER, THAYER. "Opportunities, Issues and Achievements in Development Anthropology since the Mid-1960s: A Personal View." In Eddy and Partridge, eds., *Applied Anthropology in America,* 2nd ed.

SEBEOK, THOMAS A., AND JEAN UMIKER-SEBEOK, EDS. *Speaking of Apes: A Critical Anthology of Two-Way Communication with Man.* New York: Plenum, 1980.

SELIG, R. O., AND M. R. LONDON, EDS. *Anthropology Explored: The Best of Smithsonian AnthroNotes.* Washington, DC: Smithsonian Institution Press, 1998.

SEMENOV, S. A. *Prehistoric Technology.* Trans. M. W. Thompson. Bath, England: Adams & Dart, 1970.

SENNER, WAYNE M. "Theories and Myths on the Origins of Writing: A Historical Overview." In Senner, ed., *The Origins of Writing.*

SENNER, WAYNE M., ED. *The Origins of Writing.* Lincoln: University of Nebraska Press, 1989.

SERVICE, ELMAN R. *Origins of the State and Civilization: The Process of Cultural Evolution.* New York: Norton, 1975.

SEYFARTH, ROBERT M., DOROTHY L. CHENEY, AND PETER MARLER. "Monkey Response to Three Different Alarm Calls: Evidence of Predator Classification and Semantic Communication." *Science,* November 14, 1980, 801–803.

SHANKLIN, EUGENIA. *Anthropology and Race.* Belmont, CA: Wadsworth, 1994.

SHEN, XUEFEI, AND ROBERT F. SILICIANO. "Preventing AIDS but Not HIV-1 Infection with a DNA Vaccine." *Science,* October 20, 2000, 463–65.

SHIPMAN, PAT. *The Evolution of Racism: Human Differences and the Use and Abuse of Science.* New York: Simon & Schuster, 1994.

SHIPMAN, PAT. *The Man Who Found the Missing Link: Eugene Dubois and His Lifelong Quest to Prove Darwin Right.* New York: Simon & Schuster, 2001.

SHIPMAN, PAT. "Scavenging or Hunting in Early Hominids: Theoretical Framework and Tests." *American Anthropologist,* 88 (1986): 27–43.

SIMMONS, ALAN H., ILSE KÖHLER-ROLLEFSON, GARY O. ROLLEFSON, ROLFE MANDEL, AND ZEIDAN KAFAFI. "'Ain Ghazal: A Major Neolithic Settlement in Central Jordan." *Science,* April 1, 1988, 35–39.

SIMMONS, JANIE, PAUL FARMER, AND BROOKE G. SCHOEPF. "A Global Perspective." In Paul Farmer, Margaret Connors, and Janie Simmons, eds., *Women, Poverty, and AIDS: Sex, Drugs, and Structural Violence.* Monroe, ME: Common Courage Press, 1996, pp. 39–90.

SIMONS, ELWYN. "The Primate Fossil Record." In Jones, Martin, and Pilbeam, eds., *The Cambridge Encyclopedia of Human Evolution.*

SIMONS, ELWYN L. "Skulls and Anterior Teeth of *Catopithecus*

(Primates: Anthropoidea) from the Eocene Shed Light on Anthropoidean Origins." *Science,* 268 (1995): 1885–88.

SIMONS, ELWYN L., AND D. T. RASSMUSSEN. "Skull of *Catopithecus browni,* an Early Tertiary Catarrhine." *American Journal of Physical Anthropology,* 100 (1996): 261–92.

SIMPSON, GEORGE GAYLORD. *The Meaning of Evolution.* New York: Bantam, 1971.

SIMPSON, SCOTT W. "*Australopithecus afarensis* and Human Evolution." In Peregrine, Ember, and Ember, eds., *Physical Anthropology.*

SINGER, RONALD, AND JOHN WYMER. *The Middle Stone Age at Klasies River Mouth in South Africa.* Chicago: University of Chicago Press, 1982.

SINOPOLI, CARLA. "Learning about the Past through Archaeological Ceramics: An Example from Yijayanagara, India." In Peregrine, Ember, and Ember, eds., *Archaeology.*

SMITH, B. HOLLY. "Dental Development in *Australopithecus* and Early *Homo.*" *Nature,* September 25, 1986, 327–30.

SMITH, BRUCE D. *The Emergence of Agriculture.* New York: Scientific American Library, 1995.

SMITH, BRUCE D. "Prehistoric Plant Husbandry in Eastern North America." In Cowan and Watson, eds., *The Origins of Agriculture.*

SMITH, BRUCE D. *Rivers of Change.* Washington, DC: Smithsonian Institution Press, 1992.

SMITH, FRED H. "Fossil Hominids from the Upper Pleistocene of Central Europe and the Origin of Modern Humans." In F. H. Smith and Spencer, eds., *The Origins of Modern Humans.*

SMITH, FRED H., AND FRANK SPENCER, EDS. *The Origins of Modern Humans: A World Survey of the Fossil Evidence.* New York: Alan R. Liss, 1984.

SMITH, JOHN MAYNARD. *Evolutionary Genetics.* New York: Oxford University Press, 1989.

SMITH, M. W. "Alfred Binet's Remarkable Questions: A Cross-National and Cross-Temporal Analysis of the Cultural Biases Built into the Stanford-Binet Intelligence Scale and Other Binet Tests." *Genetic Psychology Monographs,* 89 (1974): 307–34.

SMUTS, BARBARA B., DOROTHY L. CHENEY, ROBERT M. SEYFARTH, RICHARD W. WRANGHAM, AND THOMAS T. STRUHSAKER, EDS. *Primate Societies.* Chicago: University of Chicago Press, 1987.

SOFFER, OLGA. "Upper Paleolithic Adaptations in Central and Eastern Europe and Man-Mammoth Interactions." In Soffer and Praslov, eds., *From Kostenki to Clovis.*

SOFFER, O. *The Upper Paleolithic of the Central Russian Plain.* Orlando, FL: Academic Press, 1985.

SOFFER, OLGA, J. M. ADOVASIO, AND D. C. HYLAND. "The 'Venus' Figurines: Textiles, Basketry, Gender, and Status in the Upper Paleolithic." *Current Anthropology,* 41 (2000): 511–37.

SOFFER, OLGA, AND N. D. PRASLOV, EDS. *From Kostenki to Clovis: Upper Paleolithic–Paleo-Indian Adaptations.* New York: Plenum, 1993.

SOUTHWORTH, FRANKLIN C., AND CHANDLER J. DASWANI. *Foundations of Linguistics.* New York: Free Press, 1974.

SPENCER, FRANK. "The Neandertals and Their Evolutionary Significance: A Brief Historical Survey." In F. H. Smith and Spencer, eds., *The Origins of Modern Humans.*

SPETH, JOHN D. "Were Our Ancestors Hunters or Scavengers?" In Peregrine, Ember, and Ember, eds., *Physical Anthropology.*

SPETH, JOHN D., AND DAVE D. DAVIS. "Seasonal Variability in Early Hominid Predation." *Science,* April 30, 1976, 441–45.

SPETH, JOHN D., AND KATHERINE A. SPIELMANN. "Energy Source, Protein Metabolism, and Hunter-Gatherer Subsistence Strategies." *Journal of Anthropological Archaeology,* 2 (1983): 1–31.

SPOONER, BRIAN, ED. *Population Growth: Anthropological Implications.* Cambridge, MA: MIT Press, 1972.

SPRING, ANITA. *Agricultural Development and Gender Issues in Malawi.* Lanham, MD: University Press of America, 1995.

STANFORD, CRAIG. "Chimpanzee Hunting and Human Evolution." In Peregrine, Ember, and Ember, eds., *Physical Anthropology.*

STANFORD, CRAIG B. "The Social Behavior of Chimpanzees and Bonobos: Empirical Evidence and Shifting Assumptions." *Current Anthropology,* 39 (1998): 399–420.

STANFORD, CRAIG B., JANETTE WALLIS, HILALI MATAMA, AND JANE GOODALL. "Patterns of Predation by Chimpanzees on Red Colobus Monkeys in Gombe National Park, Tanzania, 1982–1991." *American Journal of Physical Anthropology,* 94 (1994): 213–29.

STEEGMAN, A. T., JR. "Human Adaptation to Cold." In Damon, ed., *Physiological Anthropology.*

STEIN, GIL, AND MITCHELL ROTHMAN, EDS. *Chiefdoms and Early States in the Near East: The Organizational Dynamics of Complexity.* Madison, WI: Prehistory Press, 1994.

STEIN, P., AND B. ROWE. *Physical Anthropology.* 7th ed. Boston: McGraw-Hill, 2000.

STEWARD, T. D. "Deformity, Trephanating, and Mutilation in South American Indian Skeletal Remains." In J. A. Steward, ed., *Handbook of South American Indians.* Vol. 6: *Physical Anthropology, Linguistics, and Cultural Geography.* Bureau of American Ethnology Bulletin 143. Washington, DC: Smithsonian Institution.

STINI, WILLIAM A. *Ecology and Human Adaptation.* Dubuque, IA: Wm. C. Brown, 1975.

STRAUSS, LAWRENCE GUY. "Comment on White." *Current Anthropology,* 23 (1982): 185–86.

STRAUSS, LAWRENCE GUY. "On Early Hominid Use of Fire." *Current Anthropology,* 30 (1989): 488–91.

STRAUSS, LAWRENCE GUY. "Solutrean Settlement of North America? A View of Reality." *American Antiquity,* 65 (2000): 219–26.

STRINGER, CHRISTOPHER. "Evolution of a Species." *Geographical Magazine,* 57 (1985): 601–607.

STRINGER, CHRISTOPHER B. "Neandertals." In Tattersall, Delson, and van Couvering, eds., *Encyclopedia of Human Evolution and Prehistory.*

STRINGER, CHRISTOPHER, AND CLIVE GAMBLE. *In Search of the Neandertals.* New York: Thames and Hudson, 1993.

STRINGER, C. B., J. J. HUBLIN, AND B. VANDERMEERSCH. "The Origin of Anatomically Modern Humans in Western Europe." In F. H. Smith and Spencer, eds., *The Origins of Modern Humans.*

STRUEVER, STUART, ED. *Prehistoric Agriculture.* Garden City, NY: Natural History Press, 1971.

SUSMAN, RANDALL L. "Fossil Evidence for Early Hominid Tool Use." *Science,* September 9, 1994, 1570–73.

SUSMAN, RANDALL L., ED. *The Pygmy Chimpanzee: Evolutionary Biology and Behavior.* New York: Plenum, 1984.

SUSMAN, RANDALL L., JACK T. STERN, JR., AND WILLIAM L. JUNGERS. "Locomotor Adaptations in the Hadar Hominids." In Delson, ed., *Ancestors.*

SUSSMAN, ROBERT. "Child Transport, Family Size, and the Increase in Human Population Size during the Neolithic." *Current Anthropology,* 13 (April 1972): 258–67.

SUSSMAN, ROBERT. "Primate Origins and the Evolution of

Angiosperms." *American Journal of Primatology*, 23 (1991): 209–23.

SUSSMAN, ROBERT W., AND W. G. KINZEY. "The Ecological Role of the Callitrichidae: A Review." *American Journal of Physical Anthropology*, 64 (1984): 419–49.

SUSSMAN, ROBERT W., AND PETER H. RAVEN. "Pollination by Lemurs and Marsupials: An Archaic Coevolutionary System." *Science*, May 19, 1978, 734–35.

SWISHER, C. C., III, G. H. CURTIS, T. JACOB, A. G. GETTY, A. SUPRIJO, AND WIDIASMORO. "Age of the Earliest Known Hominids in Java, Indonesia." *Science*, February 25, 1994, 1118–21.

SZALAY, FREDERICK S. "Hunting-Scavenging Protohominids: A Model for Hominid Origins." *Man*, 10 (1975): 420–29.

SZALAY, FREDERICK S. "Paleobiology of the Earliest Primates." In R. Tuttle, ed., *The Functional and Evolutionary Biology of the Primates*. Chicago: University of Chicago Press, 1972, pp. 3–35.

SZALAY, FREDERICK S., AND ERIC DELSON. *Evolutionary History of the Primates*. New York: Academic Press, 1979.

SZALAY, FREDERICK S., I. TATTERSALL, AND R. DECKER. "Phylogenetic Relationships of *Plesiadipis*—Postcranial Evidence." *Contributions to Primatology*, 5 (1975): 136–66.

SZATHMARY, EMÖKE J. E. "Genetics of Aboriginal North Americans." *Evolutionary Anthropology*, 1 (1993): 202–20.

TAINTER, JOSEPH. *The Collapse of Complex Societies*. Cambridge: Cambridge University Press, 1988, pp. 128–52.

TATTERSALL, IAN. *The Fossil Trail: How We Know What We Think We Know about Human Evolution*. New York: Oxford University Press, 1995.

TATTERSALL, IAN. *The Human Odyssey*. Englewood Cliffs, NJ: Prentice Hall, 1993.

TATTERSALL, IAN. *The Last Neanderthal*. Boulder, CO: Westview, 1999, pp. 115–16.

TATTERSALL, IAN. "Paleoanthropology and Evolutionary Theory." In Peregrine, Ember, and Ember, eds., *Physical Anthropology*.

TATTERSALL, IAN. *The Primates of Madagascar*. New York: Columbia University Press, 1982.

TATTERSALL, IAN, ERIC DELSON, AND JOHN VAN COUVERING, EDS. *Encyclopedia of Human Evolution and Prehistory*. New York: Garland, 1988.

TATTERSALL, IAN, AND JEFFREY SCHWARTZ. *Extinct Humans*. Boulder, CO: Westview, 2000, p. 93.

TAYLOR, R. E., AND M. J. AITKEN, EDS. *Chronometric Dating in Archaeology*. New York: Plenum, 1997.

TELEKI, GEZA. "The Omnivorous Chimpanzee." *Scientific American*, January 1973, 32–42.

TEMPLETON, ALAN R. "The 'Eve' Hypotheses: A Genetic Critique and Reanalysis." *American Anthropologist*, 95 (1993): 51–72.

TEMPLETON, ALAN R. "Gene Lineages and Human Evolution." *Science*, May 31, 1996, 1363.

TERBORGH, JOHN. *Five New World Primates: A Study in Comparative Ecology*. Princeton, NJ: Princeton University Press, 1983.

THOMPSON, ELIZABETH BARTLETT. *Africa, Past and Present*. Boston: Houghton Mifflin, 1966.

THOMPSON-HANDLER, NANCY, RICHARD K. MALENKY, AND NOEL BADRIAN. "Sexual Behavior of *Pan paniscus* under Natural Conditions in the Lomako Forest, Equateur, Zaire." In Susman, ed., *The Pygmy Chimpanzee*.

THORNE, ALAN G., AND MILFORD H. WOLPOFF. "The Multiregional Evolution of Humans." *Scientific American*, April 1992, 76–83.

TIERNEY, PATRICK. *Darkness in El Dorado*. New York: Norton, 2000.

TOBIAS, PHILIP. "The Brain of *Homo habilis*: A New Level of Organization in Cerebral Evolution." *Journal of Human Evolution*, 16 (1987): 741–61.

TOBIAS, PHILIP V. "The Craniocerebral Interface in Early Hominids: Cerebral Impressions, Cranial Thickening, Paleoneurobiology, and a New Hypothesis on Encephalization." In Corruccini and Ciochon, eds., *Integrative Paths to the Past*.

TOMASELLO, MICHAEL. "Cultural Transmission in the Tool Use and Communicatory Signaling of Chimpanzees." In Parker and Gibson, eds., *"Language" and Intelligence in Monkeys and Apes*.

TORREY, E. FULLER. *The Mind Game: Witchdoctors and Psychiatrists*. New York: Emerson Hall, n.d.

TRAVIS, JOHN. "Human Genome Work Reaches Milestone." *Science News*, July 1, 2000, 4–5.

TRIGGER, BRUCE G. *A History of Archaeological Thought*. Cambridge: Cambridge University Press, 1989.

TRINGHAM, RUTH, ED. *Ecology and Agricultural Settlements*. R2. Andover, MA: Warner Modular, 1973.

TRINGHAM, RUTH, ED. *Territoriality and Proxemics*. R1. Andover, MA: Warner Modular, 1973.

TRINKAUS, ERIK. "Bodies, Brawn, Brains and Noses: Human Ancestors and Human Predation." In Nitecki and Nitecki, eds., *The Evolution of Human Hunting*.

TRINKAUS, ERIK. "The Neandertal Face: Evolutionary and Functional Perspectives on a Recent Hominid Face." *Journal of Human Evolution*, 16 (1987): 429–43.

TRINKAUS, ERIK. "The Neandertals and Modern Human Origins." *Annual Review of Anthropology*, 15 (1986): 193–218.

TRINKAUS, ERIK. "Pathology and the Posture of the La Chapelle-aux-Saints Neandertal." *American Journal of Physical Anthropology*, 67 (1985): 19–41.

TRINKAUS, ERIK. "Western Asia." In F. H. Smith and Spencer, eds., *The Origins of Modern Humans*.

TRINKAUS, E., ED. *The Emergence of Modern Humans: Biocultural Adaptations in the Later Pleistocene*. Cambridge: Cambridge University Press, 1989.

TRINKAUS, ERIK, AND WILLIAM W. HOWELLS. "The Neanderthals." *Scientific American*, December 1979, 118–33.

TRINKAUS, ERIK, AND PAT SHIPMAN. *The Neandertals: Changing the Image of Mankind*. New York: Knopf, 1993.

TRINKAUS, ERIK, AND PAT SHIPMAN. "Neandertals: Images of Ourselves." *Evolutionary Anthropology*, 1, no. 6 (1993): 194–201.

TROTTER, ROBERT T., II, ED. *Anthropology for Tomorrow: Creating Practitioner-Oriented Applied Anthropology Programs*. Washington, DC: American Anthropological Association, 1988.

TURNER, B. L. "Population Density in the Classic Maya Lowlands: New Evidence for Old Approaches." *Geographical Review*, 66, no. 1 (January 1970): 72–82.

TURNER, CHRISTY G., II. "Teeth and Prehistory in Asia." *Scientific American*, February 1989.

TURNER, CHRISTY G., II. "Telltale Teeth." *Natural History*, January 1987.

TUTIN, CAROLINE, AND L. WHITE. "The Recent Evolutionary Past of Primate Communities: Likely Environmental Impacts during the Past Three Millennia." In J. G. Fleagle, C. Janson, and K. E. Reed, eds., *Primate Communities*. Cambridge: Cambridge University Press, 1999, pp. 230–31.

TUTTLE, RUSSELL H. *Apes of the World: Their Social Behavior*,

Communication, Mentality, and Ecology. Park Ridge, NJ: Noyes, 1986.

UCKO, PETER J., AND G. W. DIMBLEBY, EDS. *The Domestication and Exploitation of Plants and Animals.* Chicago: Aldine, 1969.

UCKO, PETER J., AND ANDRÉE ROSENFELD. *Paleolithic Cave Art.* New York: McGraw-Hill, 1967.

UCKO, PETER J., RUTH TRINGHAM, AND G. W. DIMBLEBY, EDS. *Man, Settlement, and Urbanism.* Cambridge, MA: Schenkman, 1972.

UNDERHILL, ANNE. "Investigating Craft Specialization during the Longshan Period of China." In Peregrine, Ember, and Ember, eds., *Archaeology.*

URBAN INSTITUTE. "America's Homeless. II: Populations and Services." Washington, DC: Urban Institute, February 1, 2000. Published on the Web at http://www.urban.org/housing/homeless/numbers/index.htm.

VALLADAS, H., J. L. JORON, G. VALLADAS, O. BAR-YOSEF, AND B. VANDERMEERSCH. "Thermoluminescence Dating of Mousterian 'Proto-Cro-Magnon' Remains from Israel and the Origin of Modern Man." *Nature,* February 18, 1988, 614–16.

VAN DER MERWE, N. J. "Reconstructing Prehistoric Diet." In Jones, Martin, and Pilbeam, eds., *The Cambridge Encyclopedia of Human Evolution.*

VAN LAWICK-GOODALL, JANE. *In the Shadow of Man.* Boston: Houghton Mifflin, 1971.

VAN WILLIGEN, J. *Applied Anthropology: An Introduction.* Rev. ed. Westport, CT: Bergin & Garvey, 1993.

VAN WILLIGEN, JOHN, AND TIMOTHY L. FINAN, EDS. *Soundings: Rapid and Reliable Research Methods for Practicing Anthropologists.* NAPA Bulletin No. 10. Washington, DC: American Anthropological Association, 1990.

VAN WILLIGEN, JOHN, BARBARA RYLKO-BAUER, AND ANN MCELROY. *Making Our Research Useful: Case Studies in the Utilization of Anthropological Knowledge.* Boulder, CO: Westview, 1989.

VIGILANT, LINDA, MARK STONEKING, HENRY HARPENDING, KRISTEN HAWKES, AND ALLAN C. WILSON. "African Populations and the Evolution of Human Mitochrondrial DNA." *Science,* September 27, 1991, 1503–507.

VISABERGHI, ELISABETTA, AND DOROTHY MUNKENBECK FRAGASZY. "Do Monkeys Ape?" In Parker and Gibson, eds., *"Language" and Intelligence in Monkeys and Apes.*

VOGEL, GRETCHEN. "Chimps in the Wild Show Stirrings of Culture." *Science,* 284 (1999): 2070–73.

VOGEL, JOSEPH O. "De-Mystifying the Past: Great Zimbabwe, King Solomon's Mines, and Other Tales of Old Africa." In Peregrine, Ember, and Ember, eds., *Archaeology.*

VOGT, EVON Z., AND RICHARD M. LEVANTHAL, EDS. *Prehistoric Settlement Patterns: Essays in Honor of Gordon R. Willey.* Albuquerque: University of New Mexico Press, 1983.

VRBA, ELIZABETH S. "On the Connection between Paleoclimate and Evolution." In E. S. Vrba, G. H. Denton, T. C. Partridge, and L. H. Burckle, eds., *Paleoclimate and Evolution.* New Haven, CT: Yale University Press, 1995, pp. 24–45.

WALKER, ALAN, AND R. LEAKEY. "The Evolution of *Australopithecus boisei.*" In Grine, ed., *Evolutionary History of the "Robust" Australopithecines,* pp. 247–58.

WALKER, ALAN, AND RICHARD LEAKEY, EDS. *The Nariokotome Homo erectus Skeleton.* Cambridge, MA: Harvard University Press, 1993.

WALKER, ALAN, AND M. PICKFORD, "New Postcranial Fossils of Proconsul Africanus and Proconsul Nyanzae." In Ciochon

and Corruccini, eds., *New Interpretation of Ape and Human Ancestry.*

WALKER, ALAN, AND PAT SHIPMAN. *The Wisdom of the Bones: In Search of Human Origins.* New York: Knopf, 1996.

WALLACE, ALFRED RUSSELL. "On the Tendency of Varieties to Depart Indefinitely from the Original Type." *Journal of the Proceedings of the Linnaean Society,* August 1858. In Young, ed., *Evolution of Man.*

WALLACE, ANTHONY. "Mental Illness, Biology and Culture." In Hsu, ed., *Psychological Anthropology.*

WALLACE, ANTHONY, J. LAWRENCE ANGEL, RICHARD FOX, SALLY MCLENDON, RACHEL SADY, AND ROBERT SHARER, EDS. *Perspectives on Anthropology 1976.* American Anthropological Association Special Publication No. 10. Washington, DC: American Anthropological Association, 1977.

WANNER, ERIC, AND LILA R. GLEITMAN, EDS. *Language Acquisition: The State of the Art.* Cambridge: Cambridge University Press, 1982.

WARD, S. "The Taxonomy and Phylogenetic Relationships of *Sivapithecus* Revisited." In *Function, Phylogeny and Fossils: Miocene Hominoid Evolution and Adaptation.* D. R. Begun, C. V. Ward, and M. D. Rose, eds. New York: Plenum, 1997, pp. 269–90.

WARD, STEVE, B. BROWN, A. HILL, J. KELLEY, AND W. DOWNS. "*Equatorius;* A New Hominoid Genus from the Middle Miocene of Kenya." *Science,* 285 (1999): 1382–86.

WARREN, DENNIS M. "Utilizing Indigenous Healers in National Health Delivery Systems: The Ghanaian Experiment." In van Willigen, Rylko-Bauer, and McElroy, eds., *Making Our Research Useful.*

WARRY, WAYNE. "Doing unto Others: Applied Anthropology, Collaborative Research and Native Self-Determination." *Culture,* 10 (1990): 61–62.

WASHBURN, S. L., ED. *Social Life of Early Man.* Chicago: Aldine, 1964.

WASHBURN, S. L., AND PHYLLIS C. JAY, EDS. *Perspectives on Human Evolution.* Vol. 1. New York: Holt, Rinehart & Winston, 1968.

WASHBURN, SHERWOOD. "Tools and Human Evolution." *Scientific American,* September 1960, 62–75.

WEAVER, MURIEL PORTER. *The Aztecs, Maya, and Their Predecessors.* 3rd ed. San Diego: Academic Press, 1993.

WEINER, JONATHAN. *Beak of the Finch.* New York: Vintage, 1994.

Weiner, J. S. "Nose Shape and Climate." *Journal of Physical Anthropology,* 4 (1954): 615–18.

WEISS, HARVEY, M. A. COURTY, W. WETTERSTROM, F. GUICHARD, L. SENIOR, R. MEADOW, AND A. CURNOW. "The Genesis and Collapse of Third Millennium North Mesopotamia Civilization." *Science,* 261 (1993): 995–1004.

WELLER, SUSAN C. "The Research Process." In C. R. Ember, Ember, and Peregrine, eds., *Research Frontiers in Anthropology.* Vol. 3.

WENDORF, FRED, AND ANGELA E. CLOSE, EDS. *Advances in World Archaeology.* Vol. 3. Orlando, FL: Academic Press, 1984.

WENKE, ROBERT J. *Patterns in Prehistory: Humankind's First Three Million Years.* 2nd ed. New York: Oxford University Press, 1984.

WENKE, ROBERT. *Patterns in Prehistory: Humankind's First Three Million Years.* 3rd ed. New York: Oxford University Press, 1990.

WHEAT, JOE B. "A Paleo-Indian Bison Kill." *Scientific American,* January 1967, 44–52.

WHEATLEY, PAUL. *The Pivot of the Four Quarters.* Chicago: Aldine, 1971.

WHEELER, PETER. "The Evolution of Bipedality and Loss of Functional Body Hair in Hominids." *Journal of Human Evolution,* 13 (1984): 91–98.

WHEELER, PETER. "The Influence of Bipedalism in the Energy and Water Budgets of Early Hominids." *Journal of Human Evolution,* 23 (1991): 379–88.

WHITE, BENJAMIN. "Demand for Labor and Population Growth in Colonial Java." *Human Ecology,* 1, no. 3 (March 1973): 217–36.

WHITE, F. J. "*Pan paniscus* 1973 to 1996: Twenty-three Years of Field Research." *Evolutionary Anthropology,* 5 (1996): 11–17.

WHITE, LESLIE A. "The Expansion of the Scope of Science." In Morton H. Fried, ed., *Readings in Anthropology.* 2nd ed. Vol. 1. New York: Thomas Y. Crowell, 1968.

WHITE, RANDALL. "Rethinking the Middle/Upper Paleolithic Transition." *Current Anthropology,* 23 (1982): 169–75.

WHITE, TIM D., DONALD C. JOHANSON, AND WILLIAM H. KIMBEL. "*Australopithecus africanus:* Its Phyletic Position Reconsidered." *South African Journal of Science,* 77 (1981): 445–70.

WHITE, TIMOTHY D., G. SUWA, AND B. ASFAW. "*Australopithecus ramidus,* a New Species of Early Hominid from Aramis, Ethiopia." *Nature,* 371 (1994): 306–33.

WHITE, TIMOTHY D., G. SUWA, AND B. ASFAW. "Corrigendum: *Australopithecus ramidus,* a New Species of Early Hominid from Aramis, Ethiopia." *Nature,* 375 (1995): 88.

WHITTAKER, JOHN C. *Flintknapping: Making and Understanding Stone Tools.* Austin: University of Texas Press, 1994.

WIENER, STEVE, Q. XI, P. GOLDBERG, J. LIU, AND O. BAR-YOUSEF. "Evidence for the Use of Fire at Zhoukoudian, China." *Science,* 281 (1998): 251–53.

WILFORD, JOHN NOBLE. "The Transforming Leap, from 4 Legs to 2." *New York Times,* September 5, 1995, p. C1ff.

WILFORD, JOHN NOBLE. "Ancient German Spears Tell of Mighty Hunters of Stone Age." *New York Times,* March 4, 1997, p. C6.

WILKINSON, ROBERT L. "Yellow Fever: Ecology, Epidemiology, and Role in the Collapse of the Classic Lowland Maya Civilization." *Medical Anthropology,* 16 (1995): 269–94.

WILLIAMS, GEORGE C. *Natural Selection: Domains, Levels, and Challenges.* New York: Oxford University Press, 1992.

WILLIAMS, MELVIN D. "Racism: The Production, Reproduction, and Obsolescence of Social Inferiority." In C. R. Ember, Ember, and Peregrine, eds., *Research Frontiers in Anthropology.* Vol. 3.

WILSON, ALLAN C, AND REBECCA L. CANN. "The Recent African Genesis of Humans." *Scientific American,* April 1992, 68–73.

WILSON, EDMUND O. *Sociobiology: The New Synthesis.* Cambridge, MA: Belknap Press of Harvard University Press, 1975.

WINKELMAN, MICHAEL JAMES. "Magico-Religious Practitioner Types and Socioeconomic Conditions." *Behavior Science Research,* 20 (1986): 17–46.

WITTFOGEL, KARL. *Oriental Despotism: A Comparative Study of Total Power.* New Haven, CT: Yale University Press, 1957.

WOLF, ERIC. "Culture: Panacea or Problem." *American Antiquity,* 49 (1984): 393–400.

WOLF, ERIC R., ED. *The Valley of Mexico: Studies in Pre-Hispanic Ecology and Society.* Albuquerque: University of New Mexico Press, 1976.

WOLF, NAOMI. *The Beauty Myth: How Images of Beauty Are Used against Women.* New York: Morrow, 1991.

WOLFF, RONALD G. *Functional Chordate Anatomy.* Lexington, MA: D. C. Heath, 1991.

WOLPOFF, MILFORD H. "*Ramapithecus* and Human Origins: An Anthropologist's Perspective of Changing Interpretations." In Ciochon and Corruccini, eds., *New Interpretations of Ape and Human Ancestry.*

WOLPOFF, MILFORD H. "Competitive Exclusion among Lower Pleistocene Hominids: The Single Species Hypothesis." *Man,* 6 (1971): 601–13.

WOLPOFF, MILFORD. *Paleoanthropology.* 2nd ed. Boston: McGraw-Hill, 1999, pp. 501–504, 727–31.

WOLPOFF, MILFORD H., AND ABEL NIKINI. "Early and Early Middle Pleistocene Hominids from Asia and Africa." In Delson, ed., *Ancestors.*

WOLPOFF, MILFORD, A. G. THORNE, J. JELINEK, AND ZHANG YINYUN. "The Case for Sinking *Homo erectus:* 100 years of *Pithecanthropus* Is Enough!" In J. L. Franzen, ed., *100 Years of* Pithecanthropus: The Homo Erectus *Problem. Courier Forshungsinstitut Senckenberg,* 171 (1993): 341–61.

WOOD, BERNARD A. "Evolution of Australopithecines." In Jones, Martin, and Pilbeam, eds., *The Cambridge Encyclopedia of Human Evolution.*

WOOD, BERNARD. "Hominid Paleobiology: Recent Achievements and Challenges." In Corruccini and Ciochon, eds., *Integrative Paths to the Past.*

WORLD BANK. *World Development Report 1995. Workers in an Integrating World.* Oxford: Oxford University Press, 1995.

WRANGHAM, RICHARD W. "An Ecological Model of Female-Bonded Primate Groups." *Behaviour,* 75 (1980): 262–300.

WRIGHT, GARY A. "Origins of Food Production in Southwestern Asia: A Survey of Ideas." *Current Anthropology,* 12 (1971): 447–78.

WRIGHT, HENRY T. "The Evolution of Civilizations." In Meltzer, Fowler, and Sabloff, eds., *American Archaeology Past and Future.*

WRIGHT, HENRY T., AND GREGORY A. JOHNSON. "Population, Exchange, and Early State Formation in Southwestern Iran." *American Anthropologist,* 77 (1975): 267–77.

WYNN, THOMAS. "The Intelligence of Later Acheulean Hominids." *Man,* 14 (1979): 371–91.

YAMEI, HOU, R. POTTS, Y. BAOYIN, ET AL. "Mid-Pleistocene Acheulean-like Stone Technology of the Bose Basin, South China." *Science,* 287 (2000): 1622–26.

YOUNG, LOUISE B., ED. *Evolution of Man.* New York: Oxford University Press, 1970.

YOUNG, T. CUYLER, JR. "Population Densities and Early Mesopotamian Urbanism." In Ucko, Tringham, and Dimbleby, eds., *Man, Settlement and Urbanism.*

ZEDER, MELINDA A. "After the Revolution: Post-Neolithic Subsistence in Northern Mesopotamia." *American Anthropologist,* 96 (1994): 97–126.

ZEDER, MELINDA. *The American Archaeologist: A Profile.* Walnut Creek, CA: Alta Mira, 1997.

ZEDER, MELINDA. *Feeding Cities: Specialized Animal Economy in the Ancient Near East.* Washington, DC: Smithsonian Institution Press, 1991.

ZIHLMAN, ADRIENNE L. "The Emergence of Human Locomotion: The Evolutionary Background and Environmental Context." In Nishida et al., eds., *Topics in Primatology,* Vol. 1.

ZIHLMAN, ADRIENNE. "Women's Bodies, Women's Lives: An Evolutionary Perspective." In M. E. Morbeck, A. Galloway, and A. Zihlman, eds., *The Evolving Female: A Life-History Perspec-*

tive. Princeton, NJ: Princeton University Press, 1997, pp. 185–97.

ZIMMER, CARL. "Kenyan Skeleton Shakes Ape Family Tree." *Science,* 285 (1999): 1335–337.

ZOHARY, DANIEL. "The Progenitors of Wheat and Barley in Relation to Domestication and Agriculture Dispersal in the Old World." In Ucko and Dimbleby, eds., *The Domestication and Exploitation of Plants and Animals.*

The Evolution of Human Sexuality　　　　　　　　**Anthropology 173**
Week One (complete in class)

Names of group members:

_____

_____

This group exercise is intended to help you start thinking about the scientific method, and to give you hands-on experience generating hypotheses, making predictions, and coming up with ways to test your hypothesis.

The question below was generated from observations made about human behavior.

1.　Why do humans have sex in private and other primates don't?
2.　Why don't humans have hair all over their bodies like apes?
3.　Why do human males invest so much time and energy in their children?
4.　In college, why are men on average more interested in dating than women are?
5.　Why do women spend more time and money on beauty products than men do?

Hypothesis:

Predictions if your hypothesis is true:

Predictions if your hypothesis is false:

Way or ways to test our hypothesis—be creative!

Darwinopoly Rules

Darwinopoly is desgined to let the players explore male and female reproductive strategies in a hunter-gatherer society. At the end of the game, there will be two winners: the female with the most adult children, and the male with the most adult children. Players can explore whether fidelity, promiscuity, or a mixed strategy is the best tactic.

1) There should be equal numbers of "female" and "male" players. Each player starts with $1000 from the forest.

2) Players roll the dice, move around the board, and collect or lose the amounts of money indicated.

3) When it's your turn, after rolling and moving, you can do one of the following:
   - propose marriage: if the proposal is accepted, the newlyweds together must pay the forest $1000. Polygamy is allowed.
   - divorce your spouse: you must pay $500.
   - propose sex with any other player, married or not: if accepted, see rule 4
   - give birth: see rule 5

4) When a "female" player passes "CAVE" or "Youngest child killed by lion" she finds out whether or not she is pregnant, depending on the number of times she had sex since she last passed one of these squares:
   - no sex: no chance of pregnancy.
   - sex once: pregnant if she rolled 4, 8, or 12.
   - sex twice: pregnant if she rolled an even number.
   - sex three or more times: pregnant unless she rolled 2, 3, 11 or 12.
   If she is pregnant, she gets a birth certificate for the child, on which she should record the potential fathers (the actual father will not be determined until the child reaches adulthood).

5) "Female" players give birth on the turn after they found out they were pregnant. The mother must pay the forest $1000 at childbirth. If she doesn't have the money, her husband must make up the difference. If he doesn't have the money, or the mother is unmarried, then the mother can try to persuade other players to help. If the baby isn't paid for, it dies at birth.

6) When it's your turn, you must pay the forest for food for your children as follows:
   - If you are an unmarried female, pay $600 for each of your children.
   - If you are a married female, pay $300 for each of your children.
   - If you are a married male, pay $300 for each of your wife's (wives') children, regardless of whether they are biologically yours or not.
   If there is not enough money to pay for a child, the child dies. When a total of $3000 has been invested in support for a child, the child becomes an adult, and no longer requires parental support. See the birth certificate for rules on determining paternity.

7) If a player runs out of money, the player dies.

8) When it is your turn, you can give money to any other player, and request and accept money from any other player, for any reason whatsoever.

Birth Certificate   Name of Child: Mother:

Possible Fathers (circle the actual father when the child reaches adulthood, see below):

1)   2)

3)   4)

Tick off amount paid in child support (the $1000 paid at birth doesn't count):

300 600 900 1200 1500 1800 2100 2400 2700 3000   __ Died __ Reached adulthood.

When a child with more than one possible father reaches adulthood, roll the dice to determine paternity as follows:

- two possible fathers:
    #1 is the father if the number is odd; #2 is the father if the number is even.
- three possible fathers:
    #1 is the father if the number is 2, 5, 8, or 11;
    #2 is the father if the number is 3, 6, 9, or 12;
    #3 is the father if the number is 4, 7, or 10.
- four possible fathers:
    #1 is the father if the number is 2, 3, 4, or 10;
    #2 is the father if the number is 5 or 6;
    #3 is the father if the number is 7, 11, or 12;
    #4 is the father if the number is 8 or 9.